STOCHASTIC MODELS FOR SOCIAL PROCESSES

Stochastic Models
for Social Processes

David J. Bartholomew
Professor of Statistics,
University of Kent at Canterbury

JOHN WILEY & SONS
London — New York — Sydney

Printed in Great Britain at the Pitman Press, Bath

PREFACE

This book is a contribution to the study of social phenomena by means of the theory of stochastic processes. It is written primarily for two groups of people. First of all for social scientists who wish to see what this relatively new branch of mathematics has to offer in their own field. Professor Coleman's *Introduction to Mathematical Sociology* has already demonstrated the fruitfulness of the stochastic approach in many parts of sociology. Social scientists who are acquainted with this and related work and are excited by the possibilities which it opens up will be well equipped to continue their study here. Unlike Coleman I have considered a relatively narrow range of topics and, viewing them as a statistician, have laid greater emphasis on the mathematical analysis. However, I have offered some advice to ease the path of the non-mathematical reader at the end of Chapter 1.

The book is also written for research workers, teachers and students of mathematics and statistics to whom it offers a field of application which is both mathematically stimulating and practically important. Although not written primarily as a textbook I hope that it will be used in conjunction with post-graduate or final year undergraduate courses. On the mathematical side it might well supplement the current range of texts whose applications are almost exclusively oriented towards the physical and biological sciences. The book is not intended to give a systematic account of the theory of stochastic processes but the student who works carefully through it will become acquainted with many of the main branches of that theory. No exercises have been included but there are many points at which the student can attempt to justify or extend the argument.

When the idea for writing this book was conceived nearly ten years ago the amount of material available was very limited but during the last few years there has been a rapid growth of interest in the mathematical study of social systems. One of the more conspicuous signs of this interest was the international conference on Operational Research and the Social Sciences held at Cambridge in 1964. A NATO conference on Operational and Personnel Research in the Management of Manpower Systems which took place in Brussels in 1965 is another of many examples which could be quoted. The time is perhaps ripe for a full discussion of some of the basic tools which have been developed in this area.

Some parts of the book are based upon research which has not previously appeared in print. When I began writing in 1964 I imagined that existing published material could be incorporated into an ordered account with little modification. It soon became apparent that nothing less than a wholesale recasting of some of the older work would suffice. Most of the material in Chapters 4 and 5 and parts of Chapters 2, 3 and 8 has been modified to a degree which may make its origins hard to discern. Chapters 6 and 7 are largely an account of my own research.

An author who ventures into the no-man's land between established disciplines runs many risks. In trying to speak to both sides he may fail to communicate with either. Writing as a statistician it is difficult to avoid being carried away by the love for generality which is of the very essence of mathematics. To counteract this tendency I have worked out numerical examples wherever possible and have tried to draw out the practical implications of the results. The social scientist may feel, justifiably, that some of the examples are artificial and that the interpretations placed upon the conclusions are naive. The mathematician may become impatient with the amount of time spent on mathematical trivia. To go ahead with the project in the face of such known hazards may seem foolhardy to many but I am optimistic enough to hope that the next decade will see collaboration between mathematicians and social scientists to a point where apologies are no longer necessary.

D. J. BARTHOLOMEW

Aberystwyth

ACKNOWLEDGMENTS

The final form of this book owes much to the advice, criticism and encouragement of many people. It is impossible at this stage to list all their names or to identify their contributions which have long since become part of my own thinking. However, I cannot overlook the assistance I have received from four of these people.

Clive Payne was my research assistant during the academic year 1965–66 and has collaborated closely with me since then. Almost all of the new calculations in Chapters 3 and 8 are his work. Without his prompt and efficient programming assistance the content of these chapters would have been seriously impoverished. He has also helped in the preparation of the other chapters. His willing help has often exceeded the bounds of duty.

Daryl Daley's interest in Chapter 8 has been invaluable. This began when he introduced me to the models which he and D. G. Kendall were developing for the spread of rumours. More recently he has read and checked the manuscript of Chapter 8, offering numerous ideas for its improvement and extension. My only regret is that I have not yet had an opportunity to follow up all of his suggestions.

After giving a seminar in Cambridge in February 1966 I discovered that John Pollard had developed the theory for finding the moments of the strata sizes for the models of Chapters 2 and 3. He gave generously of his time to explain the method to me and then carried out extensive calculations from which those in Table 3.2 have been extracted. His reading of the manuscript of these chapters has served to remove several errors.

Professor James Coleman read the final version of the manuscript and I have much appreciated his advice and encouragement.

Early versions of Chapter 2 and the first part of Chapter 8 were written early in 1965 at Harvard University when the work was supported by contract Nonr 1866(37) between the Office of Naval Research and Harvard University.

Permission to quote from their publications was given by the D. Van Nostrand Company Inc. in respect of Kemeny and Snell's *Finite Markov Chains* and by the New York State School of Industrial and Labour Relations, Cornell University, in respect of Blumen, Kogan, and McCarthy's *The Industrial Mobility of Labour as a Probability Process*.

I owe a special debt to Mrs. Nona Rees of the Department of Statistics, Aberystwyth, who typed the manuscript accurately and cheerfully amid many other demands on her time. The final word of thanks must be to my wife who has accepted this piece of work as part of the domestic scene and has shared in all those chores without which the idea could never have become a reality.

CONTENTS

CHAPTER 1

INTRODUCTION

1. STOCHASTIC THEORY AND SOCIAL PHENOMENA

A stochastic process is one which develops in time according to probabilistic laws. This means that we cannot predict its future behaviour with
certainty; the most that we can do is to attach probabilities to the various
possible future states. Such processes occur widely in nature and their
study has provided the impetus for the rapid development of the theory of
stochastic processes in the last two decades. Most of the applications of
the theory have been to problems in the physical and biological sciences
where the ideas of quantitative analysis were already familiar. Progress
has been much slower in the social sciences, one reason being the lack of
persons qualified in both mathematics and the social sciences. A more
fundamental reason is that many of the basic problems of measurement in
the social sciences remain unsolved and so constitute a barrier to the
application of sophisticated mathematical techniques. In spite of these
difficulties there have been some notable achievements. For example, in
psychology Bush and Mosteller (1955), have developed stochastic learning
models. More recently, Steindhl (1965) has demonstrated the possibilities
for stochastic analysis in the field of economics. Coleman (1964), in his
Introduction to Mathematical Sociology, has laid the foundations for the
stochastic treatment of many parts of sociological theory. At a more
elementary level the book by Kemeny and Snell (1962) introduces under-
graduates to the mathematical and stochastic study of the social sciences.
There have been other contributions scattered throughout journals whose
fields of interest impinge on the social sciences. These represent the work
of psychologists, statisticians, actuaries, biologists, mathematicians and
others but lack of effective communication between them has hindered the
full development of this work.

In this book our aim is to contribute to the understanding of social
phenomena by subjecting them to stochastic analysis. We shall not attempt
to cover the whole spectrum of the social sciences or even to give an
exhaustive treatment of any one branch. All the topics which will be
discussed can be broadly classified as being within the province of sociology. Some of them could equally well be included under such headings
as 'Management Science' or 'Operational Research' but arguments about
subject boundaries seem particularly futile when exploring new territory.

Some of the possibilities for co-operation between specialists in these fields is fore-shadowed in Lawrence (1966).

In common with most branches of applied mathematics we lay the foundations for the theoretical study by constructing mathematical models. The non-mathematical reader will be aware of the use made of actual physical models by engineers. For example, facts about the behaviour of an aircraft are deduced from the behaviour of the model under simulated flight conditions. The accuracy of these deductions will depend on the success with which the model embodies the features of the actual aircraft. The aircraft and the model differ in many respects. They may be of different size and made of different materials; many of the detailed fittings not directly concerned with flight behaviour will be omitted from the model. The important thing about the model is not that it should be exactly like the real thing but that it should behave in a wind tunnel like the aircraft in flight. The basic requirement is thus that the aircraft and the model should be *isomorphous* in all *relevant* respects.

A mathematical model is used in an entirely analogous way. In the social systems, which we shall discuss, the constituent parts are inter-related. When one characteristic is changed there will be consequential changes in other parts of the system. Provided that the changes in question can be quantified these inter-relationships can be described, in principle at least, by mathematical equations. A set of equations which purports to describe the behaviour of the system is a mathematical model. Its adequacy is judged by the success with which it can predict the effects of changes in the social system which it describes and by whether or not it can account for changes which have occurred in the past. The model is an abstraction of the real world in which the relevant relations between the real elements are replaced by similar relations between mathematical entities.

Mathematical models may be deterministic or stochastic. If the effect of any change in the system can be predicted with certainty the system is said to be deterministic. In practice, especially in the social sciences, this is not the case. Either because the system is not fully specified or because of the unpredictable character of much human behaviour there is usually an element of uncertainty in any prediction. This uncertainty can be accommodated if we introduce probability distributions into the model in place of mathematical variables. More precisely this means that the equations of the model will have to include random variables. Such a model is described as stochastic.

The necessity of using stochastic models in this book can be seen by considering some of the phenomena which we shall discuss. In the case of social mobility for instance, no one can predict with certainty whether or not a son will follow in his father's footsteps. Similarly there is, in general, no certain means of telling when a man will decide to change his job or whether a student will pass his examination. In the same way the diffusion of news in a social group depends, to a large extent, on chance encounters between members of the group. It is the inherent uncertainty brought about by the freedom of choice available to the individual which compels us to formulate our models in stochastic terms. As we shall see later, there are often advantages in using deterministic methods to obtain approximations to stochastic models but this does not affect the basic nature of the process. There has often been debate among sociologists about the rival merits of deterministic and stochastic methods. It should be clear from the above discussion that any model describing human behaviour should be formulated in stochastic terms. When it comes to the solution of the models it may be advisable to use a deterministic approximation. The greater simplicity of the deterministic version of a model may also make it easier to grasp the nature of the phenomena in question. Nevertheless these are tactical questions which do not affect the basic principle which we have laid down.

2. FUNCTIONS OF THE MODEL

Stochastic models of social phenomena have been constructed in the past with different objects in view. For our purposes it will be useful to distinguish four main functions of models. The first is to give *insight* into and *understanding* of the phenomenon in question. This is the activity characteristic of the pure scientist. The investigation begins with the collection of data on the process and the formulation of a model which embodies the observed features of the system. This we shall describe as the *model-building* stage. The next step is to use the model to make predictions about the system which can be tested by observation. This activity will require the use of mathematics to make deductions from the model and will be referred to as *model-solving*. The final phase is to compare the deductions with the real world and to modify the original model if it proves to be inadequate; this is the procedure of *model-testing*. An investigation of this kind is not complete until the operation of the system has been accurately and comprehensively described in mathematical terms and when the solution of the equations which arise has been obtained.

The second and third objectives in model building fall within the province of the applied social scientist. Of these the use of models for *prediction* is widely recognized. The social planner wants to know what is likely to happen if specific policies are implemented. The manager wishes to know, in advance, the consequences of various recruitment or promotion policies for the staffing of his firm. A model which adequately describes the behaviour of the system will be capable of providing answers to such questions.

Closely related to the problem of prediction is the question of the *design* of social systems and their mode of operation. Some of the models for hierarchical organizations described in Chapters 3, 5 and 7 were first constructed to establish principles for the design of recruitment and promotion policies. The management structure of a firm has to be such that it provides the correct number of people with the requisite skills and experience at each level to carry out the functions of the organization efficiently. Whether or not this object is achieved depends on the man-power policies of the firm. Hence it is necessary to evaluate competing policies in terms of their success in attaining the stated objectives. In the natural sciences it is usually possible to conduct experiments to answer questions analogous to those above. In the social sciences this is rarely possible or desirable. For example, it is not feasible to alter the manage-ment structure of a firm or to change a person's occupation in the interests of pure research. Even if such an experiment were permissible it would not achieve the ends for which it was designed. The very fact that people know themselves to be the subject of experiment is sufficient to influence their behaviour and so vitiate the experiment†. To some extent the model provides the social scientist with a substitute for the natural scientist's laboratory. It is possible to experiment in the 'world' generated by the model; if this faithfully mirrors reality the results of these experiments will be applicable to the real world.

The suggestion that mathematical methods may lead to the manipulation of social systems is often viewed with misgivings by sociologists and others who have a concern for individual freedom. A discussion of this important question would be out of place here. Let it suffice to remark that the problem is not peculiar to sociology but arises whenever new knowledge places power in the hands of its discoverers. It can be used for good or ill.

The fourth contribution which stochastic modelling can make to social research is in the field of measurement. This statement may appear para-doxical in view of our earlier remark that lack of suitable measures has itself hindered the development of stochastic models. Both statements are true but at different levels of sophistication as the following examples will show. In several applied fields research workers have become aware that the obvious but crude measures they were using were inadequate. For example, the success of a treatment for cancer is often assessed by calcu-lating the proportion of patients who survive for a given period, say 5 years. However, this measure is influenced by irrelevant factors such as

† Professor R. Emerson has pointed out to me that such a situation may neverthe-less be worth studying even though the object of the experiment is not achieved.

'natural' mortality which should, ideally, be eliminated from the measure. Fix and Neyman (1951), showed how this could be done by constructing a stochastic model of the post-treatment period and estimating one of its parameters (see Chapter 4). Another example arose in the study of labour turnover. A widely used method of measuring turnover is to express the number of people leaving a firm per unit time as a percentage of the average labour force during the same period. Large values of the measure were often taken as indicative of low morale. The measure is inadequate because it ignores the strong dependence of propensity to leave on length of service. This dependence is such that a firm with a large number of new recruits will have a misleadingly high figure of turnover. By constructing the renewal theory model of Chapter 6, it was possible to demonstrate the limitations of the usual index and to determine the conditions under which it could be meaningfully used. The results of this study emphasized the advantages of measures of turnover based on the mean or median length of service.

3. OBJECTIONS TO THE USE OF STOCHASTIC THEORY IN THE SOCIAL SCIENCES

The use of mathematical methods in the social sciences is in its infancy. It is not surprising therefore that the advocates of the quantitative approach should find their methods subject to criticism. This is especially true in the case of the application of stochastic processes where few sociologists have the competence to judge the claims which are made. Some of this criticism doubtless arises from reluctance to change established methods and habits of thought but some deserves serious consideration. Our object in dealing with the substantive objections is not primarily to contribute to the debate but to clarify the nature and especially the limitations of our methods.

It is often argued that there is a fundamental discontinuity between the natural and social sciences. According to this view the attempt to extend the application of stochastic theory into the social sciences is doomed to failure because of the essential difference in the subject matter of the two branches of science. While it may be reasonable to use stochastic models for molecular or even animal behaviour it is absurd to suppose, the argument runs, that the same laws are applicable to human behaviour; to treat human beings as subject to 'laws' seems to be depriving them of freedom of choice. This objection rests on a misunderstanding of the role of probability theory in model-building. It is precisely because man is a free agent that his behaviour is unpredictable and hence must be described in probabilistic terms. The only alternative is to adopt a deterministic point of view; it is this and not the stochastic approach which is open to the charge of making man an automaton. An example may help to reinforce the point. In Chapter 2, we shall discuss a model of labour mobility. As part of this model we shall postulate a chance mechanism to describe the movement of workers from one job to another. The objection in this case would be that a man does not make this decision by resort to dice or fortune tellers. Instead he considers the advantages and disadvantages of remaining in his present employment and so arrives at a responsible and rational decision. Our contention is not that the employee actually uses a chance device to make the decision but that the group behaves *as if* its individual members did use such a method. The function of probability theory is thus simply to describe observed variability; it carries no implications about the freedom, or otherwise, of human choice. It is a fact of experience that 'choice may mimic chance'.

A second objection arises from the complexity of social phenomena. This is often expressed by saying that social situations are far too complicated to allow mathematical study and that to ignore this fact is to be led into dangerous over-simplification. The premiss of this objection must be accepted. Social phenomena are often exceedingly complex and our models are bound to be simplifications. Even if it is allowed that our model need only reproduce the relevant features of the real process the problem remains formidable. However, we would argue that there is no alternative to simplification. The basic limiting factor is not the mathematical apparatus available but the ability of the human mind to grasp a complex situation. There is no point in building models whose ramifications are beyond our comprehension. Perhaps the only safeguard against over-simplification is to use a battery of models instead of a single one. Any particular model will be a special case of the more complex model which would be needed to achieve complete realism. Greater confidence can be placed in conclusions which are common to several special cases than in those applicable to one arbitrarily selected model. In many places, especially Chapter 7, the strategy dictated by these considerations will be evident. Instead of making 'realistic' assumptions and accepting the complexity which goes with them we have made two, or more, 'unrealistic' but simple assumptions. Where possible these have been selected as extremes between which the true situation must lie. If the conclusions about a particular question are similar we may apply them to the real life situation without abandoning the framework of thought provided by the simple model.

The art of model building is to know where and when to simplify. The object, as Coleman (1964) has expressed it, is to condense as much as possible of reality into a simple model. Not only does this give us understanding of the system but it provides a convenient base-line with which to compare the behaviour of actual systems.

The remarks made above should not be interpreted as justifying unlimited simplification. They apply, of course, to the model building stage of the process but this cannot be considered in isolation from the model solving aspects. In the past the temptation to trim the model to a form having a tractable mathematical solution has been strong. The situation has been radically altered by the wide availability of high speed computers but the habits of thought of the old era linger on. It is no longer necessary for a solution to be obtainable in closed form in terms of simple functions in order to yield useful information about the process.

The presence of computers leads to a third and more subtle objection to the model-solving aspects of the subject. A parallel situation is found in the theory of queues where a great volume of effort has been devoted to the solution of special models. It is argued that, from a practical point of view, the results can be obtained more easily and rapidly by simulation on a computer. The same argument applies in the social sciences. If our objective is simply to obtain a quick answer in a specific situation, simulation will usually be the best method of attack. In applied social science this will be the norm and the practitioner in the field will find that his interest is in the model building aspects of the book. On the other hand, if our primary interest in stochastic models is to gain insight into the workings of social phenomena, simulation is less satisfactory. In essence, we are then searching for general solutions whereas simulation provides us with solutions in special cases only. The economy and clarity of a conclusion conveyed by a simple formula is such that the effort of problem solving is well worthwhile even if we have to be content with an approximation.

4. PLAN OF THE BOOK

In a new and rapidly developing subject it would be premature to claim that a complete and systematic treatment of our subject can be given. It is not possible to cast the presentation of each model into a standard mould. Many of the models were first published in research journals covering many subjects and spanning a period extending over 30 years. The different backgrounds and interests of the authors gives the original material a fragmentary appearance. We have attempted to unify the notation, terminology and methodology and to extend the analysis where possible. In some cases this treatment has been very drastic especially for that work which originated in an actuarial context. In spite of the extensive re-working which has been undertaken much unevenness remains. Some of the models are well-established; they have passed through the stages of model building, solving, testing and rebuilding. Their adequacy can be tested and demonstrated by reference to published data. Other models are much more recent in origin and the data required to test their adequacy is not yet available. It is to be hoped that the incompleteness revealed by our presentation will serve to stimulate further research.

In spite of the variety of models and methods there is a common basic pattern underlying the discussion of each model. The members of the system being studied will, at any given time, be in one of a set of possible 'states'. These states may be discrete—for example, the social or occupational classes—or they may form a continuum. An example of the latter is the number of people in a given occupational group with x years of service in that group. The principal object of the analysis is to find the expectations of the numbers in the classes at any time. After an introduction we shall usually begin by describing the basic model. This involves a description of the system and of the probabilistic laws which govern transitions between states. Where possible the assumptions which are made at this stage are tested against data. Next we proceed as far as possible with the model solving aspect of the problem and conclude with any generalizations which are possible and a discussion of the light which the analysis throws on the general problem.

The line of development in the book is from the simple to the complex. This applies, broadly speaking, both to the social phenomena studied and to the mathematical theory. In order to help the reader trace this line of development we shall describe three methods of classifying the models.

One method of classification is according to whether the model is closed or open. These terms appear to have various connotations in sociology. They are used here in a direct and obvious sense which carries no judgement value. The membership of a closed system does not change over time; no persons leave and none are admitted. Models of this kind are described in Chapters 2, 4 and 8. Our interest there centres upon the changing internal structure of the system. An open system has both gains and losses. We are still interested in internal changes but, in addition, there are changes in the input, output and total size to be considered. Some of the systems we shall study lose members but have no input of new members. Such systems are treated as closed by introducing a state to include all the losses and regarding it as part of the system. It is, of course, possible to convert open systems into closed ones by this kind of device but we have not found this to be convenient and so prefer to retain the distinction.

A second method of classification depends on whether time is treated as discrete or continuous. The choice is partly a matter of realism and partly one of convenience. In some applications changes of state can only take place at fixed intervals of time. If the model of Chapter 3 is used to predict university enrolments then the natural unit of time is the term, quarter or year and a discrete time model is thus more realistic. In the case of the labour mobility models changes of job can take place at any time and a continuous time model is therefore appropriate. However, we can sometimes profitably take advantage of the fact that a discrete time model can be used to approximate a system in continuous time and vice versa. In applied research where it is necessary to compute solutions the discrete version of a model is usually easier to handle. But if we are interested mainly in the mathematical analysis of the model we shall often find that the techniques for handling the continuous time version are more readily available.

Finally, the models presented in this book can be dichotomized according to whether or not they possess the Markov property. In essence this requires that it be possible to deduce the future development of the process from knowledge of its present state. Information about the history of the process has no predictive value. This is a severe and sometimes unrealistic restriction. The advantage of working with Markovian models is that the mathematical analysis is more tractable. In consequence the theory of Markov processes is much better developed. However, even when the Markov assumption is invalid, it may not prove to be critical. In other cases the assumption can be made more realistic by re-defining the states of the system. Where necessary we have used non-Markovian models, for example in Chapters 6, 7 and 8, but it will usually be found in such cases that the results obtained are more limited in their scope.

Throughout the book we have concentrated on finding the mean values of the random variables of interest. This emphasis reflects the rudimentary state of the theory and future developments should be directed to finding the complete distribution theory. In physical applications where, for example, the number of molecules in a system is very large the mean values are sufficient. In a social system the number of members may be relatively small and the mean values will then give an incomplete and perhaps misleading picture of the process. Some recent work by Pollard (1966 and 1967), giving a method of finding the distribution theory for the Markov chain models of Chapters 2 and 3, has been included. Elsewhere we have sometimes quoted results of simulation studies but much more remains to be done.

At the model testing stage problems of statistical inference arise. Methods of estimating the parameters of a model and of testing the goodness of fit are often required. The statistical theory which is available for this purpose in the theory of stochastic processes is still very meagre. We have made no contribution to this problem. Where it has proved necessary to estimate a parameter we have used the most obvious method available without considering its efficiency. While such a practice is permissible in the early stages of the development of a subject in order to establish a bridgehead, it should not be taken as a pattern for future work.

5. NOTES FOR THE NON-MATHEMATICAL READER

It will be evident from a quick perusal of the following pages that a wide range of mathematical techniques has been used. The treatment is informal and non-rigorous but even so, many social scientists who are interested in the subject matter may find themselves in difficulty. The only completely satisfactory solution to this problem is for the person concerned to learn more mathematics. In the long term we hope that mathematics will become a regular part of the sociologist's education in rather the same way as it is for the engineer today. Nevertheless it should be possible to obtain a good idea of the problems, methods and results by reading between the formulae. We have tried to express the conclusions in words but they are more adequately conveyed by the formulae and tables which follow from the analysis. Conclusions which seem to have considerable practical importance and generality have been printed in italics. The non-mathematical reader must appreciate that mathematics is a very condensed language and hence be prepared to spend the time necessary to extract the meaning of simple formulae. He would be well-advised to compute numerical examples and draw graphs until the meaning conveyed by a formula is clear to him. In some cases this has already been done in the text but, to conserve space, we have usually been content to point out only the most important results of the analysis. The ability to write computer programmes in a language such as FORTRAN or ALGOL would be a great advantage for those who wish to fully explore the models.

The newcomer to the theory of stochastic processes will find that much of the treatment is self-contained. The remainder draws frequently upon standard results. There are now many textbooks and monographs on the theory of stochastic processes. Those most commonly referred to in this book are those by Bailey (1964), Parzen (1962), Cox and Miller (1965) and Bartlett (1955), but this list is far from being exhaustive.

CHAPTER 2

MODELS FOR SOCIAL AND LABOUR MOBILITY

1. INTRODUCTION

Human societies are often stratified into classes on the basis of such things as income, occupation or family background. A great deal of quantitative research has been carried out by sociologists and others into the class structure of society. Much of this work seeks to describe the structure and to correlate it with other attributes of the population. It is thus usually concerned with presenting a static picture of the society at a particular point in time. In this chapter we shall be concerned with the dynamic aspects of the problem. That is, we shall construct models to represent the changes which take place in the structure as time progresses. Our development will be centred upon two basic models. The first, for social mobility, was originally proposed by Prais (1955). The second, for labour mobility, is the work of Blumen, Kogan and McCarthy (1955). Similar models have been used by Hart and Prais (1956), Adelman (1958) and Preston and Bell (1961), to account for the distribution of the size of firms. Prais's work has been developed in a demographic context by Matras (1960a), (1960b) and (1966). The present chapter contains a presentation of the basic theory underlying these models and some new developments of them. In particular we have used a method due to Pollard (1966), to derive variances and covariances of strata sizes.

The dynamics of social structure can only be adequately described in stochastic terms. Sons do not always follow in their fathers' footsteps and even if they did the varying numbers of offspring in the different classes would lead to fluctuations in the class sizes. Similarly, in a free society, a man has some degree of choice about changing his employment. The inherent uncertainty of such processes means that their future cannot be predicted with certainty but only in probabilistic terms. The advantage of a stochastic model of social or occupational mobility is that it enables us to make predictions for the future and also to assess the likely error of those predictions. As we have already remarked in the first chapter it also serves as a guide in the construction of measures of phenomena such as mobility. The practical value of prediction for occupational mobility is considerable. It enables changes in demand for special skills to be

11

anticipated and provides a necessary ingredient for long term economic planning.

In formulating and analysing our models we shall make much use of the theory of Markov chains in discrete time. Elementary accounts of the theory can be found, for example, in Kemeny and Snell (1960), Parzen (1962), Bailey (1964) and Cox and Miller (1965). In Section 2.5, we shall encounter a branching process and the model of Section 3, is a semi-Markov process. However, in both cases our treatment will be elementary and self-contained. The Markov chain models of the present chapter also form the basis of the models developed in Chapter 3.

A characteristic of both of the main models described in this chapter is that they are closed. Strictly speaking neither of the social systems to which we shall apply our theory is closed in an absolute sense. Nevertheless we shall find it possible to treat them as closed without any significant loss of realism. As we pointed out in Chapter 1, an open system can always be turned into a closed one by introducing artificial strata from which new members come and to which departing members go. Adelman (1958) used this device but we shall find it more convenient to dispense with it and to retain the distinction between open and closed systems.

An important difference between the models lies in the nature of the 'time' variable. In the case of social mobility we shall consider changes in structure from one generation to the next. Time is thus measured in terms of generations and will take positive integer values. The application to occupational mobility requires us to work in 'real' time since a man may change his job at any time. In practice, data on the state of the system are often only available at equidistant points in time. Thus, although our model will be formulated in terms of a continuous time variable, we shall have to analyse it in discrete terms.

2. MODELS FOR SOCIAL MOBILITY

2.1. The Basic Model

First we consider a very simple model for the development of a single family line and then, in later sections, investigate the consequences of removing its more unrealistic features. The fundamental requirement in a model is that it must specify the way in which changes in social class occur. We shall assume that these are governed by transition probabilities which are independent of time. Let p_{ij} denote the probability that the son of a father in class i is in class j; since the system is closed

$$\sum_{=1}^{k} p_{ij} = 1$$

where k is the number of classes. Following Bailey (1964), we denote by **P** the *transpose* of the matrix of transition probabilities.† This convention introduces notational simplification while still retaining the usual order of subscripts for the transition probability. If we consider only family lines in which each father has exactly one son the class history of the family will be a Markov chain. By regarding society as composed of such family lines we could make deductions about the changing structure of society. In practice the requirement that each father shall have exactly one son is not met. As a result some lines become extinct and others branch. However, in a population whose size remains constant over a period of time, each father will have *on average* one son. We may expect our results for the simple model to apply in an average sense in such an actual society. In Section 2.5, we shall place this reasoning on a firmer footing and show that this expectation is fulfilled.

Suppose that the probability that the initial progenitor of a family line is in class j at time zero is $p_j(0)$. Let the probability that the line is in class j at time T $(T = 1, 2, 3, \ldots)$ be $p_j(T)$. The probabilities $\{p_j(T)\}$ can then be computed recursively from the fact that

$$p_j(T) = \sum_{i=1}^{k} pi(T-1)\, p_{ij} \quad (i = 1, 2, \ldots, k). \tag{2.1}$$

In matrix notation these equations may be written as

$$\mathbf{p}(T) = \mathbf{P}\mathbf{p}(T-1) \tag{2.2}$$

where $\mathbf{p}(T) = (p_1(T), p_2(T), \ldots, p_k(T))'$. Repeated application of equation (2.2), gives

$$\mathbf{p}(T) = \mathbf{P}^T \mathbf{p}(0). \tag{2.3}$$

The elements of $\mathbf{p}(T)$ may also be interpreted as the expected proportions of the population in the various classes at time T. If the original classes of the family lines are known the vector $\mathbf{p}(0)$ would then represent the initial class structure.

The matrix $\mathbf{P}^T$ plays a fundamental role in the theory of Markov chains. It can be used to obtain the 'state' probabilities from equation (2.3), but its elements also have a direct probabilistic interpretation. Let $p_{ij}^{(T)}$ denote the (i, j)th element in the transpose of $\mathbf{P}^T$ then equation (2.3), may be written

$$p_j(T) = \sum_{i=1}^{k} p_i(0) p_{ij}^{(T)} \quad (i = 1, 2, \ldots k). \tag{2.4}$$

---

† When writing out tables of transition probabilities we shall follow the usual practice of putting the value of p_{ij} in the ith row and jth column.

It is clear from this representation that $p_{ij}^{(T)}$ is the probability that a family line goes from class i to class j in T generations. The case $i = j$ is of special interest as the probabilities $p_{ii}^{(T)}$ can be made the basis of measures of mobility.

In many applications the population has been in existence for many generations so that the 'present' state corresponds to a large value of T. It is therefore of considerable practical interest to investigate the behaviour of the probabilities $\{p_i(T)\}$ and $\{p_{ij}^{(T)}\}$ as T tends to infinity. It is shown in the general theory of Markov chains that this limiting behaviour depends on the structure of the matrix $\mathbf{P}$. Provided that the matrix $\mathbf{P}$ is *regular* it may be shown that these probabilities all approach limits as T tends to infinity. A regular (finite) Markov chain is one in which it is possible to be in any state (class) after some number, T, of generations, no matter what the initial state. More precisely, a necessary and sufficient condition for the chain to be regular is that all of the elements of $\mathbf{P}^T$ are non-zero for some T. All transition matrices which are likely to occur in the present context are regular but, later in the book, we shall meet examples which do not possess this property.

With the existence of the limits assured it is a straightforward matter to calculate them. Thus if we write $\lim_{T \to \infty} p_j(T) = p_j$ it follows from equation (2.2) that the limiting structure must satisfy

$$\mathbf{p} = \mathbf{P}\mathbf{p} \qquad (2.5)$$

with

$$\sum_{j=1}^{k} p_j = 1.$$

The limiting structure, or distribution, can thus be obtained by solving a set of simultaneous equations. An important property of the solution is that it does not depend on the initial state of the system. Since, by our assumptions, each family line extant will have reached the equilibrium given by equation (2.5), the vector $\mathbf{p}$ gives the expected structure of the population at the present time. If this structure is all that can be observed we have no means of reconstructing the transition matrix. Neither, in fact, can we deduce $\mathbf{P}$ from two consecutive observed structures $\mathbf{p}(T)$ and $\mathbf{p}(T - 1)$ although White (1963) and Matras (1966) have considered what incomplete information can be obtained in these circumstances. The limiting value of $\mathbf{P}^T$, denoted by $\mathbf{P}^\infty$, can be deduced from equation (2.3). It must satisfy

$$\mathbf{p} = \mathbf{P}^\infty \mathbf{p}\,(0)$$

which can only be so if

$$\mathbf{P}^{\infty} = \begin{pmatrix} p_1 & \cdot & \cdot & p_1 & \cdot & \cdot & p_1 \\ p_2 & \cdot & \cdot & p_2 & \cdot & \cdot & p_2 \\ & \cdot & & & \cdot & & \cdot \\ & \cdot & & & \cdot & & \cdot \\ & \cdot & & & \cdot & & \cdot \\ p_k & \cdot & \cdot & p_k & \cdot & \cdot & p_k \end{pmatrix} \tag{2.6}$$

which implies that

$$\lim_{T \to \infty} p_{ij}^{(T)} = p_j. \tag{2.7}$$

The foregoing analysis shows that if our model provides an adequate description of actual societies then their future development depends only on their initial structure and the transition matrix. Of these two features the initial distribution has a diminishing influence as time passes. In the long run, therefore, the structure of the society is determined by its transition matrix. This conclusion implies that the study of mobility must be centred upon the transition probabilities. In particular, *measures* of mobility should be functions of the elements of **P**. Before pursuing this proposal we may test the adequacy of the model using actual data on mobility.

2.2. Test of the Adequacy of the Model

Two empirical studies of mobility have been published which give sufficient data to provide a partial test of the theory. One of these due to Glass and Hall (Glass, 1954) is based on a random sample of 3,500 pairs of fathers and sons in Britain. A second study made by Rogoff (1953) is based on data from marriage licence applications in Marion County, Indiana. Rogoff obtained data for two periods; one from 1905 to 1912, with a sample size of 10,253 and a second from 1938 to 1941, when the sample size was 9,892.

The data obtained by Glass and Hall were used by Prais (1955) and much of the material in this section is taken from his paper. Glass and Hall classified the members of their sample according to the seven occupational groups listed in Table 2.1, which also gives the estimated transition probabilities.

The last row and last column of the table give the class structure of the population in two succeeding generations. If the Markov model is adequate and if the society has reached equilibrium we would expect these distributions to be the same apart from sampling fluctuations. We would

TABLE 2.1

Estimated transition probabilities for England and Wales in 1949
(Glass and Hall's data).

		Son's Class					
Father's Class	1	2	3	4	5	6	7
1. Professional and higher administrative	0.388	0.146	0.202	0.062	0.140	0.047	0.015
2. Managerial and executive	0.107	0.267	0.227	0.120	0.206	0.053	0.020
3. Higher grade supervisory and non-manual	0.035	0.101	0.188	0.191	0.357	0.067	0.061
4. Lower grade supervisory and non-manual	0.021	0.039	0.112	0.212	0.430	0.124	0.062
5. Skilled manual and routine non-manual	0.009	0.024	0.075	0.123	0.473	0.171	0.125
6. Semi-skilled manual	0.000	0.013	0.041	0.088	0.391	0.312	0.155
7. Unskilled manual	0.000	0.008	0.036	0.083	0.364	0.235	0.274

also expect them both to agree with the equilibrium distribution obtained
from equation (2.5). Prais (1955) made the calculations necessary for this
comparison and his results are given in Table 2.2.

TABLE 2.2

Actual and equilibrium distributions of the social
classes in England and Wales (1949), estimated from
Glass and Hall's data.

Class	Fathers	Sons	Predicted Equilibrium
1	0.037	0.029	0.023
2	0.043	0.046	0.042
3	0.098	0.094	0.088
4	0.148	0.131	0.127
5	0.432	0.409	0.409
6	0.131	0.170	0.182
7	0.111	0.121	0.129

The differences between the three distributions are not large although
there does appear to be a shift towards the lower classes as we move across
the table. If this trend is genuine and not merely the result of sampling
fluctuations it might be taken to indicate that the process had not reached
equilibrium. Another possible explanation is discussed in Section 2.4. A

complete answer to the question of sampling error is not available but a first step towards the solution of the problem is given in Section 2.3. Although we cannot obtain a complete test of the model using these data it does appear that there is a broad compatibility between the data and the predictions of the theory.

Rogoff's data lead to similar conclusions about the applicability of Markov chain theory to social mobility. She obtained information at two dates separated by 30 years and so we can see whether there had been any significant change in the transition probabilities during that period. The two transition matrices are given in Table 2.3.

TABLE 2.3

Transition probabilities estimated from Rogoff's data for
Marion County, Indiana.†

	1905–1912			1938–1941		
	1	2	3	1	2	3
1. Non-manual	0.594	0.396	0.009	0.622	0.375	0.003
2. Manual	0.211	0.782	0.007	0.274	0.721	0.005
3. Farm	0.252	0.641	0.108	0.265	0.694	0.042

† Taken from Kemeny and Snell's *Finite Markov Chains*. Copyright 1959, D. Van Nostrand Company, Inc., Princeton, N.J.

We have followed Kemeny and Snell (1960) in adopting a coarse grouping for the classes in place of Rogoff's very fine breakdown. Allowing for sampling error it appears that changes did take place in the transition matrix over the period in question. However, the changes are not large and suggest that we shall not be involved in gross error if we treat them as constant over moderately short periods.

Neither set of data allows us to make a direct test of the Markov property. This property requires that a son's class should depend only on that of his father and not on that of his grandfather. To test this assumption we need records of family history over at least three generations. Indirect support for the assumption is provided by the close agreement between the equilibrium class structure predicted by Markov theory and the observed class structure.

There are theoretical grounds for believing that the Markov property will not hold exactly for a social mobility process. These grounds arise from the fact that the class boundaries are drawn somewhat arbitrarily. Thus, for example, we could subdivide the seven categories used by Glass and Hall. Alternatively some classes could be amalgamated to give a smaller number of categories. It is known (see Kemeny and Snell 1960, Chapter 6), that if the states of a Markov chain are pooled then the new chain does not, in general, have the Markov property. In the present context this means that we cannot arbitrarily re-arrange the classes and retain the Markov property. Even if there is one system of classification for which the property holds this may not be the one which we happen to have chosen. However, as we have pointed out in Chapter 1, it is sufficient if our model embodies the main features of the process without being correct in every detail. To summarize: although the assumptions on which the theory depends are not completely realistic the model is sufficiently near to reality to justify its further use and development.

2.3. The Measurement of Mobility

It is convenient, especially when comparing two societies, to have a measure of mobility. According to the Markov model the society is characterized by the transition matrix and hence we are led to construct measures of mobility from the elements of the matrix. Numerous descriptive measures of mobility which depend on the transition proportions have been devised for empirical work. Some examples are listed in Matras (1960b). It is not our intention to give a full account of this important topic but rather to show the bearing which stochastic theory has upon the problem of measurement. We may begin by considering the form of the transition matrix under extreme degrees of mobility. In a completely immobile society sons will have the same class as their fathers and $\mathbf{P}$ will have 1's along its principal diagonal and zero's elsewhere. It is less easy to decide on the other end-point of our scale of mobility. Prais (1955) defined a perfectly mobile society as one in which the son's class is independent of his father's class. For such a society the columns of $\mathbf{P}$ will be identical. This may be a desirable social norm with which to compare existing societies but it does not coincide with the maximum amount of movement which can take place between classes. The point may be illustrated by considering the following transition matrices for $k = 2$:

$$\text{(a)} \begin{pmatrix} 1 & 0 \\ 0 & 1 \end{pmatrix} \quad \text{(b)} \begin{pmatrix} \frac{1}{2} & \frac{1}{2} \\ \frac{1}{2} & \frac{1}{2} \end{pmatrix} \quad \text{(c)} \begin{pmatrix} 0 & 1 \\ 1 & 0 \end{pmatrix}.$$

Case (a) represents the immobile society in which sons follow fathers; case (b) is one example of the perfectly mobile society as defined by Prais and (c) represents the extreme of movement in which every son has a different class from his father. We must therefore decide whether we are primarily interested in movement as such, or in deviation from some ideal such as that represented by (b). In practice it is likely that transition matrices will be intermediate between (a) and (b), but it could be important not to confuse (a) and (c).

One of the simplest measures of mobility when $k = 2$ is obtained by taking the determinant of $\mathbf{P}$. This takes the value 1 for an immobile society, 0 for Prais's perfectly mobile society and -1 when the maximum amount of movement takes place. This measure is less satisfactory when $k > 2$. It is zero whenever two columns of $\mathbf{P}$ are equal which implies perfect mobility for only two classes. Also, there is some ambiguity in deciding on the appropriate form of matrix to take the place of case (c). If we select the matrix

$$\begin{pmatrix} 0 & 0 & 1 \\ \frac{1}{2} & 0 & \frac{1}{2} \\ 1 & 0 & 0 \end{pmatrix}$$

for $k = 3$, the determinant is zero and the measure has the same value as for the very different situation when the columns are identical.

A more direct and meaningful measure is obtained by counting the class boundaries crossed in passing from one generation to the next. If $f_1, f_2, \ldots f_k$ are the numbers in the classes of a given generation then the expected number of class boundaries crossed in moving to the next generation is

$$\sum_{i=1}^{k} \sum_{j=1}^{k} f_i p_{ij} |i - j|.$$

This measure depends on which generation we choose as our base line. A more satisfactory version is obtained by replacing the f's by the equilibrium class structure. Our measure would then be defined as

$$D = \sum_{i=1}^{k} \sum_{i=1}^{k} p_i p_{ij} |i - j|. \tag{2.8}$$

This is near to zero if the p_{ii}'s are close to 1 for all i† and increases in value with the amount of movement. The behaviour of D in the case $k = 2$ is easily investigated. Here we have

$$p_1 = \frac{p_{21}}{p_{12} + p_{21}} \qquad p_2 = \frac{p_{12}}{p_{12} + p_{21}}$$

$$0 < p_{12}, p_{21} < 1$$

and hence

$$D = \frac{2p_{12}p_{21}}{p_{12} + p_{21}}.$$

† If $p_{ii} = 1$ for all i, $\mathbf{P}$ is not regular and the equilibrium distribution $\mathbf{p}$ does not exist. In this case we may define $D = 0$.

D varies between 0 for the immobile society and 1 for the extreme degree of movement represented by case (c) above. For Prais's perfectly mobile society $p_{12} = 1 - p_{21}$ and hence $D = 2p_{12}(1 - p_{12}) \leq \frac{1}{2}$. Our proposed measure is thus a genuine measure of movement rather than of closeness to the ideal represented by (c). A disadvantage of D for $k > 2$ is that it cannot be used for comparing two societies with different groupings of the classes.

Any measure which attempts to summarize the contents of the transition matrix into a single number is bound to result in over-simplification. A more detailed picture of the process can be obtained if we replace the single number by a set of numbers. Two proposals were made by Prais (1955), and these will now be described.

The first set of measures is obtained by considering only the main diagonal of **P**. Thus we consider only whether or not a transition takes place and we ignore the kind of transition. It is easy to see that the duration of stay in the jth class has a geometric distribution with mean $\mu_j = 1/(1 - p_{jj})$. In a mobile society these means will be small and in an immobile society they will be large. Prais suggested that the means might be standardized by expressing them in terms of the means for a standard population. He chose the perfectly mobile society with the same equilibrium structure as the given population. The measures are thus

$$\mu_j^* = (1 - p_j)/(1 - p_{jj}) \quad (i = 1, 2, \ldots, k). \tag{2.9}$$

The values of the μ_j^* for the data given in Table 2.1 are given in the following table:

TABLE 2.4

The expected stay in each social class for Glass and Hall's data.

Class (j)	$(1 - p_{jj})^{-1}$	$(1 - p_j)^{-1}$	$\mu_j^* = (1 - p_j)/(1 - p_{jj})$
1	1.63	1.02	1.59
2	1.36	1.04	1.30
3	1.23	1.10	1.12
4	1.27	1.15	1.11
5	1.90	1.69	1.12
6	1.45	1.22	1.19
7	1.38	1.15	1.20

Most of the figures in the last column of the table are close to 1, indicating that a high degree of mobility existed in England and Wales in 1949. The relatively high values for classes 1 and 2 are suggestive but may not be significant. Prais calculated standard errors for the μ_i and found that they lay between 0.54 and 1.30. It is thus clear that differences between entries in the last column must be treated with caution.

The measures $\{\mu_j^*\}$ depend only on the diagonal elements of **P**. The information contained in the off-diagonal elements can be utilized by enlarging the set of measures still further. A convenient and meaningful way to do this is to consider the diagonal elements of the matrices $\mathbf{P}^T$ for $T = 2, 3, \ldots$. The quantity $p_{jj}^{(T)}$ is the probability that a family line which is initially in class j is also in class j, T generations later. This probability will be near to 1 in an immobile society and relatively small in a mobile society. If we standardize this probability by dividing by $p_j = \lim_{T \to \infty} p_{jj}^{(T)}$ we obtain Prais's 'immobility ratios'. However, a point is rapidly reached where our set of measures contains more elements than the transition matrix itself. The immobility ratios are best regarded as an alternative way of presenting the information contained in **P** rather than summary measures of mobility.

2.4. The Variability of the Class Sizes

The theory developed so far enables us to calculate expected numbers, or proportions, in each class at any time in the future. So far we have no means of determining the variances and covariances of our predictions. A method for obtaining the moments and product moments of the class numbers has been given by Pollard (1966), and we shall now describe its application to this problem.

Let N denote the number of family lines in the population; this remains constant through time. Let the size of the jth class at time T be $n_j(T)$ and let the number of transitions between class i and class j between T and $T + 1$ be $n_{ij}(T)$. It follows from the definitions that

$$n_j(T + 1) = \sum_{i=1}^{k} n_{ij}(T) \quad (j = 1, 2, \ldots, k). \tag{2.10}$$

If we take expectations on each side of this equation we arrive at equation (2.1) because $En_j(T + 1) = Np_j(T + 1)$ and $En_{ij}(T) = Np_i(T)p_{ij}$. Consider the covariance of $n_j(T + 1)$ with $n_l(T + 1)$. It will simplify the presentation of the theory if we adopt the convention that cov $(x_i x_j) \equiv$ var (x_i) if $i = j$. We then have

$$\text{cov}\,\{n_j(T + 1)n_l(T + 1)\}$$

$$= E\{n_j(T + 1)n_l(T + 1)\} - En_j(T + 1)En_l(T + 1)$$

$$= \sum_{i=1}^{k} \sum_{i'=1}^{k} [E\{n_{ij}(T)n_{i'l}(T) - En_{ij}(T)En_{i'l}(T)\}] \tag{2.11}$$

by equation (2.10). In order to evaluate the expectations in equation (2.11), we make use of a well-known result about conditional expectations to the effect that $E(x) = E_X(x|X)$. In the present case we obtain the expectations conditional upon $n_i(T)$. These follow from the fact that, given $n_i(T)$, $n_{ij}(T)$ $(j = 1, 2, \ldots, k)$ are multinomially distributed with probabilities p_{ij} $(j = 1, 2, \ldots, k)$. Hence

$$E\{n_{ij}(T)|n_i(T)\} = n_i(T)p_{ij} \tag{2.12}$$

and

$$E\{n_{ij}(T)n_{i'l}(T)|n_i(T), n_i'(T)\} = n_i(T)n_{i'}(T)p_{ij}p_{i'l} \qquad (i \neq i'),$$

$$E\{n_{ij}(T)n_{il}(T)|n_i(T)\} = n_i(T)\{n_i(T) - 1\}p_{ij}p_{il} + \delta_{jl}n_i(T)p_{ij} \tag{2.13}$$

where $\delta_{jl} = 1$ if $j = l$ and is zero otherwise. The unconditional expectations are now obtained from equations (2.12) and (2.13), by taking the expectations of the right hand sides with respect to $n_i(T)$. Substituting these expressions in equation (2.11) then gives,

$$\text{cov}\{n_j(T+1), n_l(T+1)\} = \sum_{i=1}^{k} \sum_{i'=1}^{k} p_{ij}p_{i'l} \, \text{cov}\{n_i(T), n_{i'}(T)\}$$

$$+ \sum_{i=1}^{k} (\delta_{jl}p_{ij} - p_{ij}p_{il})En_i(T). \tag{2.14}$$

We have thus obtained a recurrence relation between the expectations and covariances at time T and the covariances at time $T + 1$. Since the covariances at $T = 0$ are zero the complete set can be computed from equations (2.14) and (2.1). If we require them the same method can be extended to yield the higher moments and product moments.

Since the expectations and covariances at $T + 1$ are linear functions of the corresponding quantities at T we can express the relationship in matrix notation. To do this we introduce the vector of means and covariances and denote it by $\mu(T)$. In this vector we first list the k means followed by the k^2 covariances in dictionary order, that is

$$\mu = [E(n_1), \ldots, E(n_k), \text{cov}(n_1n_1), \text{cov}(n_1n_2), \ldots, \text{cov}(n_1n_k),$$

$$\text{cov}(n_2n_1), \text{cov}(n_2n_2), \ldots, \text{cov}(n_2n_k), \ldots, \text{cov}(n_kn_k)],'$$

where we have omitted the arguments of the n's and μ for brevity. There is some redundancy in this listing because, for example, the covariance between n_1 and n_2 appears as $\text{cov}(n_1n_2)$ and as $\text{cov}(n_2n_1)$ but by retaining this the symmetry of the expressions is preserved. Equations (2.1) and (2.14) may now be combined and written in the form

$$\mu(T + 1) = \Pi\mu(T) \tag{2.15}$$

where the elements of the $k(k + 1) \times k(k + 1)$ matrix $\boldsymbol{\Pi}$ are functions of the p_{ij}'s. The matrix $\boldsymbol{\Pi}$ may be partitioned as follows

$$\begin{array}{c|c} \mathbf{P} & \mathbf{O} \\ \hline \mathbf{X} & \mathbf{Y} \end{array}$$

where $\mathbf{P}$ is the $k \times k$ transition matrix, $\mathbf{Q}$ is a $k \times k^2$ zero matrix, $\mathbf{X}$ is a $k^2 \times k$ matrix with elements of the form $\delta_{jl}p_{ij} - p_{ij}p_{il}$ and $\mathbf{Y}$ is a $k^2 \times k^2$ matrix with elements of the form $p_{ij}p_{i'l}$.† In the case of $\mathbf{X}$ and $\mathbf{Y}$, (j, l) indexes the row and i or (i, i') the columns.

Equation (2.15), is a generalization of equation (2.2) and it can be used in the same way. It is no longer true that $\mathbf{q}$ is a stochastic matrix because it has negative elements but the columns still sum to one. This fact can be used to deduce that the elements of $\boldsymbol{\mu}(T)$ tend to limits as T tends to infinity. Consequently these limits must satisfy the equations

$$\left.\begin{array}{c} \boldsymbol{\mu}(\infty) = \boldsymbol{\Pi}\boldsymbol{\mu}(\infty) \\ \sum_{i=1}^{k} \bar{n}_i(\infty) = N. \end{array}\right\} \tag{2.16}$$

where here, and subsequently, the bar denotes the expectation of the random variable. A computer programme is available to generate the vector $\boldsymbol{\mu}(T)$ for all T. We shall give some results of calculations in Chapter 3, for a more general model. We can get an idea of the kind of solution one obtains in the present application by considering a special case.

Suppose that we have a perfectly mobile society in Prais's sense with $p_{ij} = p_j$ $(i = 1, 2, \ldots, k)$. Equation (2.14) then simplifies to give

$$\operatorname{cov}\{n_j(T + 1), n_l(T + 1)\}$$
$$= N\delta_{jl}p_j - Np_jp_l + p_jp_l\sum_{i=1}^{k}\sum_{i'=1}^{k}\operatorname{cov}\{n_i(T), n_{i'}(T)\}. \tag{2.17}$$

Now

$$\sum_{i=1}^{k}\sum_{i'=1}^{k}\operatorname{cov}\{n_i(T), n_{i'}(T)\} = E\{\sum_{i=1}^{k}(n_i - \bar{n}_i)\}^2 = 0$$

so that the last term in equation (2.17) vanishes. The part which remains will be recognized as giving the variances and covariances of the multinomial distribution. In fact it is easy to see directly that $\{n_j(T)\}$ has a multinomial distribution with parameters N and p_j $(j = 1, 2, \ldots, k)$ for all T. The class distribution at time $T + 1$ is independent of that at time

† $\mathbf{Y}$ is the *direct matrix product* $\mathbf{P} \times \mathbf{P}$. The direct matrix product can be used to facilitate the solution of the more general problem of finding the higher moments and product moments of the $\{n_j\}$. See Pollard (1966).

T. Hence we may regard the *N* family lines as being allocated independently to classes with probabilities p_j $(j = 1, 2, . . ., k)$ which is the condition for the distribution to be multinomial. In this case, therefore, the standard error of the predicted proportion p_j will be $\{p_j(1 - p_j)/N\}^{\frac{1}{2}}$.

2.5. Time-dependent Models

In this and the following section we shall examine the effect of relaxing two of the assumptions on which the foregoing model depends. The first of these is that the transition probabilities are time-homogeneous. Rogoff's data suggests that this assumption may be reasonable in some societies but it is of interest to point out that the generalization is straightforward.

Suppose that the transition matrix for the *T*th generation is $P(T)$. Equation (2.2) still holds with **P** replaced by $P(T - 1)$. Solving this equation recursively then gives, in place of equation (2.3),

$$\mathbf{p}(T) = \prod_{i=1}^{T} \mathbf{P}(i)\mathbf{p}(0). \tag{2.18}$$

It is thus possible to investigate the effect of any specified changes in the transition matrix. In general there will not be an equilibrium class structure and the complexity of the model makes it difficult to devise useful measures of mobility. Matras (1966) has suggested that the transition probabilities relating to movements between times *T* and *T* + 1 might be made functions of the class structure at time *T*. This would seem especially plausible if the classes were based on occupational categories. The movement in or out of a class might then depend on the demand for the skills possessed by its members. The future development of the system would then be completely determined by the initial structure **p**(0) and the function relating the transition matrix to the structure on which it operates. The development of this model should prove to be very worthwhile.

Another kind of time-dependence was envisaged by Prais (1955). He postulated that the discrepancy between the class structure for fathers and sons revealed by Table 2.2 might be due to a change in the definitions of the classes. Thus, suppose that, in the past, the process was time-homogeneous and had attained an equilibrium structure like that observed for fathers. The changes which occur in the next generation are then supposed to take place in two parts. The first is a change of 'true' class governed by the time-homogeneous matrix **P**; the second is a change in 'apparent' class resulting from a change in the system of classification. If the second transition has an associated matrix $R(T)$ then the observed transition matrix would be $\mathbf{PR}(T)$. If it were possible to estimate $R(T)$ from census or other information, it would be possible, in turn, to estimate **P** and so predict the development of the process. Prais (1955) showed that a matrix $\mathbf{R}(T)$ could be constructed that would account for the observed difference in the class distributions of fathers and sons in Glass and Hall's data.

2.6. A Model Allowing for a Differential Birth-rate

The most restrictive and unrealistic of our assumptions is that each father has exactly one son. We have used a rough argument to suggest that our model will be a reasonable approximation if each father has, on average, one son. In this section we shall develop the theory necessary to place these remarks on a firmer footing.

Suppose that the distribution of the number of sons born to a member of the jth class is $P_j(i)$, $(i = 0, 1, 2, \ldots)$ and assume that these probabilities are time-homogeneous. The dependence of the distribution on j enables us to introduce differential birth rates between classes. We assume also that family sizes are independent. Let the mean number of male offspring in the jth class be denoted by v_j. Under this model the population size will not remain constant from one generation to the next so we must work in terms of class numbers instead of proportions. Using a simple conditional probability argument based on conditional expectations we have

$$\bar{n}_j(T) = \sum_{i=1}^{k} \bar{n}_i(T - 1)v_i P_{ij} \quad (i = 1, 2, \ldots, k; T \geq 1) \qquad (2.19)$$

where $\bar{n}_i(0) = n_i(0)$ is the initial number in class i. This equation generates the expected class sizes in a manner analogous to equation (2.1). In order to make comparisons with the simple model we shall find it easier to work in proportions writing

$$p_j(T) = \bar{n}_j(T) / \sum_{i=1}^{k} \bar{n}_i(T) \quad (j = 1, 2, \ldots, k).$$

It is not strictly accurate to use this notation because the ratio of expected values is not, in general, equal to the expected value of the proportion. However, the distinction is not important for the heuristic reasoning which follows and we shall refer to $p_j(T)$ as defined above as an expected proportion.

If we divide both sides of equation (2.19), by

$$\sum_{i=1}^{k} \bar{n}_i(T)$$

and use the fact that

$$\sum_{i=1}^{k} \bar{n}_i(T) = \sum_{i=1}^{k} \bar{n}_i(T - 1)v_i$$

we obtain the following expression;

$$p_j(T) = \sum_{i=1}^{k} p_i(T-1)\nu_i p_{ij}/\bar{\nu}(T-1) \quad (j = 1, 2, \ldots, k) \quad (2.20)$$

where

$$\bar{\nu}(T-1) = \sum_{i=1}^{k} p_i(T-1)\nu_i / \sum_{i=1}^{k} p_i(T-1).$$

This equation was given by Matras (1960b). When the classes have the same birth rate, ν_i is independent of i and equation (2.20) reduces to equation (2.1). We therefore conclude that, as far as expectations are concerned, the theory developed in Section 2.1 is still applicable when the single family line is replaced by a more realistic branching process.

The effect of a differential birth rate can most easily be seen by writing $p_j(T)$ in the following form.

$$p_j(T) = \sum_{i=1}^{k} p_i(T-1)\nu_i p_{ij} / \sum_{i=1}^{k} p_i(T-1)\nu_i. \quad (2.21)$$

Consider first the perfectly mobile society in which $p_{ij} = p_j$. In this case equation (2.21) gives

$$p_j(T) = p_j.$$

Expressed in words, this means that the social structure of a perfectly mobile society is unaffected by a differential birth rate between class. This conclusion is intuitively obvious. By contrast the birth rates are of crucial importance in an immobile society. In that case $p_{ij} = 1$ if $i = j$ and zero otherwise. From equation (2.19) we find

$$En_j(T) = \nu_j En_{j-1}(T-1)$$
$$= \nu_j^T n_j(0) \quad (j = 1, 2, \ldots, k; T \geq 1).$$

The corresponding expression for $p_j(T)$ is

$$p_j(T) = \nu_j^T n_j(0) / \sum_{i=1}^{k} \nu_i^T n_i(0) \quad (j = 1, 2, \ldots, k). \quad (2.22)$$

It is clear from the form of this equation that the class with the largest birth rate will eventually dominate the population. In the limit as T tends to infinity we shall have

$$p_j(\infty) = 1 \text{ if } j \text{ refers to the class with the highest birth rate}$$
$$= 0 \text{ otherwise.}$$

For degrees of mobility intermediate between the two extremes which we have considered we would expect to find some tendency for classes with high birth rates to increase in size relative to the others. Some idea of the extent to which this is possible can be deduced from equation (2.21). The right-hand side of this equation is a weighted average of the probabilities p_{ij} $(j = 1, 2, \ldots, k)$ with positive weights. Hence it follows that

$$\min_i p_{ij} \leq p_j(T) \leq \max_i p_{ij} \quad (j = 1, 2, \ldots, k) \quad (2.23)$$

for all T. Thus, however much the birth rates of the classes may differ, the class structure is bounded by the inequalities (2.23). For example, using the data of Table 2.1, the expected proportion in class 5 (skilled manual and routine non-manual) can never fall below 0.140 or exceed 0.470 as long as the model remains valid.

The theory presented above is clearly capable of further development. Matrix methods have been used in demographic work for many years. Matras (1966) has pointed out that these can easily be adapted to include changes in social class as well as changes in the age structure of a population. Now that Pollard's method for obtaining the moments of class sizes is available, considerable progress should be possible.

3. MODELS FOR LABOUR MOBILITY

3.1. The Basic Model

There are obvious affinities between the movement of workers between industries and the movement of family lines between social classes. However, we cannot take over the social mobility model as it stands because it does not specify when transitions take place. This was not necessary when time was measured in generations but in the case of labour mobility there is no such natural unit of time. People change their jobs at irregular intervals of time and an adequate stochastic model must take account of this fact.

The stochastic models which we shall describe were proposed by Blumen, Kogan and McCarthy (1955) (referred to hereafter as the BKM study). They devised the models for a study of labour mobility in the United States using data for the total employed population. These authors were interested in the flow of manpower between the main occupational categories but the models could serve equally well for movements between individual employers in a given locality.

We shall follow the same pattern of development as in Section 2, beginning with a very simple model and then generalizing it in various ways suggested by the data on mobility. It will be assumed throughout that we have a closed system of employers (or industries) and employees. An equivalent assumption is that any losses from the system are made good by new members who are similar in all relevant respects to those that they replace. In practice it will usually be necessary to introduce 'unemployed' as an occupational category if the system is to be closed. Our model must specify the means by which changes of state are determined and also the timing of these changes. We do this as follows.

In the employment history of a given individual we postulate a number of 'decision' points at which he considers changing his employment. At each of these points he may move to another job or remain where he is. We assume that the changes of employment are governed by time-homogeneous transition probabilities p_{ij} $(i, j = 1, 2, . . ., k)$, where k is the number of employment categories. Thus the diagonal elements $\{p_{ii}\}$ of the transition matrix give the probabilities that no change is made. The model can be given a slightly different interpretation as follows. Suppose that the k categories represent fairly broad industrial classifications. The decision points could be replaced by 'change' points at which the employee leaves his present employer. Under this interpretation the probabilities $\{p_{ii}\}$ would relate to a move to a different employer within the same industrial classification. We shall use the terminology appropriate to the first variant of the model but our results can easily be translated into the language of the second. The specification of the model is completed by supposing that the decision points for each individual are realizations of the same time-homogeneous point process. The number of decision points in the interval $(0, T)$ will be a random variable which we shall denote by $m(T)$. Let $\Pr \{m(T) = m\}$ be denoted by $P_m(T)$. In some applications in which employees can only leave their jobs at the end of a week or month it would be more realistic to treat the intervals between decision points as discrete variables. This refinement does not seem justified at the present stage and we shall confine the discussion to the continuous case. A process in which changes of state occur according to a Markov chain and in which the time intervals between changes are random variables is sometimes known as a semi-Markov Process or a Markov Renewal Process. The theory of such processes has been discussed, for example, by Pyke (1961a and b) and Taga (1963).

If a complete job history were available for each employee in the system, then its two main features could be studied separately. The data on job changes, or decisions on whether to change, could be used to estimate the transition probabilities and hence predict the equilibrium occupational structure in the same way as the model for social mobility. Similarly the record of decision points could be made the basis for studying the stochastic process $m(T)$. In the BKM study, complete information was lacking because the records only gave the current occupations at quarterly intervals. There was no record of changes that had taken place during these intervals. This is a common situation and the particular interest of the BKM model is that it shows what can be learned from such limited data.

We suppose that a job census is taken at regular intervals recording the numbers of employees in each occupational category. For convenience we shall refer to the interval between censuses as a quarter as in the BKM investigation. In the formulae we shall retain full generality denoting it by τ. Let $p_{ij}(\tau)$ be the probability that a man who is in category i at the beginning of a quarter is in category j at the beginning of the next quarter. We shall assume that the process $\{m(T)\}$ is time-homogeneous and hence that the transition probabilities $p_{ij}(\tau)$ do not depend on T. If there are exactly m decision points during the quarter we have $p_{ij}(\tau) = p_{ij}^{(m)}$. However, m is itself a random variable with distribution $P_m(\tau)$. Hence

$$p_{ij}(\tau) = \sum_{m=0}^{\infty} P_m(\tau) p_{ij}^{(m)} \quad (i, j = 1, 2, \ldots, k), \tag{3.1}$$

where we define $p_{ii}^{(0)} = 1$ and $p_{ij}^{(0)} = 0 \ (i \neq j)$. The matrix $\mathbf{P}(\tau) = \{p_{ij}(\tau)\}'$ can be observed in practice whereas $\mathbf{P}$ cannot. Our analysis will therefore be devoted to discovering how much about the future of the process can be deduced from $\mathbf{P}(\tau)$ alone.

The answer to this question would present no problems if the states of the system at successive quarters could be treated as a Markov chain. We would then be in a situation identical with that of the last section with the 'generations' replaced by 'quarters'. Unfortunately this is the case only in rather special circumstances. An obvious condition for the system to be a Markov chain, which is both necessary and sufficient, is that

$$p_{ij}(r\tau) = p_{ij}^{(r)}(\tau) \quad (r = 1, 2, 3, \ldots), \tag{3.2}$$

where $p_{ij}^{(r)}(\tau)$ denotes the r-quarter transition probability for the Markov chain with transition matrix $\mathbf{P}(\tau)$. We now ask for what kinds of stochastic process $\{m(T)\}$, if any, does equation (3.2) hold. The probability on the left-hand side of equation (3.2) is

$$\sum_{m=0}^{\infty} P_m(r\tau) p_{ij}^{(m)}.$$

That on the right-hand side is the (j, i)th element in the matrix

$$\{\sum_{m=0}^{\infty} P_m(\tau) \mathbf{P}^m\}^r$$

where we define $\mathbf{P}^0$ to be the unit matrix $\mathbf{I}$. The condition expressed by equation (3.2) is thus equivalent to

$$\sum_{m=0}^{\infty} P_m(r\tau) \mathbf{P}^m = \{\sum_{m=0}^{\infty} P_m(\tau) \mathbf{P}^m\}^r. \tag{3.3}$$

There are only two stochastic processes $\{m(T)\}$ of practical interest for which this condition holds. The first is the degenerate case when decision points occur at regular intervals. Under these circumstances

$$P_m(\tau) = 1 \text{ if } n = n_0$$
$$= 0 \text{ otherwise}$$

and

$$P_m(r\tau) = 1 \text{ if } n = rn_0,$$

where n_0 is the fixed number of decisions made in an interval of length τ. The second case when equation (3.3) is satisfied, is when $\{m(T)\}$ is a Poisson process. Then we have, when the parameter of the process is λ,

$$\left. \begin{aligned} P_m(\tau) &= \frac{(\lambda\tau)^m}{m!} e^{-\lambda\tau} \\[2mm] P_m(r\tau) &= \frac{(\lambda\tau r)^m}{m!} e^{-\lambda r\tau} \end{aligned} \right\} \qquad (m = 0, 1, 2, \ldots)$$

and equation (3.3) is satisfied. The Poisson process implies that the intervals between decision points are independently and exponentially distributed.

The foregoing theory shows that the one-quarter transition matrix only defines a Markov chain if the decision points occur either regularly or randomly in time. If, therefore, we observe a discrepancy in practice between the predicted and observed 'r-quarter' transition matrices, one explanation could be that the stochastic process governing when movements take place is neither regular nor random. Such a discrepancy did, in fact, occur in the BKM study. Using the observed one-quarter matrix the authors estimated those for 4 and 8 quarters using Markov chain theory. The result was that the actual matrices for the longer periods did not agree with the predictions. A typical example is given in Table 2.5 which shows that the Markov prediction underestimates the elements on the main diagonal.

The letters A–K denote industry codes and U is the unemployed category. It is thus clear that, within the framework of the model, the hypothesis of regular or completely random spacing of decision points is untenable. We shall therefore present a more general model and show that it is capable of explaining the discrepancies which we have observed.

3.2. A Model Allowing for Individual Differences

The direct approach to the problem of reconciling the differences between theory and observation would be to search for a stochastic process $\{m(T)\}$ which gives a better fit. We shall find such a process but it will be arrived at indirectly. According to our model the number of decision points in each quarter for any individual will vary. On the simple model the pattern of variation will be the same for all individuals in the population. Although we have no direct evidence on this point it would be remarkable if there were no individual differences in the rate of occurrence.

TABLE 2.5

Comparison of observed and predicted 8-quarter transition probabilities for males, aged 20–24. The upper figure is the observed proportion and the lower that predicted by Markov theory.†

Industry code	A	B	C	D	E	F	G	H	J	K	U
A	0.000	0.062	0.062	0.000	0.125	0.156	0.312	0.000	0.000	0.000	0.281
	0.002	0.086	0.105	0.042	0.116	0.053	0.181	0.016	0.058	0.004	0.337
B	0.003	0.449	0.039	0.020	0.048	0.035	0.079	0.014	0.023	0.006	0.284
	0.002	0.144	0.087	0.040	0.104	0.050	0.163	0.018	0.052	0.004	0.336
C	0.002	0.037	0.461	0.023	0.046	0.021	0.101	0.007	0.022	0.002	0.278
	0.002	0.077	0.176	0.039	0.103	0.046	0.163	0.016	0.050	0.004	0.324
D	0.000	0.064	0.044	0.459	0.083	0.024	0.091	0.011	0.030	0.002	0.192
	0.001	0.070	0.080	0.218	0.099	0.046	0.141	0.015	0.047	0.003	0.279
E	0.002	0.045	0.042	0.034	0.489	0.031	0.094	0.010	0.023	0.002	0.227
	0.001	0.072	0.075	0.040	0.276	0.046	0.147	0.013	0.044	0.004	0.279
F	0.003	0.056	0.033	0.022	0.054	0.440	0.090	0.020	0.026	0.010	0.245
	0.002	0.081	0.076	0.038	0.097	0.166	0.152	0.017	0.050	0.004	0.316
G	0.002	0.047	0.051	0.025	0.046	0.038	0.491	0.020	0.044	0.002	0.235
	0.002	0.080	0.084	0.039	0.098	0.049	0.261	0.017	0.053	0.004	0.314
H	0.000	0.044	0.007	0.015	0.026	0.085	0.096	0.439	0.074	0.000	0.214
	0.001	0.077	0.077	0.035	0.090	0.048	0.170	0.158	0.052	0.004	0.287
J	0.002	0.061	0.033	0.018	0.054	0.035	0.145	0.019	0.339	0.000	0.294
	0.002	0.084	0.085	0.038	0.105	0.049	0.178	0.018	0.105	0.004	0.333
K	0.000	0.113	0.097	0.032	0.121	0.048	0.137	0.032	0.024	0.048	0.347
	0.002	0.089	0.096	0.047	0.130	0.048	0.179	0.023	0.056	0.006	0.325
U	0.001	0.069	0.068	0.035	0.077	0.040	0.153	0.018	0.055	0.004	0.482
	0.002	0.090	0.095	0.042	0.112	0.052	0.179	0.019	0.058	0.004	0.346

† Data from Blumen and others (1955).

of decision points. We shall therefore generalize the original model in such a way that each individual may have a different 'decision rate'. Let us assume that the random variable $m(T)$ has a distribution $P_m(T; \lambda)$, where λ is a parameter which characterizes the individual. If the variation of λ in the population is described by a distribution function $F(\lambda)$ then the observed probability law of the process will be

$$P_m(T) = \int_0^\infty P_m(T; \lambda) dF(\lambda). \tag{3.4}$$

Without loss of generality we may define λ in such a way that it is proportional to $\bar{m}(T)$ and hence its range of variation may be limited to $(0, \infty)$.

It will be shown below that the probabilities given by equation (3.4) do not satisfy the condition of equation (3.3), even if $P_m(T; \lambda)$ is a Poisson distribution. Hence there is no immediate need to take $m(T)$ as anything other than a Poisson process. We must therefore first consider whether it is possible to find an $F(\lambda)$ which, when combined with a Poisson process, leads to a tenable hypothesis. No general results have been obtained but the following example, due to Blumen and others (1955), answers the question we have raised. Suppose that the transition matrix $\mathbf{P}'$, which would be unknown in practice, is

$$\begin{pmatrix} 0.70 & 0.15 & 0.15 \\ 0.20 & 0.60 & 0.20 \\ 0.25 & 0.25 & 0.50 \end{pmatrix} \tag{3.5}$$

Let $P_m(T; \lambda)$ be a Poisson distribution with mean λT. We suppose that for half of the employees $\lambda = 1/10$ and that for the other half $\lambda = 7/10$. Then

$$P_m(\tau) = \frac{1}{2m!} \left\{ \left(\frac{\tau}{10} \right)^m e^{-\tau/10} + \left(\frac{7\tau}{10} \right)^m e^{-7\tau/10} \right\} \quad (m = 1,2,3,\ldots). \tag{3.6}$$

If the unit of time between censuses is unity we shall require that

$$P_0(1) = 0.701, \quad P_1(1) = 0.219, \quad P_2(1) = 0.063,$$
$$P_3(1) = 0.014, \quad P_4(1) = 0.002.$$

The mean of this distribution is 0.395 and the variance is 0.473 indicating a higher dispersion than the Poisson distribution having the same mean. Substitution of these values and the matrix (3.5) in equation (3.1) gives

$$\mathbf{P}'(\tau = 1) = \begin{pmatrix} 0.90 & 0.05 & 0.05 \\ 0.07 & 0.87 & 0.06 \\ 0.08 & 0.08 & 0.84 \end{pmatrix} \tag{3.7}$$

This is the matrix which would be calculated from the data collected for two successive quarters. Treating it as the transition matrix of a Markov chain we would predict the 8-quarter matrix by raising the matrix (3.7) to the eighth power. Thus

$$\{\mathbf{P}'(\tau = 1)\}^8 = \begin{pmatrix} 0.54 & 0.25 & 0.21 \\ 0.33 & 0.44 & 0.24 \\ 0.35 & 0.30 & 0.36 \end{pmatrix}. \tag{3.8}$$

However, the 8-quarter matrix which we would expect from our present model is

$$\mathbf{P}'(\tau = 8) = \begin{pmatrix} 0.63 & 0.21 & 0.17 \\ 0.26 & 0.55 & 0.19 \\ 0.28 & 0.23 & 0.48 \end{pmatrix}. \tag{3.9}$$

The heterogeneity which we have introduced thus leads us to underestimate the diagonal elements. This is exactly what Blumen and others (1955) found in practice.

It is not necessary to assume that there are individual differences in the population. The same result would be obtained if the decision points occurred according to equation (3.6) for each person. This might be the case if decision points were of two kinds, one kind occurring at rate $\lambda = 1/10$ and the other at rate $\lambda = 7/10$. It is an unfortunate fact that we cannot, on the data available, distinguish between these two models for the decision point process. For predictive purposes they are identical; if we require a full explanation of the process, data on individual case histories is necessary.

3.3. The 'Mover-stayer' Model

Having shown that heterogeneity in the process $\{m(T)\}$ is a desirable ingredient of the model we must consider what form this should take. There is a certain plausibility in what Blumen and others (1955) termed the 'mover-stayer' model. According to this model a certain proportion, $F(0)$, of employees do not change their jobs at all. These are the 'stayers'. The 'movers' are those who change employment in the way postulated by our model. If we retain the assumption of heterogeneity for the movers the one-quarter transition matrix will now be

$$\mathbf{P}(\tau) = F(0)\mathbf{I} + \int_0^\infty \sum_{m=0}^\infty P_m(\tau; \lambda)\mathbf{P}^m \mathrm{d}F(\lambda), \tag{3.10}$$

where **I** is the unit matrix. Blumen and others (1955) assumed homogeneity and supposed that the decision process was Poisson with the same λ for all movers. In this case equation (3.10) becomes

$$\mathbf{P}(\tau) = F(0)\mathbf{I} + \{1 - F(0)\} \sum_{m=0}^{\infty} \frac{(\lambda\tau)^m}{m!} \, e^{-\lambda\tau}\mathbf{P}^m. \qquad (3.11)$$

Even with this crude model the predictions obtained were a marked improvement over the simple Markov version, in the case of the 8-quarter matrix. The improvement was less marked for the 4- and 11-quarter matrices. Table 2.6 shows the observed and predicted values of the diagonal elements of the two matrices for the example used in Table 2.5.

TABLE 2.6

Comparison of observed and predicted values of the diagonal elements in the 8-quarter transition matrices for males aged 20–24.†

Industry code	A	B	C	D	E	F	G	H	J	K	U
Observed	0.000	0.449	0.461	0.459	0.489	0.440	0.491	0.439	0.339	0.048	0.482
Predicted	0.003	0.442	0.464	0.474	0.512	0.444	0.489	0.446	0.338	0.049	0.536

† Data from Blumen and others (1955).

Other generalizations of the basic model are possible. We could allow the matrix **P** to be time-dependent as we did in the social mobility model. In addition we could introduce more elaborate stochastic processes to account for the decision points. Since the models developed above are capable of describing mobility patterns which have been observed in practice there is no immediate need for such generalizations. However, if data can be obtained on such things as individual job histories the scope for useful model building will be enlarged.

3.4. Limiting Behaviour of the Models

When we turn to the limiting occupational structure the differences between all but one of our models vanish. First we consider the basic model of Section 3.1, and show that the limiting behaviour does not depend on the stochastic process $m(T)$. More precisely we shall show that, if **P** is regular, then

$$\lim_{r \to \infty} \mathbf{P}^r(\tau) = \lim_{r \to \infty} \mathbf{P}^r. \qquad (3.12)$$

This is an extremely useful result. It means that we can compute the limiting occupational structure from $\mathbf{P}(\tau)$ by treating the quarterly structures *as if* they were realizations of a Markov chain. To prove equation (3.12), we find the limit of the left-hand side as follows.

$$\mathbf{P}(\tau) = \sum_{m=0}^{\infty} P_m(\tau)\mathbf{P}^m \qquad (3.13)$$

by equation (3.1). We may thus think of $\mathbf{P}(\tau)$ as a matrix-valued generating function of the probability distribution $P_m(\tau)$. On raising the right-hand side of equation (3.13) to the rth power we thus obtain the generating function of the r-fold convolution of the distribution of $m(\tau)$. Hence we may write

$$\mathbf{P}^r(\tau) = \sum_{m=0}^{\infty} Pr\{S(r) = m\}\mathbf{P}^m,$$

where $S(r)$ is the sum of r independent observations on $m(\tau)$. By applying Chebychev's inequality to the distribution of $S(r)$ we may show that

$$\lim_{r \to \infty} Pr\{S(r) \leq m\} = 0$$

for any finite m and therefore

$$\lim_{r \to \infty} \sum_{m=0}^{\infty} Pr\{S(r) = m\}\mathbf{P}^m = \lim_{m \to \infty} \mathbf{P}^m.$$

If we assume that the system we are studying has reached equilibrium we can test whether the changes of state follow a Markov chain. This test can easily be made with the BKM data. Taking the observed quarterly transition matrix we can predict the equilibrium distribution using equation (2.5). A comparison of an observed and predicted structure taken from Blumen and others is given in Table 2.7.

TABLE 2.7

Actual and predicted occupation structure using the Markov model and the quarterly transition matrix.†

Occupational Group	(C, D, E)	G	(F, H)	(A, B, J, K)	U	Total
Average percentage of workers observed	28.2	17.0	6.8	13.7	34.3	100.0
Predicted percentage using Markov model	27.0	18.0	8.0	15.0	32.0	100.0

† Data from Blumen and others (1955).

The close agreement supports the hypothesis that the changes of occupation are accounted for by the Markov chain model. The discrepancies between the predicted and observed 4- and 8-quarter transition matrices, noted earlier, point to the need for $\{m(T)\}$ to be a non-Poissonian point process. We must now consider whether the agreement observed in Table 2.7 is compatible with the models involving individual differences described in Section 3.2 and 3.3. This is obviously the case because we have proved the result for any distribution $P_m(T)$ and hence, in particular, for those having the form of equation (3.4).

The mover-stayer model requires special treatment. Our theory as developed above applies only to the movers. They will reach an equilibrium structure **p** while the stayers remain in their original categories. The transpose of the matrix giving the probabilities of transitions from state i to state j in r steps will thus have the limiting form

$$F(0)\mathbf{I} + \{1 - F(0)\}\mathbf{P}^\infty.$$

This is not the same form as we would get by finding $\lim_{r \to \infty} \{\mathbf{P}(\tau)\}^r$ from equation (3.11). The matrix $\mathbf{P}(\tau)$ for the mover-stayer model can be written in the form of equation (3.13) and hence it follows that

$$\lim_{r \to \infty} \{\mathbf{P}(\tau)\}^r = \mathbf{P}^\infty.$$

Therefore, if we treat $\mathbf{P}(\tau)$ as the transition matrix of a Markov chain, the limiting structure that we shall predict is that of the movers only. The reason for this result is worth elaborating. On the basis of the one-quarter transition matrix alone we cannot distinguish between the mover-stayer model and one in which *all* members are movers with transition matrix $F(0)\mathbf{I} + \{1 - F(0)\}\mathbf{P}$. The limiting result obtained is the one appropriate to the second model rather than the first. We cannot therefore treat the mover-stayer model as a Markov process in discrete time with transition matrix $\mathbf{P}(\tau)$. This fact raises interesting estimation problems which have been discussed by Blumen and others (1955), and Goodman (1961). They lie outside the scope of this book.

3.5. Concluding Remarks

We have assumed that the system we have been studying is closed. This is a reasonable assumption in the short term but in view of our emphasis on limiting results it requires further comment. We remarked in the introduction that our model would cover open systems in which all losses were made good by 'equivalent' replacements. In a labour force whose size remains constant over long periods we may expect this requirement to be met in an average sense. A full justification of this remark must await the development of a theory of open systems to which we turn in the following chapter.

When discussing social mobility we included a section on the measurement of social mobility. It was argued there that any such measures should be based on the matrix of transition probabilities. In the case of labour mobility we would similarly argue that the transition matrix and the stochastic process $\{m(T)\}$ need to be taken into account. This is a problem which would repay further research.

CHAPTER 3

DISCRETE TIME MODELS FOR GRADED SOCIAL SYSTEMS

1. INTRODUCTION

The social systems described in Chapter 2 were closed. This meant either that no members moved in or out of the system or that any losses were replaced immediately by identical recruits. Our interest in that chapter was in the changing internal structure of the system. The assumption of a closed system was reasonable for the applications to social class and labour mobility for reasons which have already been explained. Nevertheless there are many systems in which gains and losses are an important feature of the process. In this chapter we shall, therefore, give two generalizations of the closed Markov model in which recruitment and loss appear explicitly.

A feature common to each model is the stochastic mechanism governing losses from the system. This can easily be incorporated into the Markov chain model by associating a time-homogeneous loss probability with each grade or stratum. The difference between the two models lies in the factors which are supposed to control the input. For clarity we shall describe the situation by reference to two applications without intending thereby to place any limitation on the applicability of the models.

In the first model the number of recruits to the system at time T is either a known quantity or a realization of a known stochastic process. Under these conditions the sizes of the individual grades will be random variables with distributions determined by the stochastic nature of the loss and input. One example of a situation in which such a model is appropriate is provided by an educational system. The model described in Section 2, was, in fact, proposed by Gani (1963), for the university system of Australia. He wished to predict the total enrolment in universities and the numbers of degrees to be awarded in the future. The system thus consisted of the total university population of the country. The strata, or grades, were the four undergraduate and three postgraduate years of study. At the end of each year three alternatives were available to any student. He could move into the next higher year, by passing an examination; he could repeat the year if he failed the examination, or he could leave the university. Past data showed that it was reasonable to suppose that each kind of transition had a fixed probability. The input to the educational system consists of the total number of qualified students reaching the age for university entrance. This number could be accurately predicted up to 18 years ahead from the known numbers in each age cohort. In practice there might be constraints affecting the size of the system but this does not detract from the usefulness of the model for predicting the demand for university places.

Gani has adapted his model to be suitable for the American university system as it exists in Michigan State University. In this case progress is by 'credits' and not by 'years'. In addition there may be transfers between the various schools of the university. A further complication is introduced by the fact that the transition probabilities vary between the Fall, Winter and Spring terms. Only the last of these differences introduces any new point of principle and this will be discussed in Section 2.6. An educational system is a good example of the type of organization for which our model is likely to be suitable because the input is fixed without regard to the state of the system. A study of the whole educational system for the United Kingdom is being undertaken by the Committee for Economic and Statistical Studies in Higher Education based at the London School of Economics. The model described in Section 2 has also been used in that investigation. The staffing structure of a firm is another example if conditions are such that all qualified applicants can be employed. This would be the case at a time when the demand for labour exceeded the supply. To summarize: the model is characterized by transitions according to a time-homogeneous Markov chain, constant loss probabilities and given (fixed or random) input.

In the second model it is the total size at time T and not the number of recruits which is given. The number of new entrants required at any time is then a random variable with distribution depending on the loss mechanism and the required size of the system. In contrast to the first model we are here assuming that there is an unlimited supply of potential recruits. As originally formulated by Young and Almond (1961) the model was designed for expanding organizations but it can be adapted for systems which are declining or fluctuating in size. In the original application the members of an organization were divided into grades according to status. At the end of each year some members were promoted to a higher grade, others left the organization and the remainder continued in the same grade. It was found that the proportions in each of these 3 categories were effectively constant from year to year. The object of the investigation was to predict the future grade structure assuming a given rate of overall expansion and fixed promotion and loss probabilities. Since the planned expansion, or contraction, of graded social systems is of widespread occurrence the development of a satisfactory theory of their behaviour is of considerable importance. Young's model represents a first but very substantial step towards this goal.

Gani's model is described in Section 2 of the present chapter. Section 3 contains a discussion of Young's model and ends with some general conclusions about the effect of the promotion and recruitment policies on the structure of hierarchical organizations.

2. A MODEL FOR A SYSTEM WITH GIVEN INPUT

2.1. The Basic Model

We consider a population whose members are divided into k strata. In many applications these will be ranked according to seniority but this feature will not be considered explicitly until later. As far as possible the notation of Chapter 2 will be retained. Thus $n_j(T)$ denotes the number of people in grade j between time T and $T + 1$ ($T = 0, 1, 2, \ldots$). The initial grade sizes, $n_j(0)$ ($j = 1, 2, \ldots, k$), are assumed to be given and we define

$$N(T) = \sum_{j=1}^{k} n_j(T).$$

For $T > 0$ the grade sizes are random variables and we shall be concerned mainly with their expectations. These will be denoted as before by placing a bar over the symbol representing the random variable; thus $\bar{n}_j(T)$ is the expected number in grade j at time T. The number of new entrants to the system at time T will be written as $R(T)$. As remarked above, this may be a constant or a random variable. In the latter case $R(T)$ is to be understood as the expected number of entrants. The assumptions and notation for the transitions between grades used in the model of social mobility are retained. A member of grade i moves to grade j with probability p_{ij} but it is no longer true that

$$\sum_{j=1}^{k} p_{ij} = 1.$$

In general

$$\sum_{j=1}^{k} p_{ij} < 1$$

because, in an open system, transitions out of the system are possible. The probability of loss from the ith grade at time T is denoted by $p_{i,k+1}$ and we note that

$$p_{i,k+1} = 1 - \sum_{j=1}^{k} p_{ij}.$$

To complete the specification of the model we must say how new entrants are allocated to the various grades. In many applications all recruits are placed in the lowest grade but we shall make the more general assumption that a proportion p_{0j} enter the jth grade. Obviously

$$\sum_{j=1}^{k} p_{0j} = 1$$

and the distribution $\{p_{0j}\}$ will be referred to as the 'recruitment distribution'. An alternative assumption about entry to the system is that a new recruit is allocated to grade j with *probability* p_{0j}. The actual numbers entering the various grades will then be multinomially distributed instead of fixed. Our theory covers both cases as long as it refers only to expectations because it then makes no difference whether p_{0j} is regarded as an actual or an expected proportion. The difference becomes important for the discussion of variances and covariances given in Section 2.5.

The probabilities which specify the process can be conveniently set out in standard form as follows:

p_{01}	p_{02}	$\cdots$	p_{0k}	
p_{11}	p_{12}	$\cdots$	p_{1k}	$p_{1,k+1}$
p_{21}	p_{22}	$\cdots$	p_{2k}	$p_{2,k+1}$
.	.	.	.	
.	.	.	.	
.	.	.	.	
p_{k1}	p_{k2}	$\cdots$	p_{kk}	$p_{k,k+1}$

As before $\mathbf{P}$ will be the transpose of the matrix with elements $\{p_{ij}\}$ $(i, j = 1, 2, \ldots, k)$; $\mathbf{p}_0$ denotes the recruitment distribution and $\bar{\mathbf{n}}(T)$ the vector of expected grade sizes between T and $T + 1$.

Now that the operation of the system has been specified it is easy to write down equations relating the expected grade sizes at successive points in time. A straightforward argument using conditional expectations gives

$$\bar{n}_j(T) = \sum_{i=1}^{k} p_{ij}\bar{n}_i(T-1) + R(T)p_{0j} \quad (T = 1, 2, 3, \ldots) \qquad (2.1a)$$

$$(j = 1, 2, \ldots, k).$$

or

$$\bar{\mathbf{n}}(T) = \mathbf{P}\bar{\mathbf{n}}(T-1) + R(T)\mathbf{p}_0. \qquad (2.1b)$$

Since $R(T)$ is known for all T this equation may be used to compute the expected grade sizes recursively. Repeated application of equation (2.1b) gives

$$\bar{\mathbf{n}}(T) = \mathbf{P}^T \bar{\mathbf{n}}(0) + \left\{ \sum_{\tau=0}^{T-1} R(T - \tau) \mathbf{P}^\tau \right\} \mathbf{p}_0. \tag{2.2}$$

where $\mathbf{P}^0$ is again defined to be the unit matrix $\mathbf{I}$. The probabilities $\{p_{i,k+1}\}$ do not appear explicitly in these formulae but, because they are the complements of the column sums of $\mathbf{P}$, $\mathbf{P}^\tau$ and hence $\bar{\mathbf{n}}(T)$ depend upon their values. If $R(T)$ has a suitable mathematical form it may be possible to sum the matrix series appearing in equation (2.2) and so obtain the solution in closed form. This is the case if $R(T)$ is constant for all T or, more generally, if

$$R(T) = Rx^T, \quad (R > 0, x > 0, T \geq 1). \tag{2.3}$$

We then have

$$\bar{\mathbf{n}}(T) = \mathbf{P}^T \bar{\mathbf{n}}(0) + Rx(x\mathbf{I} - \mathbf{P})^{-1}(x^T\mathbf{I} - \mathbf{P}^T)\mathbf{p}_0, \tag{2.4}$$

provided that the inverse of $x\mathbf{I} - \mathbf{P}$ exists. This will be so unless x is equal to any of the k eigen values of the matrix $\mathbf{P}$. For a matrix with non-negative elements and column sums strictly less than unity, the eigen values lie between 0 and 1. In particular $x = 1$ is not an eigen value and hence equation (2.4) applies for the case of constant input. However, as we shall see in Section 2.4, the chief value of this form is for the light which it throws on the limiting behaviour of the system.

The analysis of the following sections is designed to yield general results about the form of the solutions and their implications for the social process in question.

2.2. The Spectral Representation of $\bar{\mathbf{n}}(T)$

An alternative representation of $\bar{\mathbf{n}}(T)$ which has some advantages may be obtained by using a standard result in matrix theory known as Sylvester's theorem.[†] The theorem states that the Tth power of $\mathbf{P}$ can be expressed in the form

$$\mathbf{P}^T = \sum_{r=1}^{k} \lambda_r^T \mathbf{A}_r. \tag{2.5}$$

[†] A basic reference is Frazer, Duncan and Collar (1946); an application of the theorem to powers of stochastic matrices is given in Bailey (1964), pages 47–56.

The constants $\lambda_1, \lambda_2, \ldots, \lambda_k$ are the eigen values, assumed distinct, of the matrix $\mathbf{P}$ and the matrices $\{\mathbf{A}_r\}$ have the following properties:

$$\mathbf{A}_r\mathbf{A}_s = 0 \text{ if } r \neq s$$
$$= \mathbf{A}_r \text{ if } r = s$$

and

$$\sum_{r=1}^{k} \mathbf{A}_r = \mathbf{I}.$$

Equation (2.5) is described as the spectral representation of $\mathbf{P}^T$ and the matrices $\{\mathbf{A}_r\}$ are known as the 'spectral set'. If there are multiplicities among the eigen values, $\mathbf{P}^T$ can still be expressed in terms of powers of the eigen values but the expressions are more complicated.

If we substitute the expression for $\mathbf{P}^T$ given by equation (2.5), in equation (2.2), we shall have

$$\bar{\mathbf{n}}(T) = \sum_{r=1}^{k} [\lambda_r^T \mathbf{A}_r \bar{\mathbf{n}}(0) + \{\sum_{\tau=0}^{T-1} R(T - \tau)\lambda_r^\tau\}\mathbf{A}_r\mathbf{p}_0]. \qquad (2.6)$$

This representation will be particularly useful if the series

$$\sum_{\tau=0}^{T-1} R(T - \tau)\lambda_r^\tau$$

can be expressed in closed form. If this is possible $\bar{\mathbf{n}}(T)$ will be a sum of k terms for all T; it can be found without having to calculate the structure for intermediate values of T. Equation (2.6) is also a good starting point for the investigation of the limiting behaviour of $\bar{\mathbf{n}}(T)$. In general, the determination of the eigen values and the spectral set involves extensive calculations if k is large but these are routine operations for which computer programmes are available. However, the analysis is simplified considerably in certain special cases of practical interest. One such example arises when the organization is hierarchical in form with downward movement not permitted. We shall discuss this special case and illustrate the foregoing theory in the following section.

2.3. Hierarchical Structure with no Demotions

Let us suppose that the k grades are arranged in increasing order of seniority and assume that transitions within the organization are to a higher grade only. This was certainly the case in the application to the

Australian university system and is sufficiently common to warrant special attention. The matrix $\mathbf{P}$ is now lower triangular thus

$$\mathbf{P} = \begin{pmatrix} p_{11} & 0 & \cdots & 0 \\ p_{12} & p_{22} & \cdots & 0 \\ & \cdot & \cdot & \cdot \\ & \cdot & \cdot & \cdot \\ & \cdot & \cdot & \cdot \\ p_{1k} & p_{2k} & \cdots & p_{kk} \end{pmatrix}.$$

The eigen values of such a matrix are obtained at once as $\lambda_r = p_{rr}$. Hence the eigen values will be distinct if the diagonal elements of $\mathbf{P}$ are distinct. In this case it is also possible to give an explicit expression for the elements of the matrices $\{\mathbf{A}_r\}$. If we denote the (i, j)th element of $\mathbf{A}_r$ by $A_{r.ij}$ then

$$A_{r.ij} = \sum_{m=1}^{i-j} \left(\prod_{s=j}^{i-m} p_{s,s+m} \Bigg/ \prod_{\substack{s=j+m-1 \\ s \neq r}}^{i} (p_{rr} - p_{ss}) \right), \quad \left. \begin{pmatrix} i > r > j \\ i \geq r > j \\ i > r \geq j \end{pmatrix} \right) $$
$$= 1 \text{ if } i = r = j \qquad\qquad\qquad\qquad\qquad (2.7)$$
$$= 0 \text{ otherwise.}$$

Substitution of the eigen values and the spectral set in equation (2.6) gives an expression from which $\bar{\mathbf{n}}(T)$ can be calculated.

Further simplification is possible if we place additional restraints on the kind of promotions which can occur. Suppose, for example, that promotion can only occur into the next highest grade so that $p_{s,s+m} = 0$ for $m > 1$. The first expression given in equation (2.7) can then be replaced by

$$A_{r.ij} = \prod_{s=j}^{i-1} p_{s,s+1} \Bigg/ \prod_{\substack{s=j \\ s \neq r}}^{i} (p_{rr} - p_{ss}). \qquad (2.8)$$

If $R(T)$ has the geometric form Rx^T

$$\bar{\mathbf{n}}(T) = \sum_{r=1}^{k} \left\{ p_{rr}^T \mathbf{A}_r \mathbf{n}(0) + Rx \left(\frac{x^T - p_{rr}^T}{x - p_{rr}} \right) \mathbf{A}_r \mathbf{p}_0 \right\} \quad (x \neq p_{rr}). \qquad (2.9)$$

It is thus clear that the diagonal elements of $\mathbf{P}$ and the value of x play a crucial role in determining the development of the process in time.

To illustrate the calculations required and to give some insight into the behaviour of hierarchical systems we shall discuss a numerical example with $k = 5$. The table of transition probabilities which we assume is set out in standard form below.

0.75	0.25	0	0	0	
0.65	0.20	0	0	0	0.15
0	0.70	0.15	0	0	0.15
0	0	0.75	0.15	0	0.10
0	0	0	0.85	0.10	0.05
0	0	0	0	0.95	0.05

The figures in this table have been chosen to reflect the kind of conditions which one might find in a typical management hierarchy. In an educational system the diagonal elements would tend to be much smaller. Three-quarters of new recruits enter the lowest grade and one-quarter the next lowest. The wastage probabilities, $\{p_{i,k+1}\}$, decrease as we move up the hierarchy since mobility between firms is usually more common at the lower levels. Loss from grade 5, would include retirements as well as transfers and so might well have a higher probability than the figure of 0.05 used in this example. The average time spent in grade i is $(1 - p_{ii})^{-1}$; in the present case this is between 3 and 4 years for the lowest 3 grades. The expected time to reach the highest grade is almost 17 years.

The matrix $\mathbf{P}$ is triangular and hence the eigen values are equal to the diagonal elements. It therefore remains to calculate the spectral set $\{\mathbf{A}_r\}$. To do this we have to substitute numerical values given above in equation (2.8). For example,

$$A_{1.11} = 1, \quad A_{1.21} = p_{12}/(p_{11} - p_{22}) = (0.20)/(-0.05) = -4,$$

$$A_{1.31} = p_{12}p_{23}/(p_{11} - p_{22})(p_{11} - p_{33}) = (0.20)(0.15)/(-0.05)(-0.10) = 6$$

etc. Written out in full the matrices are

$$\mathbf{A}_1 = \begin{pmatrix} 1 & 0 & 0 & 0 & 0 \\ -4 & 0 & 0 & 0 & 0 \\ 6 & 0 & 0 & 0 & 0 \\ -4.5 & 0 & 0 & 0 & 0 \\ 1.5 & 0 & 0 & 0 & 0 \end{pmatrix}$$

$$A_2 = \begin{pmatrix} 0 & 0 & 0 & 0 & 0 \\ 4 & 1 & 0 & 0 & 0 \\ -12 & -3 & 0 & 0 & 0 \\ 12 & 3 & 0 & 0 & 0 \\ -4.8 & -1.2 & 0 & 0 & 0 \end{pmatrix}$$

$$A_3 = \begin{pmatrix} 0 & 0 & 0 & 0 & 0 \\ 0 & 0 & 0 & 0 & 0 \\ 6 & 3 & 1 & 0 & 0 \\ -9 & -4.5 & -1.5 & 0 & 0 \\ 4.5 & 2.25 & 0.75 & 0 & 0 \end{pmatrix}$$

$$A_4 = \begin{pmatrix} 0 & 0 & 0 & 0 & 0 \\ 0 & 0 & 0 & 0 & 0 \\ 0 & 0 & 0 & 0 & 0 \\ 1.5 & 1.5 & 1.5 & 1 & 0 \\ -1.5 & -1.5 & -1.5 & -1 & 0 \end{pmatrix}$$

$$A_5 = \begin{pmatrix} 0 & 0 & 0 & 0 & 0 \\ 0 & 0 & 0 & 0 & 0 \\ 0 & 0 & 0 & 0 & 0 \\ 0 & 0 & 0 & 0 & 0 \\ 0.3 & 0.45 & 0.75 & 1 & 1 \end{pmatrix}.$$

Of the quantities appearing in equation (2.9) the initial grade structure $\bar{n}(0)$ and the input sequence $\{R(T)\}$ remain to be specified. Let us assume that

$$\mathbf{n}(0) = N(0) \begin{pmatrix} 0.40 \\ 0.30 \\ 0.15 \\ 0.10 \\ 0.05 \end{pmatrix} \quad \text{and} \quad R(T) = R.$$

If we compute the total population size and the individual grade sizes at time T $(T > 0)$ as multiples of $N(0)$ we need only express R as a fraction of $N(0)$. For the illustrative calculations we have chosen $N(0) = 9.8333R$. The reason for this particular choice is that it makes $N(\infty) = N(0)$. This ensures that there is no long-term trend in the overall size and so enables us to concentrate on the changes in structure which take place. Under the assumptions we have made

$$\bar{\mathbf{n}}(T) = \sum_{r=1}^{5} \left\{ p_{rr}^{T} \mathbf{A}_r \mathbf{n}(0) + R \left(\frac{1 - p_{rr}^{T}}{1 - p_{rr}} \right) \mathbf{A}_r \mathbf{p}_0 \right\} \quad (2.10)$$

and, in the limit,

$$\bar{\mathbf{n}}(\infty) = R \sum_{r=1}^{5} (1 - p_{rr})^{-1} \mathbf{A}_r \mathbf{p}_0. \quad (2.11)$$

In the example the vectors $\{\mathbf{A}_r \mathbf{p}_0\}$ are found to be

$$\mathbf{A}_1\mathbf{p}_0 = \begin{pmatrix} 0.75 \\ -3.00 \\ 4.50 \\ -3.375 \\ 1 \cdot 125 \end{pmatrix} \quad \mathbf{A}_2\mathbf{p}_0 = \begin{pmatrix} 0 \\ 3.25 \\ -9.75 \\ 9.75 \\ -3.90 \end{pmatrix} \quad \mathbf{A}_3\mathbf{p}_0 = \begin{pmatrix} 0 \\ 0 \\ 5.25 \\ -7.875 \\ 3 \cdot 9375 \end{pmatrix}$$

$$\mathbf{A}_4\mathbf{p}_0 = \begin{pmatrix} 0 \\ 0 \\ 0 \\ 1.50 \\ -1.50 \end{pmatrix} \quad \mathbf{A}_5\mathbf{p}_0 = \begin{pmatrix} 0 \\ 0 \\ 0 \\ 0 \\ 0.3375 \end{pmatrix}.$$

Substitution in equation (2.11), thus gives the limiting structure as

$$\bar{\mathbf{n}}(\infty) = N(0) \begin{pmatrix} 0.218 \\ 0.230 \\ 0.138 \\ 0.138 \\ 0.275 \end{pmatrix}. \quad (2.12)$$

The difference between this and the initial structure is quite striking. The highest grade has increased more than five-fold in size and the sizes of the lower grades have become more nearly equal. This feature is primarily due to the long average stay of 20 years in grade 5. In order to counteract this excessive growth at the top one might be able to increase p_{rr} for $r < 5$ by reducing the promotion probabilities. *This example illustrates the fact that a promotion policy which seems reasonable in itself may lead to undesirable consequences for the structure of the organization. In particular it suggests that the pressure to grow at the top which is exhibited in many organizations may be the direct consequence of a rigid promotion policy.*

To calculate the intermediate structures we must first calculate the vectors $\{\mathbf{A}_r\mathbf{n}(0)\}$. We omit the details and proceed directly to the table of $\bar{\mathbf{n}}(T)$ for selected values of T.

TABLE 3.1

Values of $\bar{\mathbf{n}}(T)/N(0)$ for the example discussed in the text.

				T		
Grade	0	1	2	5	10	∞
1	0.400	0.336	0.295	0.239	0.220	0.218
2	0.300	0.315	0.313	0.280	0.243	0.230
3	0.150	0.158	0.165	0.174	0.159	0.138
4	0.100	0.107	0.115	0.136	0.154	0.138
5	0.050	0.058	0.065	0.091	0.137	0.275
$\sum_j \bar{n}_j(T)/N(0)$	1.000	0.974	0.953	0.920	0.913	1.000

The approach to equilibrium exhibits a pattern which we have observed in other instances. In the lower grades the limiting expectations are attained relatively quickly but the approach is very slow in grade 5. After 10 years the expected size of grade 5 is still only half its equilibrium value while grades 1 and 2 have almost attained theirs. The total expected size of the population shows a steady decrease over the period 0 to 10 years but ultimately recovers its original value. The slowness of the approach to equilibrium in the upper grades and in the total size is accounted for by the term involving $(0.95)^T$ which occurs in equation (2.10). With a coefficient of -0.6864 its value does not become negligible until T is of the order of 100. In cases like this the limiting structure of the system is of little direct practical interest although it does indicate the general direction of change. For some purposes it might be of greater interest to look at the expected proportions in each grade instead of the expected numbers. These can easily be obtained from Table 3.1 but they do not materially alter the general picture.

2.4. Limiting Behaviour of $\bar{\mathbf{n}}(T)$

We have already considered the limiting behaviour of the model for a special case with constant input. Although the limits may be approached too slowly to be attained in practice they give valuable information about the inherent tendencies in the system and so we shall pursue the question in the general case. For this purpose we use the spectral representation given by equation (2.6), in conjunction with a theorem due to Perron and Frobenius (see, for example, Cox and Miller 1965, p. 120). When applied to the matrix $\mathbf{P}$ this states that

$$0 < \max_i \lambda_i \leq \max_i \sum_{j=1}^{k} p_{ij},$$

where the equality sign holds only if all of the row sums are equal. The largest eigen value will thus be strictly less than 1 unless all the row sums are equal to 1. This cannot be so for an open system which requires that some, at least, of the inequalities

$$\sum_{j=1}^{k} p_{ij} < 1 \quad (i = 1, 2, \ldots, k)$$

must hold. These results ensure that

$$\lim_{T \to \infty} \lambda_r^T = 0$$

for all T and hence that the leading term of equation (2.6) vanishes. The limiting solution thus depends on the behaviour of the series

$$S_{T,r} = \sum_{\tau=0}^{T-1} R(T - \tau)\lambda_r^\tau \tag{2.13}$$

as $T \to \infty$ for $0 < \lambda_r < 1$ and $r = 1, 2, \ldots, k$. Although we cannot obtain further detailed results without specifying the function $R(T)$ we can usefully distinguish three kinds of behaviour as follows.

(a) $\lim_{T \to \infty} R(T) = 0$. In this case $S_{T,r}$ tends to zero for all r and hence $\bar{\mathbf{n}}(\infty) = \mathbf{0}$. This result expresses the obvious fact that if the input vanishes the population will ultimately become extinct. We might ask what happens to the *relative* grade sizes as $T \to \infty$ but no general results are available.

(b) $\lim_{T \to \infty} R(T) = R$, a constant. Under this condition

$$\lim_{T \to \infty} S_{T,r} = R\sum_{j=0}^{\infty}\lambda_r^j = R(1 - \lambda_r)^{-1}$$

which gives

$$\bar{\mathbf{n}}(\infty) = R\sum_{r=1}^{k} (1 - \lambda_r)^{-1}\mathbf{A}_r\mathbf{p}_0. \tag{2.14}$$

A special case of this result was given earlier in equation (2.11). It should be noted that the limiting size and structure do not depend on $\mathbf{n}(0)$. The ultimate size is, in fact, proportional to R, the input per unit time. The same result holds if the eigen values are not all distinct.

(c) $\lim_{T \to \infty} R(T) = \infty$. If the input increases without limit it is obvious that the size of the organization will grow in like manner. Again it would be interesting to have information on the limiting values of the relative grade sizes. No general results are available but a special case will be considered later.

The three cases listed above are not exhaustive because $R(T)$ need not tend to a limit; it might fluctuate indefinitely in a more or less erratic manner. If this is the case there will be no limiting grade structure in the ordinary sense but it will still be true that the initial structure will exert a diminishing influence as T increases. The general results we have obtained about $\bar{n}(\infty)$ could have been derived, though in a less complete form, by allowing T to approach infinity on both sides of the difference equation, equation (2.1b).

We shall illustrate the foregoing discussion by supposing that $R(T) = Rx^T (x, R > 0)$. By varying the value of x we can generate examples falling into each of the above three categories. If $x < 1$

$$\lim_{T \to \infty} R(T) = 0$$

and the total input is finite. Under these conditions $N(T)$ and the individual grade sizes tend to zero as T increases. If $x = 1$ case (b) above obtains and an expression for the expected limiting grade structure has been given in equation (2.14). In certain special cases explicit expressions can be found for the limiting structure. For example, if recruitment is into the lowest grade only and if promotion is restricted to the next highest grade then $\lambda_r = p_{rr} (r = 1, 2, \ldots k)$; the spectral set is given by equation (2.8), and hence

$$\bar{n}_j(\infty) = R \prod_{r=1}^{j-1} p_{r,r+1} \Big/ \prod_{r=1}^{j} (1 - p_{rr}) \quad (j = 1, 2, \ldots, k). \tag{2.15}$$

This formula clearly demonstrates how grade sizes depend on the values of the p_{rr}'s and, in particular, on their closeness to 1.

If $x > 1$ the term in x^T in equation (2.9) becomes dominant as $T \to \infty$, so that

$$\bar{n}(T) \sim Rx^{T+1} \sum_{r=1}^{k} \mathbf{A}_r \mathbf{p}_0 / (x - \lambda_r). \tag{2.16}$$

This result shows that the total size and the grade sizes will tend to grow geometrically. It is theoretically interesting to ask whether the *relative* grade sizes approach limits as T increases. If

$$p_j(T) = \bar{n}_j(T) \bigg/ \sum_{i=1}^{k} n_i(T)$$

then it is clear from equation (2.16), that

$$\mathbf{p}(T) \propto \sum_{r=1}^{k} \mathbf{A}_r \mathbf{p}_0/(x - \lambda_r). \tag{2.17}$$

Making the same assumptions about recruitment and promotion as in the discussion leading up to equation (2.15), we have

$$\mathbf{p}_j(\infty) \propto \prod_{r=1}^{j-1} p_{r,r+1} \bigg/ \prod_{r=1}^{j} (x - p_{rr}). \tag{2.18}$$

Alternative, but equivalent, expressions for $\bar{\mathbf{n}}(\infty)$ and $\mathbf{p}(\infty)$ can be obtained from the matrix expression given in equation (2.4). The result for $\mathbf{p}(\infty)$ is

$$\mathbf{p}(\infty) \propto (x\mathbf{I} - \mathbf{P})^{-1}\mathbf{p}_0. \tag{2.19}$$

The constants of proportionality in the above equations are, of course, determined by the fact that

$$\sum_{j=1}^{k} p_j(\infty) = 1.$$

If x is very large $(x\mathbf{I} - \mathbf{P})^{-1} \sim x\mathbf{I}$ and

$$\mathbf{p}(\infty) \sim \mathbf{p}_0. \tag{2.20}$$

This equation expresses the obvious fact that, with a very high rate of expansion, the recruitment distribution dominates the structure. The rate at which this situation is approached when equation (2.18) applies, can be judged by noting that $p_j(T)$ is proportional, in the limit, to x^{-j}.

2.5. Variances and Covariances of the Grade Sizes

The theory for closed systems given in Section 2.4 of Chapter 2, can be generalized to include open systems. For an open system equation (2.11) of that chapter must be replaced by

$$n_j(T) = \sum_{i=1}^{k} n_{ij}(T - 1) + n_{0j}(T) \quad (j = 1, 2, \ldots, k), \tag{2.21}$$

where $n_{0j}(T)$ is the number of new entrants to grade j at time T. On taking expectations of both sides of this equation we are led back to equation

(2.1). If we assume that the input is stochastically independent of the internal movements of the system then

$$\text{cov}\{n_j(T)n_l(T)\}$$

$$= \text{cov}\left\{\sum_{i=1}^{k}n_{ij}(T-1)\sum_{i=1}^{k}n_{il}(T-1)\right\} + \text{cov}\{n_{0j}(T)n_{0l}(T)\}. \quad (2.22)$$

The first term on the right-hand side of equation (2.22) is essentially the same as the expression given in equation (2.11) of Chapter 2. Its evaluation can be carried through as in that chapter without any modification. All that we have to do to make the result of equation (2.15) of Chapter 2 applicable in the present case is to add on the last covariance term given in equation (2.22), above. Thus in matrix notation we have

$$\mu(T) = \Pi\mu(T-1) + \mu_0(T), \quad (2.23)$$

where $\mu(T)$ and Π are as defined in Chapter 2. The first k elements of the vector $\mu_0(T)$ are the expected number of entrants to each grade at time T listed in ascending order; the remaining k^2 elements are the covariances of these numbers listed in dictionary order. In our examples the input will be time homogeneous so we shall suppress the argument of μ_0 and write μ_0 instead of $\mu_0(T)$. In this case equation (2.2) yields

$$\mu(T) = \Pi^T\mu(0) + (I - \Pi)^{-1}(I - \Pi^T)\mu_0. \quad (2.24)$$

The inverse of $I - \Pi$ exists because the dominant eigen value of Π is strictly less than one.

The form of μ_0 will depend upon the stochastic nature of the input and the method of allocation to grades. We shall illustrate the point using the two cases mentioned in Section 2.1. First suppose that the input $\{R(T)\}$ is a sequence of independently and identically distributed random variables and that, at time T, a proportion p_{0j} go to grade j. In this case the first k elements of μ_0 are $\bar{R}(T)p_{0j}$ $(j = 1, 2, \ldots, k)$, where $\bar{R} = ER(T)$. The covariance elements take the form

$$\text{var}\{R(T)\}p_{0j}p_{0l} \quad (j, l = 1, 2, \ldots, k).$$

Our second assumption about the allocation of recruits was that each one was to be allocated to the jth grade with probability p_{0j}. In this case the k means in the vector μ_0 are $\bar{R}(T)p_{0j}$ $(j = 1, 2, \ldots, k)$ as before, but the covariances are now given by

$$\text{cov}\{n_{0j}(T)n_{0l}(T)\}$$
$$= \text{var}\{R(T)\}p_{0j}p_{0l} + \bar{R}(T)(\delta_{jl}p_{0j} - p_{0j}p_{0l}) \quad (i, j = 1, 2, \ldots, k). \quad (2.25)$$

This result is obtained by first finding expectations conditional upon $R(T)$ and then averaging over the distribution of $R(T)$. Under either assumption about allocation the determination of the successive values of $\mu(T)$ is straightforward. Some examples are discussed below but first we consider the limiting behaviour of the system.

If the input to the system is time-homogeneous, μ_0 does not depend on T. Under these circumstances we may investigate the limiting form of the vector $\mu(T)$ as $T \to \infty$. We already know that the limit exists for the first k elements of the vector and it may be shown that the same result holds for all of the elements. This being so it is clear from equation (2.23) that the limiting vector must satisfy

$$\mu(\infty) = \mathbf{\Pi}\mu(\infty) + \mu_0$$

or

$$\mu(\infty) = (\mathbf{I} - \mathbf{\Pi})^{-1}\mu_0. \tag{2.26}$$

Once the matrix $(\mathbf{I} - \mathbf{\Pi})^{-1}$ has been computed the effects of different kinds of input can easily be compared. If $R(T)$ is a fixed quantity R, then var $\{R(T)\} = 0$ and there is a substantial simplification in μ_0.

To illustrate the foregoing theory we shall present some calculations for two different kinds of input. In the first case we shall suppose that $R(T)$ is a fixed number, R, independent of T and in the second that $\{R(T)\}$ is a sequence of independent Poisson variates with constant mean equal to R. These two assumptions represent fairly extreme degrees of variability in the input. We shall assume, for the purposes of this illustration, that each new recruit is allocated to grade j with probability p_{0j}. The covariance elements of μ_0 are obtained from equation (2.25), where var $\{R(T)\}$ is zero for constant input and equal to $\bar{R}$ for Poisson input. The calculations in Table 3.2 relate to the example discussed in Section 2.3 for which the expected grade sizes were given in Table 3.1. We have further supposed that the initial size of the organization was 590 and that $\bar{R} = 60$.

The equilibrium values are approached quite rapidly for the lower grades but only very slowly for the highest grade. For both types of input there is considerable uncertainty in predictions of the size of the fifth grade in the distant future. The difference between the two kinds of input is most apparent in the lowest grades. It is not until $T = 5$ that the input has any effect on the top grade and thereafter it is only slight. In the lowest grade the effect of Poisson variability is to roughly double the variance as compared with fixed input. All of the covariances are either zero or negative but in the Poisson case they vanish in the limit. This fact coupled with equality of the limiting means and variances suggests that the grade sizes are asymptotically distributed like independent Poisson variates. Pollard (1967) has proved this to be true in the general case when the input consists of an independent sequence of Poisson variates. A proof is as follows.

TABLE 3.2

Variance-covariance matrices for the grade sizes for the the example of Section 2.3 with (a) fixed input, (b) Poisson input where, in each case, $N(0) = 9.8333\,\bar{R}(T)$ and $\bar{R}(T) = 60$.

T	Fixed input					Poisson input				
1	64.94	−41.93	0	0	0	98.69	−30.68	0	0	0
		86.18	−18.59	0	0		89.93	−18.59	0	0
			39.16	−9.96	0			39.16	−9.96	0
				18.81	−5.02				18.81	−5.02
					6.71					6.71
2	83.82	−47.68	−4.09	0	0	131.83	−26.92	−2.99	0	0
		115.16	−21.51	−1.95	0		125.25	−20.78	−1.95	0
			60.94	−12.81	−0.75			61.02	−12.81	−0.75
				31.86	−7.99				31.86	−7.99
					12.61					12.61
5	80.20	−38.20	−7.69	−1.22	−0.07	137.86	−5.70	−2.82	−0.67	−0.05
		124.69	−17.15	−5.07	−0.57		149.79	−11.25	−4.24	−0.52
			85.60	−11.20	−2.56			87.63	−10.85	−2.54
				58.36	−11.47				58.43	−11.46
					28.83					28.83
10	71.54	−34.71	−6.73	−1.51	−0.24	129.97	−0.19	−0.25	−0.21	−0.07
		111.69	−11.99	−4.68	−1.16		142.27	−1.53	−1.57	−0.65
			84.77	−6.72	−2.91			90.83	−4.20	−2.39
				79.43	−10.50				80.80	−10.18
					56.05					56.13
∞	70.13	−34.58	−6.58	−1.43	−0.24	128.57	0	0	0	0
		104.79	−11.10	−3.97	−1.05		135.71	0	0	0
			74.13	−4.35	−1.86			81.43	0	0
				76.84	−3.74				81.43	0
					154.50†					162.26
Expected grade sizes for $T = \infty$	128.6	135.7	81.4	81.4	162.3	128.6	135.7	81.4	81.4	162.3

† This is the value for $T = 100$ at which point the limiting value had not been attained. The calculations in this table were carried out by J. H. Pollard on the Cambridge University Titan computer.

At time T an individual who entered the system at time $T - t$ will be in one of the k grades or will have left. Let the probability that he is in grade j be $\pi_j(T - t)$, $(j = 1, 2, \ldots, k + 1)$, where $j = k + 1$ refers to those who have left. These probabilities will be functions of the recruitment probabilities $\{p_{0j}\}$ and the transition probabilities $\{p_{ij}\}$. The joint distribution of the numbers in the $k + 1$ grades at time T who entered at time $T - t$ may thus be expressed as

$$P(n_1, n_2, \ldots, n_{k+1}) = Pr\{R(T - t) = n_0\}P(n_1, n_2, \ldots, n_{k+1}|n_0) \quad (2.27)$$

where

$$n_0 = \sum_{j=1}^{k} n_{0j}.$$

The first term on the right-hand side of equation (2.27) is the Poisson probability with parameter $\bar{R}$ and the second is the multinomial probability with parameters n_0 and $\{\pi_j(T - t)\}$. Hence

$$P(n_1, n_2, \ldots, n_{k+1}) = \left(\frac{e^{-R}\bar{R}^{n_0}}{n_0!}\right)\left(\frac{n_0!}{n_1!n_2!\ldots!n_{k+1}!}\right)\prod_{j=1}^{k+1} \pi_j^{n_j}(T - t)$$

$$= \prod_{j=1}^{k+1} \frac{\{\bar{R}\pi_j(T - t)\}^{n_j}}{n_j!} e^{-\bar{R}\pi_j(T-t)}. \quad (2.28)$$

The numbers of individuals in the k grades at time T who entered at time $T - t$ are thus mutually independent Poisson variates. Since the $\{R(T)\}$ are mutually independent, the total number of *recruited* members in grade j at time T is the sum of T mutually independent Poisson variates and hence is itself a Poisson variate. In addition we may deduce that the total numbers of recruited members in the k grades are mutually independent. The initial members of the system will ultimately consist wholly of recruited members and so the result follows. The rate at which the limiting behaviour is approached is thus seen to depend on the rate at which the original members leave.

2.6. An Example with a Periodic Transition Matrix

So far we have assumed that the transition probabilities and the recruitment distribution do not depend on T. Without this assumption equation (2.1b) still holds, although the subsequent analysis becomes more complicated. In particular, there may be several limiting structures or none at all. An interesting example of a non-homogenous process arose in Gani's study of student enrolment at Michigan State University. The academic year there consisted of three 'quarters' and transitions took place at the end of each quarter. It was not considered realistic to assume that the transition and recruitment probabilities would be the same in each quarter of a given year. However, it could be assumed that these probabilities would be the same in, say, the first quarter of one year as they had been in the first quarter of previous years. This requires us to make both $\mathbf{P}$ and $\mathbf{p}_0$ functions of T satisfying

$$\mathbf{P}(T + 3) = \mathbf{P}(T)$$

and

$$\mathbf{p}_0(T + 3) = \mathbf{p}_0(T) \quad (T = 0, 1, 2, \ldots).$$

Suppose that $T = 0$ refers to the first quarter of the first academic year and let

$$\mathbf{P}(3T + j) = \mathbf{P}_{j+1} \quad \begin{pmatrix} j = 0, 1, 2, \ldots \\ T = 0, 1, 2, \ldots \end{pmatrix}.$$
$$\mathbf{p}_0(3T + j) = \mathbf{p}_{0, j+1}$$

Then $\mathbf{P}_j$ and $\mathbf{p}_{0j}$ relate to the jth quarter of any year. The grade structures may now be computed from the following difference equations:

$$\left. \begin{array}{l} \bar{\mathbf{n}}(3T + 1) = \mathbf{P}_1 \bar{\mathbf{n}}(3T) + R(3T + 1)\mathbf{p}_{0,2} \\ \bar{\mathbf{n}}(3T + 2) = \mathbf{P}_2 \bar{\mathbf{n}}(3T + 1) + R(3T + 2)\mathbf{p}_{0,3} \\ \bar{\mathbf{n}}(3T + 3) = \mathbf{P}_3 \bar{\mathbf{n}}(3T + 2) + R(3T + 3)\mathbf{p}_{0,1} \end{array} \right\} \quad (T = 0, 1, 2, \ldots) \quad (2.30)$$

These equations express the structure in a given quarter in terms of the structure in the previous quarter. For some purposes it is more convenient to relate the structures for the same quarter of succeeding years. Thus, for example, for the first quarter, equation (2.30) gives

$$\bar{\mathbf{n}}(3T + 3) = \mathbf{P}_3 \mathbf{P}_2 \mathbf{P}_1 \bar{\mathbf{n}}(3T) + R(3T + 1)\mathbf{P}_3 \mathbf{P}_2 \mathbf{p}_{0,2}$$
$$+ R(3T + 2)\mathbf{P}_3 \mathbf{p}_{0,3} + R(3T + 3)\mathbf{p}_{0,1}. \quad (2.31)$$

Similar expressions can be obtained for the second and third quarters.

The limiting behaviour of the system may be investigated by the methods of earlier sections. The case of greatest interest is when $R(T)$ is constant or tends to a limit. When this is so the limiting grade structure in the *first* quarter will be given by

$$\bar{\mathbf{n}}(\infty) = (\mathbf{I} - \mathbf{P}_3 \mathbf{P}_2 \mathbf{P}_1)^{-1} \{\mathbf{P}_3 \mathbf{P}_2 \mathbf{p}_{0,2} + \mathbf{P}_3 \mathbf{p}_{0,3} + \mathbf{p}_{0,1}\} R \quad (2.32)$$

where R is the limiting value of the input. The corresponding expressions for the second and third quarters can either by obtained by substituting back in equations (2.30) or by a repetition of the above argument.

3. A MODEL FOR AN EXPANDING SYSTEM
WITH GIVEN SIZE

3.1. The Equations of the Model

The practical context in which the present model arose was described in Section 1. The model differs from that described in the preceding section only in that the total size of the organization rather than the input is fixed. Instead of being given the sequence of inputs $\{R(T)\}$ we now have a sequence of total sizes $\{N(T)\}$. As before, this may be a sequence of given numbers or a realization of a known stochastic process. In the latter case the symbol $N(T)$ is to be interpreted as an expected size. The distinction is of no importance until we come to consider the distributions of grade sizes in Section 3.4. Young and Almond (1961), who proposed the model, were concerned with expanding organizations and we shall follow them in this respect. Much of the theory is also applicable to the more general case of fluctuating or decreasing sequences. Some aspects of this case will be explored in Chapter 6.

Let $M(T)$ denote the increase in size which takes place between $T - 1$ and T; thus $M(T) = N(T) - N(T - 1)$ $(T = 1, 2, \ldots)$.

Equation 2.1 remains valid but cannot be used as it stands because $\{R(T)\}$ is an unknown in this version of the problem. At any time the number of recruits must be sufficient to achieve the desired expansion and to replace losses from the system. The expected number of recruits required at time T is thus

$$\bar{R}(T) = M(T) + \sum_{i=1}^{k} p_{i,k+1}\bar{n}_i(T - 1) \quad (T = 1, 2, \ldots). \tag{3.1}$$

By substituting $\bar{R}(T)$ for $R(T)$ in equation (2.1a), the difference equations for the expected grade sizes become

$$\bar{n}_j(T) = \sum_{i=1}^{k} (p_{ij} + p_{i,k+1}p_{0j})\bar{n}_i(T - 1) + M(T)p_{0j} \quad (j = 1, 2 \ldots, k). \tag{3.2a}$$

If we write $q_{ij} = p_{ij} + p_{i,k+1}p_{0j}$ this equation may be written in matrix notation as

$$\bar{\mathbf{n}}(T) = \mathbf{Q}\bar{\mathbf{n}}(T - 1) + M(T)\mathbf{p}_0, \tag{3.2b}$$

where $\mathbf{Q}$ is the transpose of the matrix $\{q_{ij}\}$. This matrix equation has the same form as equation (2.1b) and leads to the result that

$$\bar{\mathbf{n}}(T) = \mathbf{Q}^T\mathbf{n}(0) + \left\{ \sum_{\tau=0}^{T-1} M(T - \tau)\mathbf{Q}^\tau \right\}\mathbf{p}_0. \tag{3.3}$$

The foregoing formulae provide all that is necessary for the numerical investigation of the expected structure. If we wish to study the form of $\bar{n}(T)$ by analytical methods two approaches are possible. One of these is to use the spectral representation for the power of a matrix as in Section 2.2 but the advantages of this method are not as great here as when the input was fixed. In that case we were able to obtain many explicit results for the special but important case when the matrix $\mathbf{P}$ was triangular. This was because the eigen values were then equal to the diagonal elements of the matrix. It is clear from inspection of the q_{ij}'s as defined above that $\mathbf{Q}$ will not normally be triangular and hence much of the simplicity of the method is lost. An alternative approach is to use the fact that $\mathbf{Q}$ is a stochastic matrix; a conclusion which follows by observing that

$$\sum_{j=1}^{k} q_{ij} = \sum_{j=1}^{k} p_{ij} + p_{i,k+1} \sum_{j=1}^{k} p_{0j} = 1 \quad (i = 1, 2, \ldots, k).$$

This fact enables us to use known results about powers of stochastic matrices and, in particular, about their limiting behaviour. We shall use this method in the following sections.

The special case $M(T) = 0$, for all T, is particularly interesting. Our equations then relate to an open system of constant size but they are identical in form to those used in the study of closed systems in Chapter 2. They thus provide a formal justification for our earlier remark that an open system in which gains and losses were equal could be treated as closed. Each person who leaves can be paired with a new entrant and the two changes treated as one. Thus a transition from grade i to grade j can either take place within the system or by loss from grade i and replacement to grade j with total probability $p_{ij} + p_{i,k+1}p_{0j}$.

3.2. The Exact Solution for Geometric Growth Rate

In order to gain insight into the behaviour of expanding organizations we shall suppose the growth rate to be geometric. That is we suppose that

$$M(T) = Mx^T \quad (T \geq 1),$$

where M is a positive constant and x is non-negative. By varying the values of M and x we can generate a considerable variety of growth patterns. The simplest case arises when there are only two strata and we shall consider this first.

When $k = 2$ the matrix $\mathbf{Q}$ can be written in the form

$$\mathbf{Q} = \begin{pmatrix} 1 - \alpha & \beta \\ \alpha & 1 - \beta \end{pmatrix}$$

where $1 - \alpha = p_{11} + p_{01}p_{13}$, $1 - \beta = p_{22} + p_{02}p_{23}$. A well-known result (see, for example, Bailey 1964, p. 52) then gives

$$\mathbf{Q}^{\tau} = \frac{1}{\alpha + \beta} \left\{ \begin{pmatrix} \beta & \beta \\ \alpha & \alpha \end{pmatrix} + (1 - \alpha - \beta)^{\tau} \begin{pmatrix} \alpha & -\beta \\ -\alpha & \beta \end{pmatrix} \right\}. \qquad (3.4)$$

Substituting for $\mathbf{Q}^{\tau}$ in equation (3.3), with $M(T - \tau) = Mx^{T-\tau}$ we find

$$\bar{\mathbf{n}}(T) = \frac{1}{\alpha + \beta} \left\{ \begin{pmatrix} \beta & \beta \\ \alpha & \alpha \end{pmatrix} + (1 - \alpha - \beta)^{T} \begin{pmatrix} \alpha & -\beta \\ -\alpha & \beta \end{pmatrix} \right\} \mathbf{n}(0)$$

$$+ \frac{1}{\alpha + \beta} \sum_{\tau=0}^{T-1} Mx^{T-\tau} \left\{ \begin{pmatrix} \beta & \beta \\ \alpha & \alpha \end{pmatrix} + (1 - \alpha - \beta)^{\tau} \begin{pmatrix} \alpha & -\beta \\ -\alpha & \beta \end{pmatrix} \right\} \mathbf{p}_0. \quad (3.5)$$

Summing the geometric series in equation (3.5), and using the facts that $n_1(0) + n_2(0) = N(0)$ and $p_{01} + p_{02} = 1$ the vector of expected grade sizes becomes

$$\bar{\mathbf{n}}(T) = \frac{1}{\alpha + \beta} \left[\left\{ N(0) + M \frac{(x - x^{T+1})}{1 - x} \right\} \begin{pmatrix} \beta \\ \alpha \end{pmatrix} \right.$$

$$+ (1 - \alpha - \beta)^{T} \begin{pmatrix} \alpha n_1(0) - \beta n_2(0) \\ -\alpha n_1(0) + \beta n_2(0) \end{pmatrix}$$

$$\left. + M \left\{ \frac{x^{T} - (1 - \alpha - \beta)^{T}}{1 - (1 - \alpha - \beta)x^{-1}} \right\} \begin{pmatrix} \alpha p_{01} - \beta p_{02} \\ -\alpha p_{01} + \beta p_{02} \end{pmatrix} \right]. \qquad (3.6)$$

The total size of the organization at time T is

$$N(T) = N(0) + Mx(1 - x^{T})/(1 - x). \qquad (3.7)$$

The variable, T, enters the expression for $\bar{\mathbf{n}}(T)$ through the terms in x^{T} and $(1 - \alpha - \beta)^{T}$. Of these the latter exerts a diminishing influence as T increases because $1 - \alpha - \beta < 1$. If $x > 1$ the terms in x^{T} become dominant whereas if $x < 1$ they vanish in the limit. In the intermediate case where $x = 1$ the grade sizes increase without limit but their relative values approach a limit as $T \to \infty$. In fact, for $x \le 1$ we have

$$\bar{\mathbf{n}}(T) \sim \frac{N(T)}{\alpha + \beta} \begin{pmatrix} \beta \\ \alpha \end{pmatrix}. \qquad (3.8)$$

In order to appreciate the full implications of equation (3.6), it is necessary to consider special cases. One such case is considered below; the reader will find it helpful to construct others.

The following illustration is for a two-grade system in which all recruits enter grade 1. There are no demotions and the probability of withdrawal is the same for each grade. The table of transition probabilities is

$$
\begin{array}{cc}
1 & 0 \\
\hline
\tfrac{1}{2} & \tfrac{1}{4} \quad \tfrac{1}{4} \\
0 & \tfrac{3}{4} \quad \tfrac{1}{4}
\end{array}
$$

For this example

$$1 - \alpha = 1 - \beta = \tfrac{3}{4}.$$

Substitution in equation (3.6) gives

$$\bar{\mathbf{n}}(T) = N(T)\begin{pmatrix} \tfrac{1}{2} \\ \tfrac{1}{2} \end{pmatrix} + (\tfrac{1}{2})^{T+2}\begin{pmatrix} n_1(0) - n_2(0) \\ n_2(0) - n_1(0) \end{pmatrix} + Mx\begin{Bmatrix} x^T - (\tfrac{1}{2})^T \\ x - \tfrac{1}{2} \end{Bmatrix}\begin{pmatrix} \tfrac{1}{2} \\ -\tfrac{1}{2} \end{pmatrix}.$$

$$(3.9)$$

If x is fairly small the approach to the limit will be rapid. For example, if $x = \tfrac{1}{2}$

$$n_1(T) = \tfrac{1}{2}\{N(0) + M(1 - (\tfrac{1}{2})^T)\} + (\tfrac{1}{2})^{T+1}\{n_1(0) - n_2(0)\} + (\tfrac{1}{2})^{T+2}TM.$$

$$(3.10)$$

The difference between the initial and final structures and the size of M both affect the rate of approach to the limit but their effect is not great. If x is near to 1 the approach to the limit may be very slow as we shall see below.

When $k > 2$ there is no simple expression for $\mathbf{Q}^T$ but similar conclusions can be drawn. If the growth rate is geometric the matrix series in equation (3.3) can almost always be summed. It is easy to verify that

$$(x\mathbf{I} - \mathbf{Q})(\sum_{\tau=0}^{T-1}\mathbf{Q}x^{T-\tau}) = x(x^T\mathbf{I} - \mathbf{Q}^T)$$

and hence, if $x\mathbf{I} - \mathbf{Q}$ possesses an inverse,

$$\sum_{\tau=0}^{T-1}\mathbf{Q}^\tau x^{T-\tau} = x(x\mathbf{I} - \mathbf{Q})^{-1}(x^T\mathbf{I} - \mathbf{Q}^T).$$

Thus we have

$$\bar{\mathbf{n}}(T) = \mathbf{Q}^T\mathbf{n}(0) + Mx(x\mathbf{I} - \mathbf{Q})^{-1}(x^T\mathbf{I} - \mathbf{Q}^T)\mathbf{p}_0. \qquad (3.11)$$

The inverse of $x\mathbf{I} - \mathbf{Q}$ does not exist if the determinant of the matrix vanishes. This will happen whenever x is equal to an eigen value of the matrix $\mathbf{Q}$. For a stochastic matrix it is known that at least one eigen value is equal to unity and that the remainder lie between zero and one. Hence equation (3.11) holds for all $x > 1$ and when $x < 1$ for all but at most $k - 1$ values of x. For numerical work with $x < 1$ it is preferable to use the recursive formula of equation (3.2). The usefulness of the representation of equation (3.11) is that it provides direct information about the transient behaviour of the system. This behaviour depends on the terms x^T and $\mathbf{Q}^T$. It is known from the general theory of Markov chains that, if $\mathbf{Q}$ is regular, $\mathbf{Q}^T$ tends to a limit as T increases. As in the case $k = 2$ the long-term behaviour of the system depends crucially on the magnitude of x.

In order to illustrate the theory we shall take $k = 5$ and use the same transition probabilities as in the example of Section 2.3. Let the rate of growth be

$$M(T) = \frac{1}{10} N(0)x^T$$

with $x = 0, \frac{1}{2}, 1$ and 2. Because the total size of the organization is changing we have tabulated the relative expected grade sizes given by

$$a_j(T) = \bar{n}_j(T)/N(T) \quad (j = 1, 2, \ldots, k).$$

When $x = 0$ there is no expansion and the limit is approached rather slowly especially in the highest grade. This is due mainly to the big difference between the initial and limiting structures. When $x = \frac{1}{2}$ the ultimate increase in total size is 10 per cent but the rate of approach to the limiting structure is hardly affected. The case $x = 1$ shows a very slow approach to the limit though here again the lower grades attain their limiting values more quickly than the higher ones. In this example grade 5 is little more than half its limiting value after 50 years. Under this kind of expansion the structure would not achieve equilibrium in any period likely to be of practical interest. By contrast, when $x = 2$, the limit is reached quite rapidly although in this case it is a different limit. Few organizations would be able to maintain such a rapid rate of growth long enough for this final structure to be of real importance.

3.3. The Limiting Structure

We have already investigated the limiting behaviour of expanding organizations when the growth rate is geometric. In the special cases considered we observed that the quantities $\{a_j(T)\}$ approached the same limiting values for $x \leq 1$ but had different limits when $x > 1$. We shall now give a general method of finding the limiting structure and use it to show how this structure depends on the growth rate.

TABLE 3.3

Percentage values of the expected grade sizes for an organization with geometric growth rate and transition probabilities as in Section 2.3.

		$100a_i(T)$				
				i		
T	x	1	2	3	4	5
0	0	40	30	15	10	5
	$\frac{1}{2}$	40	30	15	10	5
	1	40	30	15	10	5
	2	40	30	15	10	5
1	0	35.6	32.2	15.8	10.8	5.8
	$\frac{1}{2}$	37.4	31.8	15.0	10.2	5.5
	1	39.1	31.5	14.3	9.8	5.2
	2	42.1	31.0	13.1	9.0	4.8
2	0	32.5	32.8	16.6	11.5	6.5
	$\frac{1}{2}$	34.8	32.8	15.7	10.7	6.1
	1	38.4	32.4	14.2	9.6	5.4
	2	46.6	31.3	10.9	7.2	4.1
5	0	27.8	31.1	18.2	13.8	9.1
	$\frac{1}{2}$	29.2	32.0	17.7	12.8	8.3
	1	36.3	33.2	14.8	9.6	6.1
	2	59.6	31.6	5.4	2.2	1.3
10	0	24.8	27.5	17.7	16.2	13.8
	$\frac{1}{2}$	25.3	28.2	17.9	15.7	12.8
	1	33.8	32.4	15.8	10.6	7.4
	2	63.6	31.9	3.9	0.6	0.1
25	0	22.3	23.8	14.6	15.5	23.8
	$\frac{1}{2}$	22.4	23.9	14.7	15.6	23.3
	1	29.3	29.4	15.9	13.0	13.0
	2	63.8	31.9	3.8	0.5	0.0
50	0	21.8	23.0	13.8	13.9	27.3
	$\frac{1}{2}$	21.8	23.1	13.9	14.0	27.3
	1	26.2	26.8	15.2	13.6	18.1
	2	63.8	31.9	3.8	0.5	0.0

Let us consider $\bar{n}(T)$ in the form given by equation (3.3). In Chapter 2, we made use of the fact that if $\mathbf{Q}$ is a regular stochastic matrix then

$$\lim_{T \to \infty} \mathbf{Q}^T = \mathbf{Q}^\infty$$

exists and is a matrix with identical columns. We introduce the vector $\mathbf{q} = (q_1, q_2, \ldots, q_k)'$ to denote any column of this matrix. This result enables us to deduce that the limit of the first term on the right-hand side of equation (3.3) is $N(0)\mathbf{q}$. To find the limit of the second term consider the matrix

$$\mathbf{Q}_T^* = \left(\sum_{\tau=0}^{T-1} M(T - \tau)\mathbf{Q}^\tau \right) \bigg/ \sum_{\tau=0}^{T-1} M(T - \tau). \tag{3.12}$$

The (i, j)th element in this matrix may be written in the form

$$S_{ij}(T) = \sum_{\tau=0}^{T-1} q_{ij}^{(\tau)} \mathrm{d}(T - \tau),$$

where $q_{ij}^{(\tau)}$ is the τ-step transition probability for the Markov chain with transition matrix $\mathbf{Q}$: we define $q_{ii}^{(0)} = 1$. The weights $\mathrm{d}(T - \tau)$ obviously satisfy the condition

$$\sum_{\tau=0}^{T-1} \mathrm{d}(T - \tau) = 1.$$

Further, since $0 \le q_{ji}^{(\tau)} \le 1$ and $\mathrm{d}(T - \tau) \ge 0$ for all τ, it follows that the elements of $\mathbf{Q}_T^*$ all lie in the interval $(0, 1)$ for all T. Using this notation, equation (3.3) may be written as

$$\bar{n}(T) = \mathbf{Q}^T \mathbf{n}(0) + \mathbf{Q}_T^* \mathbf{p}_0 \{ N(T) - N(0) \}. \tag{3.13}$$

Two cases must now be distinguished. If $M(T)$ is such that $N(T)$ approaches a limit then

$$\bar{n}(\infty) = N(0)\mathbf{q} + \mathbf{Q}_\infty^* \mathbf{p}_0 (N(\infty) - N(0)) \tag{3.14}$$

assuming that

$$\lim_{T \to \infty} \mathbf{Q}_T^* = \mathbf{Q}_\infty^*$$

exists. If $N(T)$ increases without limit the expected grade sizes also tend to infinity but we can still calculate their relative sizes. We then find that

$$\mathbf{a}(\infty) = \mathbf{Q}_\infty^* \mathbf{p}_0. \tag{3.15}$$

In either case the solution to our problem reduces to finding

$$\lim_{T \to \infty} \mathbf{Q}_T^*.$$

Provided $\mathbf{Q}$ is regular we know that

$$\lim_{T \to \infty} q_{ij}^{(T)} = q_i \quad (i = 1, 2, \ldots, k).$$

Thus for any positive ε, however small, there is a value T_0 of T such that for $T \geq T_0$ $|q_{ij}^{(T)} - q_i| < \varepsilon$. The element $S_{ij}(T)$ of $\mathbf{Q}_T^*$ may be written

$$S_{ij}(T) = \sum_{\tau=0}^{T_0-1} q_{ij}^{(\tau)} \mathrm{d}(T - \tau) + \sum_{\tau=T_0}^{T-1} q_i \mathrm{d}(T - \tau) + \sum_{\tau=T_0}^{T-1} (q_{ij}^{(\tau)} - q_i) \mathrm{d}(T - \tau). \quad (3.16)$$

The modulus of the last term is certainly less than ε and can thus be made arbitrarily small. To find the limit of $S_{ij}(T)$ we therefore need to consider only the first two terms. There are two cases:

    (a) If

$$\lim_{T \to \infty} \sum_{\tau=T_0}^{T-1} \mathrm{d}(T - \tau) = 1$$

the second term in equation (3.16) tends to q_i and the first term vanishes. In this case, therefore, the limit exists and is equal to q_i. We shall refer to this condition as condition A. It is a condition imposed on the rate of growth of the organization. If it is satisfied we find from both equations (3.14) and (3.15), that

$$\mathbf{a}(\infty) = \mathbf{q}. \quad (3.17)$$

This means that *the same limiting structure is reached for all rates of growth satisfying condition A*. In particular the limit is that reached by a system in which there is no expansion at all.

    (b) If condition A does not hold, $\mathbf{Q}_T^*$ may or may not tend to a limit depending on the nature of the sequence $\{M(T)\}$. An example is considered below and, in general, each problem must be considered on its own.

    Condition A may be expressed in various forms. An equivalent version is that

$$\lim_{T \to \infty} \mathrm{d}(T - C) = 0$$

for any positive integer C. Perhaps the form which shows most clearly the nature of the restraint which it imposes on growth is

$$\lim_{T \to \infty} M(T)/N(T) = 0.$$

Expressed in words this means that the *proportionate* growth rate must vanish in the limit.

    For the geometric growth rate, condition A holds whenever $x \leq 1$. The case $x = 1$ is particularly interesting because, although the organization grows without limit, the limiting grade structure is the same as when there is no growth at all. However, as we saw in Table 3.4 the rate of approach to the limit is much slower. If $x > 1$

$$\lim_{T \to \infty} \sum_{\tau=T_0}^{T-1} d(T - \tau) = 0$$

and hence condition A does not hold. The limiting grade structure may be deduced directly in this case from equation (3.11). If T is large

$$\bar{n}(T) \sim Mx(x\mathbf{I} - \mathbf{Q})^{-1}\mathbf{p}_0 \qquad (3.18)$$

and

$$\mathbf{a}(\infty) \propto (x\mathbf{I} - \mathbf{Q})^{-1}\mathbf{p}_0. \qquad (3.19)$$

The inverse matrix may be formally expanded in a power series to give

$$(x\mathbf{I} - \mathbf{Q})^{-1} = \frac{1}{x}\left(\mathbf{I} + \frac{\mathbf{Q}}{x} + \frac{\mathbf{Q}^2}{x^2} + \ldots\right). \qquad (3.20)$$

The elements of this matrix are thus

$$S_{ij}(\infty) = \frac{1}{x} \sum_{\tau=0}^{\infty} q_{ij}^{(\tau)} x^{-\tau}.$$

If x is very large the first term is dominant and

$$\mathbf{a}(\infty) \doteqdot \mathbf{p}_0. \qquad (3.21)$$

This result could have been anticipated by observing that with such a rapid rate of growth most members of the system would be new recruits.

3.4. Variances and Covariances of the Grade Sizes

The method used to obtain the variances and covariances for the model with given input is equally applicable here. The basic equation is equation (2.23). However, this can no longer be used directly because the elements of $\boldsymbol{\mu}_0(T)$ depend upon the unknown mean and variance of $R(T)$. These quantities can easily be found by an extension of the argument which gave equation (3.1). Thus we have to find the mean and variance of

$$R(T) = M(T) + \sum_{i=1}^{k} n_{i,k+1}(T - 1). \qquad (3.22)$$

The random variables $\{n_{i,k+1}(T - 1)\}$ are independent and, given $n_i(T - 1)$, $n_{i,k+1}(T - 1)$ is binomially distributed with parameter $p_{i,k+1}$. For simplicity we shall assume that $\{M(T)\}$ is a sequence of known numbers but allowing it to be a sequence of random variables presents no difficulties. Under these assumptions

$$E[R(T)|\{n_i(T-1)\}] = M(T) + \sum_{i=1}^{k} n_i(T-1)p_{i,k+1}$$

and hence, as before,

$$\bar{R}(T) = M(T) + \sum_{i=1}^{k} \bar{n}_i(T-1)p_{i,k+1}. \qquad (3.23)$$

Similarly,

$$E[R^2(T)|\{n_i(T-1)\}]$$

$$= M^2(T) + 2M(T)\sum_{i=1}^{k} n_i(T-1)p_{i,k+1}$$

$$+ \sum_{i=1}^{k}\sum_{j=1}^{k} En_i(T-1)n_j(T-1)p_{i,k+1}p_{j,k+1}.$$

Therefore

$$\operatorname{var} R(T) = \sum_{i=1}^{k}\sum_{j=1}^{k} p_{i,k+1}p_{j,k+1} \operatorname{cov}\{n_i(T-1)n_j(T-1)\}. \qquad (3.24)$$

It is clear from these results that the mean and variance of $R(T)$ depend only on the history of the process through $\mu(T-1)$. Hence the right-hand side of equation (2.23) can be evaluated from a knowledge of $\mu(T-1)$ and thus $\mu(T)$ can be calculated recursively. The unknown $\bar{R}(T)$ and var $R(T)$ which appear in μ_0 can be eliminated by means of equation (3.23) and (3.24) as follows. These equations may be written as

$$\begin{pmatrix} \bar{R}(T) \\ \operatorname{var}(T) \end{pmatrix} = \begin{pmatrix} M(T) \\ 0 \end{pmatrix} + \mathbf{V}\mu(T-1) \qquad (3.25)$$

where $\mathbf{V}$ is a $2 \times (k^2+k)$ matrix. From our earlier results it follows that μ_0 can be expressed in the form

$$\mu_0 = \mathbf{U}\begin{pmatrix} R(T) \\ \operatorname{var} R(T) \end{pmatrix},$$

where $\mathbf{U}$ is a $(k^2+k) \times 2$ matrix with known elements. Hence we may re-write equation (2.23) as

$$\mu(T) = (\mathbf{\Pi} + \mathbf{UV})\mu(T-1) + \mathbf{U}\begin{pmatrix} M(T) \\ 0 \end{pmatrix} \qquad (3.26)$$

which is a generalization of equation (3.2b). By means of this equation we can compute the means, variances and covariances of the grade sizes and investigate their limiting behaviour. The theoretical and numerical investigation of equation (3.26) remains to be carried out.

3.5. Promotion and Recruitment Policies for Hierarchical Organizations

We have seen, in the preceding sections, that the grade sizes are determined by the patterns of loss, recruitment and transfer from the organization. Of these factors the promotion and recruitment distributions are often amenable to control. This fact suggests that we might use our results to calculate what the promotion and recruitment patterns should be in order to achieve and maintain a desired structure. A full investigation of this problem is lacking but some preliminary results are set out below for Young's model.

For simplicity we shall assume that condition A holds; this enables us to ignore any expansion of the organization. Under this condition we saw in Section 3.3 that the limiting vector of relative sizes, $\mathbf{q}$, satisfies

$$\mathbf{Qq} = \mathbf{q} \tag{3.27}$$

and

$$\sum_{i=1}^{k} q_i = 1.$$

The elements of $\mathbf{Q}$ depend on the promotion, loss and recruitment probabilities. So far in this chapter we have assumed that these probabilities were fixed and have used equation (3.27), or its equivalent, to predict $\mathbf{q}$. We now reverse this procedure and ask what the promotion and recruitment probabilities must be in order to achieve some desired $\mathbf{q}$. We shall continue to assume that the loss probabilities $\{p_{i,k+1}\}$ are given.

The general problem may be formulated as follows. We want to find probabilities $\{p_{ij}\}$ and $\{p_{0j}\}$ satisfying the following conditions.

$$\left.\begin{aligned}
\mathbf{Qq} = (\mathbf{P} + \mathbf{p}_0\mathbf{p}'_{k+1})\mathbf{q} &= \mathbf{q}, \\
\sum_{j=1}^{k} p_{ij} = 1 - p_{i,k+1}, \quad \sum_{j=0}^{k} p_{0j} &= 1, \\
0 \le p_{ij} \le 1 \quad (i, j &= 1, 2, \ldots, k), \\
0 \le p_{0j} \le 1 \quad (j &= 1, 2, \ldots, k),
\end{aligned}\right\} \tag{3.28}$$

where $\mathbf{p}'_{k+1}$ is the vector of loss probabilities $(p_{1,k+1}, p_{2,k+1}, \ldots, p_{k,k+1})'$. If we require a policy which avoids the need to make demotions we would add the condition

$$p_{ij} = 0 \quad (i > j).$$

The problem is equivalent to finding a feasible solution to the restraints in linear programming. Hence existing computer programmes could be used to explore the solution. There may be no solution to the problem but, in general, there will be infinitely many sets of p_{ij}'s and p_{0j}'s which satisfy the requirements. In linear programming a choice is made between them by finding the feasible solution which also minimizes a given linear function. In this application we would hope to select a policy which satisfied some criterion of economic or social optimality. There is obviously much room for research on this question. In what follows we shall merely consider two special cases where the addition of further restraints leads to a unique policy for achieving the required structure.

First of all let us suppose that the recruitment policy is fixed and that only the promotion policy can be changed. To simplify matters further suppose that all recruits enter the lowest grade and that the only internal transfers are promotions to the next highest grade. The matrix $\mathbf{Q}$ then has the form

$$\mathbf{Q} = \begin{pmatrix} p_{11} & 0 & 0 & \ldots & 0 & 1 - p_{kk} \\ p_{12} & p_{22} & 0 & \ldots & 0 & 0 \\ 0 & p_{23} & p_{33} & \ldots & 0 & 0 \\ \cdot & \cdot & \cdot & & \cdot & \cdot \\ \cdot & \cdot & \cdot & & \cdot & \cdot \\ \cdot & \cdot & \cdot & & \cdot & \cdot \\ 0 & 0 & 0 & \ldots & p_{k-1k} & p_{kk} \end{pmatrix}$$

so that the equations (3.27) become

$$q_j = p_{j-1,j}q_{j-1} + p_{jj}q_j$$

or

$$p_{j-1,j} = \frac{q_j}{q_{j-1}}(1 - p_{jj}) \quad (j = 2, 3, \ldots, k). \tag{3.29}$$

Since, under our assumptions,

$$1 - p_{jj} = p_{j,j+1} + p_{j,k+1} \quad (j = 1, 2, \ldots, k - 1)$$
$$= p_{k,k+1} \quad (j = k)$$

the required promotion probabilities are given recursively by

$$\left. \begin{aligned} p_{j-1,j} &= \frac{q_j}{q_{j-1}}(p_{j,j+1} + p_{j,k+1}) \quad (j = 2, 3, \ldots, k - 1) \\ p_{k-1,k} &= \frac{q_k}{q_{k-1}} p_{k,k+1}. \end{aligned} \right\} \tag{3.30}$$

The promotion probabilities thus depend in a simple way upon the relative grade sizes and the loss rates. To make the position clearer suppose that the loss probabilities are the same in each grade and write $p_{i,k+1} = p_{k+1}$ for all i. Also let $q_j/q_{j-1} = C$ for $j = 2, 3, \ldots, k$. If $C < 1$ this represents an organization in which, on average, C^{-1} persons at one level report to 1 person at the next higher level. With these assumptions it is easily shown that

$$p_{j-1,j} = p_{k+1}(C + C^2 + \ldots + C^{k-j+1}) \quad (j = 2, 3, \ldots, k). \quad (3.31)$$

This result shows that it will only be possible to achieve our objective if the right-hand side of equation (3.31) is a probability and hence never exceeds unity. Thus the condition for the problem to be soluble is that

$$p_{k+1}(C - C^k) < 1 - C.$$

Assuming that this inequality holds, the promotion probabilities will be proportional to the wastage probability and are increasing functions of C. Further, whatever C or p_{k+1}, the promotion chances will decrease as we move up the hierarchy.

Secondly let us suppose that the promotion probabilities are fixed and that only the recruitment distribution can be controlled. The recruitment policy required to attain a specified equilibrium structure may be obtained directly from the first member of equation (3.28). Making $\mathbf{p}_0$ the subject of the matrix equation gives

or

$$\left.\begin{aligned}
\mathbf{p}_0 &= (\mathbf{I} - \mathbf{P})\mathbf{q}/\mathbf{p}'_{k+1}\mathbf{q}, \\[2mm]
p_{0j} &= \frac{q_j - \displaystyle\sum_{i=1}^{k} p_{ij}q_i}{\displaystyle\sum_{i=1}^{k} p_{i,k+1}q_i} \quad (j = 1, 2, \ldots, k).
\end{aligned}\right\} \quad (3.32)$$

It is easy to verify that

$$\sum_{j=1}^{k} p_{0j} = 1$$

but the values for p_{0j} given by equation (3.32) are not necessarily positive. Only when $p_{0j} \geq 0$ for *all* j will it be possible to find a recruitment policy to achieve the desired structure. As an example, consider a system with the following transition matrix where the probabilities $\{p_{0j}\}$ are at choice.

$$\begin{array}{ccccc}
\frac{1}{2} & \frac{1}{4} & 0 & 0 & \frac{1}{4} \\[1mm]
0 & \frac{1}{2} & \frac{1}{4} & 0 & \frac{1}{4} \\[1mm]
0 & 0 & \frac{1}{2} & \frac{1}{4} & \frac{1}{4} \\[1mm]
0 & 0 & 0 & \frac{3}{4} & \frac{1}{4}
\end{array}$$

If we wish to have the structure

$$q_1 = \tfrac{1}{2}, \quad q_2 = \tfrac{1}{4}, \quad q_3 = q_4 = \tfrac{1}{8}$$

then equation (3.32), gives

$$p_{01} = 1, \quad p_{02} = p_{03} = p_{04} = 0.$$

On the other hand, if we wish to make

$$q_1 = \tfrac{1}{4}, \quad q_2 = \tfrac{1}{2}, \quad q_3 = \tfrac{3}{16}, \quad q_4 = \tfrac{1}{16},$$

then both p_{03} and p_{04} as given by equation (3.32) are negative. This means that, with the promotion and loss probabilities as given, no recruitment policy can yield the required structure. It is interesting to observe that the optimum recruitment distribution is not obtained by putting $\mathbf{p}_0 = \mathbf{q}$. However, if condition A is not satisfied, we saw in equation (3.21) that this is the best allocation of recruits under conditions of very rapid growth.

We shall see in Chapter 7 that questions similar to those discussed in this section can also be approached by a renewal-type model.

CHAPTER 4

SOME SOCIAL APPLICATIONS OF CONTINUOUS TIME MARKOV PROCESSES

1. INTRODUCTION

We shall now begin the development of continuous time models. The models described in Chapters 2 and 3 are based upon the discrete time Markov chain. We began with models for closed systems and then generalized them to cover systems that were open. A parallel treatment based on continuous time Markov processes will be given in this and the following chapter. The two systems which we shall describe and analyse in this chapter are closed and the standard theory is directly applicable. In Chapter 5 the theory will be extended to give continuous time analogues of the models due to Gani and Young. Our first use of the theory of Markov processes is as a model for the survival of patients treated for cancer. Although this is outside the mainstream of applied problems which are considered in this book it provides an excellent illustration of the potentialities of the model. The second application is to the study of organizational commitment and the related topic of labour turnover.

The development of a Markov chain is determined by a set of transition probabilities. In continuous time, when changes can occur at any time, it is necessary to base the development of the theory on infinitesimal transition probabilities. Let the states of the system be labelled $S_1, S_2, \ldots, S_k$ then the probability of a transition from S_i to S_j $(i \neq j)$ in $(T, T + \delta T)$ is termed an *infinitesimal transition probability*. The set of such probabilities for all pairs of states determines the future of the process. We shall assume that these probabilities can be written in the form

$$Pr\{S_i \to S_j \text{ in } (T, T + \delta T)\} = r_{ij}(T)\delta T + o(\delta T) \quad (i \neq j). \quad (1.1)$$

For our purpose the term $o(\delta T)$ can be ignored and we shall omit it from future specifications of infinitesimal probabilities. The function $r_{ij}(T)$ will be referred to as the *rate* or *intensity* of transition between S_i and S_j at time T or, more briefly, as the transition rate. The possible dependence of the rates on T has been made explicit in the notation. In particular applications they may be constant or depend on other variables such as the length of time spent in the present state. When complications of this latter kind occur the Markov property is lost and the analysis becomes more difficult. Some examples of this kind will occur in the following chapter.

Transition rates, or intensities, are frequently used in actuarial and reliability studies though under various names; perhaps the most familiar and expressive is the term 'force of mortality'. In our present terminology this is the transition intensity at age T from the state 'life' to the state 'death'. These intensities can often be estimated in practice and have a direct intuitive meaning. They therefore provide a natural starting point for the construction of stochastic models of social phenomena which can, in principle at least, be observed continuously in time.

It is instructive to consider the link between the present formulation and the model used for labour mobility in Chapter 2. The latter was basically a continuous time process although it had to be treated as discrete because of the nature of the data available. The connexion is made apparent if $r_{ij}(T)$ is expressed in the form

$$r_{ij}(T) = \lambda_i(T)p_{ij.T},$$

with
$$\sum_{j=1}^{k} p_{ij.T} = 1 \quad (i = 1, 2, \ldots, k). \qquad (1.2)$$

When considered in this form $\lambda_i(T)\delta T$ is the probability that a member of S_i changes state at time T and $p_{ij.T}$ is the probability that the transition is to S_j. The need for separating the two processes in Chapter 2 arose because the transition matrix $\{p_{ij.T}\}$ was the only part which could be estimated from the available data. In the applications now to be discussed it is the rates $\{r_{ij}(T)\}$ which are of fundamental interest.

The theory of Markov processes in continuous time is given in most of the basic texts on stochastic theory. Of these books those by Bharucha-Reid (1960), and Cox and Miller (1965), are particularly recommended as supplementary reading for those unfamiliar with the theory. A paper by Zahl (1955) also gives an introductory account of the application of the theory to follow-up studies in cancer research and other related fields. Authors who have applied the theory to social phenomena have usually derived the theory they required by heuristic arguments without reference to the formal theory. However, in order to give a unified account of their work and to lay a foundation for further developments we shall set our exposition within the framework of the general theory of Markov processes. We shall nevertheless give a very full description of the application of the theory in each of our chosen fields.

The parallel between the models in discrete and continuous time is very close but there is one important difference in the kinds of system to which they are applied in this book. In the discrete time models it was possible to move from any state to any other state in a finite number of moves. But in both of the examples discussed in Section 2, below, there are states from which no exit is possible. These are called *terminal* states; they correspond to death in follow-up studies and to leaving in turnover studies. In a system with terminal states the investigation of limiting behaviour is still important but has rather different objectives as we shall see later.

2. DESCRIPTION OF APPLICATIONS

2.1. Survival After Treatment for Cancer

A patient who has been treated for a disease may, at any subsequent time, be in one of a number of states. These states might be, for example, 'health', 'relapsed', and 'death'; the precise classification used will obviously depend on the objects of the enquiry and the kind of records available. A stochastic model for the post-treatment history of patients treated for cancer was developed by Fix and Neyman (1951) and discussed in more general terms by Zahl (1955). Fix and Neyman used the model to provide measures of the effectiveness of a treatment and we shall describe how this can be done below. Sverdrup (1965) has discussed a similar model for a working population whose states were 'able', 'disabled' and 'dead'. The basic situation is of wide occurrence and there are many other possible applications.

In Fix and Neyman's model there were four states. The description of the states and the allowable transitions are indicated on the following diagram:

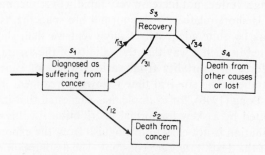

The authors emphasized the difficulty of defining 'recovery' and also pointed out that it might be desirable to subdivide some of the states. For example, S_4 might be divided into those who died from natural causes and those who were lost from observation. It might also be thought desirable to allow transitions between S_1 and S_4. We shall not digress to discuss these technical points since we are using the example primarily to illustrate the application of the theory of Markov processes in a social context.

The first objective in the cancer application was to estimate the transition rates. These were then used to provide measures of survival which did not suffer from the disadvantages associated with the commonly used measures. One such measure is the 'T-year survival rate'. This is the proportion of those receiving treatment who survive for at least T years. This measure would be satisfactory if cancer was the only cause of death and if all persons were under observation for the full T years. In practice this is not the case and the T-year survival rate may be misleading. To see this we merely note that the rate would be higher if loss or death from other causes were eliminated since then more people would survive to ultimately die of cancer. The observed value of the rate thus depends not only upon the risk of cancer death but also on other risks which have nothing to do with cancer. If a 'treatment' and 'control' group were compared by means of the crude rate the comparison would be valueless if the two groups were subject to different risks from other causes. To overcome this difficulty it is customary to calculate net rates which make allowance for such differences. Our purpose in introducing this example is to show that the stochastic model provides a more satisfactory basis for estimating net rates than the 'actuarial' method. Except for a brief discussion on pages 86 and 87 we shall ignore the important question of how best to estimate the transition rates.

In their model, Fix and Neyman, treated the transition rates between the states as constants. However, it is well-known that the force of natural mortality for human populations is not constant but, after infancy, increases with age. It does not increase very rapidly over the middle years of life and if T is short relative to the normal life span the assumption of constancy may be quite adequate. In any event we shall show that data can be collected in such a way that the validity of the assumption can be tested. The force of mortality from various kinds of cancer has been extensively studied. The survival time following treatment appears to be highly skew; Boag (1946), for example, has suggested that it can often be adequately fitted by a skew lognormal distribution. In this case the lognormal distribution is not easy to distinguish from the exponential which would arise if the death rate were constant. The assumption of a constant rate for death from cancer is thus probably not unrealistic. Direct evidence on the true nature of the transition rates between S_1 and S_3 (recovery) and between S_3 and S_1 is lacking, but it does seem plausible to assume a constant loss rate at least in the case of those who are lost to observation.

In the model we assume that there are N people in state S_1 at time zero and none elsewhere. The numbers in the four groups at any subsequent time T will be random variables which we denote by $n_j(T)$ ($j = 1, 2, 3, 4$). In conformity with the notation of earlier chapters we shall use the symbol $\bar{n}_j(T)$ to represent the expectation of $n_j(T)$. By observing these random variables at one or more points in time it will be possible to estimate the transition rates. Using these estimates it will then be possible to predict the numbers in the various states at future times. More important, it will be possible to estimate what these numbers would have been if death from cancer had been the only risk.

2.2. Organizational Commitment

The mathematical model in this application is the same as that in Section 2.1 but its interpretation and uses are rather different. It was developed by Herbst (1963) in an attempt to describe and understand the length of service distributions arising in labour turnover studies. We shall give a fuller discussion of this particular problem in Chapter 6. For the present we simply remark that there is a large body of empirical evidence to show that the distribution of an individual's total length of service, is highly skewed. This has been found to be the case in many occupations and in several countries. Herbst proposed what he called a decision process model which has proved very successful in graduating observed length of service distributions. Once again we consider a group of N people who join an organization at time zero. They then pass through two or three intermediate states until they become firmly attached to the organization or leave. Herbst gave reasons for believing that the model illustrated in the following diagram may be appropriate.

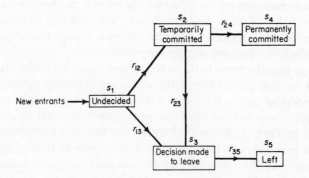

In this model there are two terminal states and particular interest is attached to the proportions of entrants who ultimately reach each of them.

An important difference between this application and the last one is that here the states S_1, S_2, S_3, and S_4 cannot be recognized by direct observation although it might be possible to distinguish them by questioning individuals. At any time, therefore, we can observe only the single random variable $n_5(T)$. If $f(T)$ is the frequency curve of the distribution of length of service then clearly

$$\bar{n}_5(T) = \int_0^T f(x)\mathrm{d}x.$$

Thus by comparing the observed distribution of length of service with that predicted by $\bar{n}_5(T)$ it is possible to estimate the transition rates $\{r_{ij}\}$ and test the goodness of fit of the model. It should be observed that the assumption of constant transition intensities is part of the model; there is no need to make them depend upon T unless empirical evidence makes the hypothesis of constant rates untenable.

2.3. Two Other Applications

The remainder of this chapter will be concerned mainly with the two applications described in Sections 2.1 and 2.2. However, to illustrate the scope for the use of Markov process models we shall briefly describe two other applications. These were both proposed by Coleman (1964). The first is a model for attitude changes. In a typical experiment persons are observed to have certain defined attitudes at the outset. They are then supplied with further information and at some later date their attitudes are ascertained again. Coleman proposed a Markov model with constant transition rates for this situation and argues that these rates are the appropriate measures of the effect of the stimuli producing the change. From the point of view of methodology the situation here is entirely analogous to the problem of Fix and Neyman, except that it is now the rates themselves which are our primary interest.

Coleman uses the same basic model to study data on social class of the kind that we used in Chapter 2. His viewpoint is slightly different to the one we adopted and a brief comparison will be instructive. Instead of describing changes in class from one generation to the next by a transition matrix he proceeds as follows. Until the son becomes independent of his father we may suppose that his class is the same as that of his father. Subsequently, as the son grows up he is subject to forces which tend to change his class. If we further assume that these forces are constant in time and operate continuously the phenomenon of change may be represented by a Markov process in continuous time. Coleman tested the validity of the model using the data collected by Glass and Svalagosta referred to in Chapter 2. A general Markov model in which transitions between all classes are possible could not be used because it would have more parameters than could be estimated from the data. It was therefore assumed that transitions were possible into adjacent classes only. This model did not provide a good fit to either set of data but, in any case, the data were not in a suitable form. A satisfactory test of the model could only have been made if each son had been exposed to the risk of transition for the same length of time. For the data collected by Glass and Svalagosta this could, at best, have only been approximately true.

We shall defer further discussion of applications until we have outlined the basic theory of Markov processes in continuous time.

3. SOME BASIC THEORY OF MARKOV PROCESSES

3.1. Transient Theory

The quantities of greatest interest to us are the transition probabilities which we denote by $p_{ij}(T)$ $(i, j = 1, 2, . . ., k)$. For given i and j this is the probability that an individual who is in S_i at time zero is in S_j at time T $(T > 0)$. We define

$$p_{ij}(0) = 0 \text{ if } i \neq j$$
$$= 1 \text{ if } i = j.$$

These transition probabilities should not be confused with the infinitesimal transition probabilities, $r_{ij}(T)\delta T$, which are used to define the process.

The first step is to set up a system of differential equations relating the $p_{ij}(T)$'s to the $r_{ij}(T)$'s. Readers who are familiar with the derivation of the equations for the birth and death process will recognize the following argument as a straightforward generalization. Consider the probability $p_{ij}(T + \delta T)$. Let us suppose that we have found $p_{ij}(T)$ for all i and j. In addition we know the probabilities of the various transitions in $(T, T + \delta T)$ because the process is defined in terms of them. We then have

$$p_{ij}(T + \delta T) = p_{ij}(T)\left\{1 - \delta T \sum_{\substack{h=1 \\ h \neq j}}^{k} r_{jh}(T)\right\} + \sum_{\substack{h=1 \\ h \neq j}}^{k} p_{ih}(T) r_{hj}(T) \, \delta T$$

$$(i, j = 1, 2, . . ., k). \qquad (3.1)$$

Subtracting $p_{ij}(T)$ from both sides of equation (3.1), dividing by δT, and allowing δT to tend to zero gives

$$\frac{dp_{ij}(T)}{dT} = -p_{ij}(T) \sum_{\substack{h=1 \\ h \neq j}}^{k} r_{jh}(T) + \sum_{\substack{h=1 \\ h \neq j}}^{k} p_{ih}(T) r_{hj}(T) \quad (i, j = 1, 2, . . ., k). \quad (3.2)$$

The transition rate $r_{ij}(T)$ has not been defined for $i = j$. However, the set of equations (3.2), can be written more compactly if we define

$$r_{jj}(T) = - \sum_{\substack{h=1 \\ j \neq h}}^{k} r_{jh}(T). \qquad (3.3)$$

We then have

$$\frac{dp_{ij}(T)}{dT} = \sum_{h=1}^{k} p_{ih}(T) r_{hj}(T) \quad (i, j = 1, 2, \ldots, k). \qquad (3.4)$$

A further notational simplification, which also facilitates the solution of the system, is obtained by adopting a matrix representation as follows. Let

$$\mathbf{P}(T) = \{p_{ij}(T)\}' \qquad \mathbf{R}(T) = \{r_{ij}(T)\}'$$

then equation (3.4) becomes

$$\frac{d\mathbf{P}(T)}{dT} = \mathbf{R}(T)\mathbf{P}(T). \qquad (3.5)$$

The differential operator on the left-hand side of equation (3.5) is to be understood as applying to each element in the matrix $\mathbf{P}(T)$. Equation (3.5) can be used to yield a system of differential equations for $\bar{\mathbf{n}}(T)$, the vector of expected grade sizes at time T. This follows when it is recognized that

$$\bar{\mathbf{n}}(T) = \mathbf{P}(T)\mathbf{n}(0). \qquad (3.6)$$

Post-multiplying both sides of equation (3.5) by $\mathbf{n}(0)$ gives

$$\frac{d\bar{\mathbf{n}}(T)}{dT} = \mathbf{R}(T)\bar{\mathbf{n}}(T). \qquad (3.7)$$

Systems of first order linear differential equations have been extensively studied and methods are available for their solution (see, for example, Frazer, Duncan and Collar, 1946). The simplest case occurs if the transition rates are all constant. Since this is the case with both models described in this chapter we shall, in the remainder of this section, assume constant rates. In the following chapter we shall solve the equations in one case when the rates are not all constants. When the transition rates are constant we shall omit the T from the notation, writing r_{ij} for the rate and $\mathbf{R}$ for the matrix.

A solution to equation (3.5) when $\mathbf{R}$ is constant is suggested by consideration of the special case when R and $P(T)$ are scalars. In that case the solution is

$$P(T) = e^{RT} = \sum_{i=0}^{\infty} (RT)^i / i!. \qquad (3.8)$$

In the matrix case we may easily verify that the matrix series on the right-hand side of equation (3.8) satisfies equation (3.5) if we define $\mathbf{R}^0 = \mathbf{I}$. It will be the solution if the series converges and this is always so if k is finite. In a similar manner it follows that the solution of equation (3.6) is

$$\bar{\mathbf{n}}(T) = \exp(\mathbf{R}T)\mathbf{n}(0), \tag{3.9}$$

where we use the exponential notation for the infinite matrix series. A direct solution of either set of equations using this representation would involve the summation of k^2 infinite series one for each element in the matrix. This is hardly feasible as a practical method unless T is very small. An alternative method is available using Sylvester's theorem (see Chapter 3, Section 2.3), which enables us to express the solution as a finite series of k terms. In general the matrix $\mathbf{R}$ admits the spectral representation

$$\mathbf{R} = \sum_{i=1}^{k} \lambda_i \mathbf{A}_i,$$

where $\{\lambda_i\}$ are the eigen values of $\mathbf{R}$ and $\{\mathbf{A}_i\}$ is the associated spectral set. The representation is only valid if all the λ_i's are distinct. It then follows from Sylvester's theorem that

$$\exp(\mathbf{R}T) = \sum_{i=1}^{k} e^{\lambda_i T} \mathbf{A}_i \tag{3.10}$$
$$= \mathbf{P}(T)$$

using the matrix form of equation (3.8).
Likewise we have

$$\mathbf{n}(T) = \sum_{i=1}^{k} e^{\lambda_i T} \mathbf{A}_i \mathbf{n}(0). \tag{3.11}$$

The behaviour of the solution, especially for large T, will clearly depend critically on the eigen values. Before proceeding to a discussion of the practical steps needed to obtain a complete solution we shall therefore obtain some general results about their values.

The eigen values are obtained by solving the equation

$$\begin{vmatrix} r_{11} - \lambda & r_{21} & \cdot & \cdot & \cdot & \cdot & \cdot & r_{k1} \\ r_{12} & r_{22} - \lambda & \cdot & \cdot & \cdot & r_{k2} \\ \cdot & \cdot & & & \cdot \\ \cdot & \cdot & \cdot & & & \cdot \\ \cdot & \cdot & & \cdot & & \cdot \\ \cdot & \cdot & & & \cdot & \cdot \\ \cdot & \cdot & & & & \cdot \\ r_{1k} & r_{2k} & \cdot & \cdot & \cdot & r_{kk} - \lambda \end{vmatrix} = 0. \tag{3.12}$$

The value of the determinant is unchanged if we replace the first row by a row whose elements are the column sums. Each element in the first row of the new determinant so formed is $-\lambda$ because of equation (3.3). The equation (3.12) is therefore always satisfied when $\lambda = 0$. It is clear from equation (3.10) that all roots must be zero or negative otherwise there would be some T for which the transition probabilities did not lie between 0 and 1.

Since we are mainly interested in the vector $\mathbf{n}(T)$ we shall consider the solution given by equation (3.11). It follows from the foregoing remarks that $\bar{n}_i(T)$'s can be expressed in the form

$$\bar{n}_i(T) = c_{i1} + \sum_{j=2}^{k} c_{ij}e^{\lambda_j T} \quad (i = 1, 2, \ldots, k), \tag{3.13}$$

where $\lambda_j < 0$ $(j = 2, 3, \ldots, k)$. This form is valid provided that all the λ's are distinct. It holds also, with a slight modification discussed below, if $\lambda = 0$ is a multiple root. The coefficients $\{c_{ij}\}$ in equation (3.13), may be found by first determining the spectral set $\{\mathbf{A}_i\}$. An equivalent, but more direct approach, is the following. Substituting $\bar{\mathbf{n}}(T)$ from equation (3.13), into equation (3.7), we have

$$\sum_{j=1}^{k} c_{ij}\lambda_j e^{\lambda_j T} = \sum_{j=1}^{k} r_{ji} \sum_{h=1}^{k} c_{jh}e^{\lambda_h T} \quad (i = 1, 2, \ldots, k), \tag{3.14}$$

where $\lambda_1 = 0$. Equating coefficients of $e^{\lambda_h T}$ we find that the c_{ij}'s must satisfy the equations

$$\sum_{j=1}^{k} r_{ji}c_{jh} = \lambda_h c_{ih}, \quad \begin{cases} i = 1, 2, \ldots, k \\ h = 1, 2, \ldots, k \end{cases}. \tag{3.15}$$

Although there are k^2 equations here for the same number of unknowns they are not independent. In fact if we sum each side of equation (3.15) over i we obtain zero in each case. In order to determine the c's we therefore require k further equations. These arise from the necessity of ensuring that the initial conditions are satisfied. Thus, setting $T = 0$ in equation (3.13), we have

$$\sum_{j=1}^{k} c_{ij} = n_i(0) \quad (i = 1, 2, \ldots, k). \tag{3.16}$$

We shall solve the equations in the case of the applications to cancer survival and labour turnover.

The theory given above covers the case when all the λ's are distinct. If multiplicities occur among the roots the form of the solution can be determined by an appropriate limiting operation on equation (3.13). For example, suppose that $\lambda_2 = \lambda_3 = \lambda$. The coefficients $\{c_{ij}\}$ are functions of the λ's and we must determine their limits as $\lambda_2 \to \lambda_3$. The terms involving λ_2 and λ_3 in the exponent require special attention. In a typical case we have

$$
\left.
\begin{aligned}
\lim_{\lambda_2 \to \lambda_3 = \lambda} & \{c_{i2}e^{\lambda_2 T} + c_{i3}e^{\lambda_3 T}\} \\
&= e^{\lambda T} \lim_{\lambda_2 \to \lambda_3} \{c_{i2} + c_{i3}e^{(\lambda_3 - \lambda_2)T}\} \\
&= e^{\lambda T} \lim_{\lambda_2 \to \lambda_3} \{c_{i2} + c_{i3} + c_{i3}((\lambda_3 - \lambda_2)T + O(\lambda_3 - \lambda_2)^2)\}.
\end{aligned}
\right\} \quad (3.17)
$$

Since the limit in curly brackets cannot be infinite in any meaningful problem, the pair of terms corresponding to $j = 2$ and $j = 3$ in equation (3.13) must be replaced by a single term of the form

$$
(d_{i2} + d_{i3}T)e^{\lambda T}. \tag{3.18}
$$

In general, if there is a root of multiplicity m with common value λ, the terms corresponding to that root in equation (3.13) must be replaced by the following expression

$$
\sum_{j=2}^{m+1} d_{ij}T^{j-2}e^{\lambda T}. \tag{3.19}
$$

A particularly simple and important case occurs when the multiple root has the value zero. The general solution then has the form

$$
\bar{n}_i(T) = \sum_{j=1}^{m} d_{ij}T^{j-1} + \sum_{j=m+1}^{k} c_{ij}e^{\lambda_j T} \quad (i = 1, 2, \ldots, k). \tag{3.20}
$$

It may be shown that, in this case, $d_{ij} = 0$ for $j > 1$ and all i. The necessity for this may be seen by considering the limit of $\bar{n}_i(T)$ as T tends to infinity. Under these conditions the second sum in equation (3.20) vanishes, the first sum will tend to $\pm\infty$ according to the sign of d_{im}. Since $\bar{n}_i(T)$ possesses a finite limit, as we shall see in the next section, we conclude that $\bar{n}_i(T)$ must have the form

$$
\bar{n}_i(T) = d_{i1} + \sum_{j=m+1}^{k} c_{ij}e^{\lambda_j T} \quad (i = 1, 2, \ldots, k). \tag{3.21}
$$

If we substitute this in equation (3.7), the equations for $\{d_{i1}\}$ and $\{c_{ij}\}$ are identical with those given in equation (3.15), if we delete those equations with $h \leqslant m - 1$ and replace c_{im} by d_{i1}.

3.2. Limiting Behaviour

The limiting behaviour of $\bar{n}_i(T)$ as $T \to \infty$ can be studied directly by reference to the results of Section 3.1. Referring to equation (3.13) and noting that $\lambda_j < 0$ $(j = 2, 3, \ldots, k)$ it is clear that

$$\lim_{T \to \infty} \bar{n}_i(T) = c_{i1} \quad (i = 1, 2, \ldots, k). \tag{3.22}$$

In the case when $\lambda = 0$ is a multiple root we merely have to replace c_{i1} by d_{i1} on the right-hand side of equation (3.22).

If we are interested only in the limiting values we can avoid the necessity of calculating the c_{ij}'s for $j > 1$. Two methods are available according to whether or not there are terminal states in the system. Suppose first that there are no terminal states, then transitions are possible both into and out of every state. Since we know that the $\bar{n}_i(T)$'s approach limits we may deduce that their derivatives vanish at infinity. It then follows from equation (3.7) that if the transition rates are constant, the limiting vector of expected state sizes must satisfy

$$\mathbf{R}\bar{\mathbf{n}}(\infty) = \mathbf{0}, \tag{3.23}$$

where $\mathbf{0}$ is a column vector of zeros. We have the additional equation

$$\sum_{j=1}^{k} \bar{n}_j(\infty) = N$$

which, with equation (3.23), determines the limits uniquely. It may also be shown that

$$\lim_{T \to \infty} p_{ij}(T) = \bar{n}_j(\infty)/N \quad (i, j = 1, 2, \ldots, k), \tag{3.24}$$

indicating that the probability of ultimate transition to S_j is independent of the original state.

The equations (3.23) are satisfied by the limiting state sizes even if there are terminal states. In this case, however, they no longer determine the expectations uniquely, since each terminal state gives rise to a column of zeros in the $\mathbf{R}$-matrix. The limiting expectations for the non-terminal states do not appear in the equations (3.23) because their coefficients all vanish. We shall not enter into a full discussion of the treatment in this case. For fairly small systems a simple direct method is available which will be sufficiently illustrated by the examples of Section 4.

4. APPLICATION OF THE GENERAL MODEL

4.1. Survival After Treatment for Cancer

We shall now use the general theory of Markov processes to answer the questions posed by the applications described at the beginning of this chapter.

The matrix $\mathbf{R}$ in this case has the form

$$\mathbf{R} = \begin{vmatrix} r_{11} & 0 & r_{31} & 0 \\ r_{12} & 0 & 0 & 0 \\ r_{13} & 0 & r_{33} & 0 \\ 0 & 0 & r_{34} & 0 \end{vmatrix} \tag{4.1}$$

where $r_{11} = -(r_{12} + r_{13})$ and $r_{33} = -(r_{31} + r_{34})$. The equation for the eigen values is $|\mathbf{I}\lambda - \mathbf{R}| = 0$ or

$$\lambda^2(r_{11} - \lambda)(r_{33} - \lambda) - \lambda^2 r_{13} r_{31} = 0. \tag{4.2}$$

This equation clearly has a double root equal to zero; the two remaining roots which we label λ_3 and λ_4 are

$$\lambda_3, \lambda_4 = \tfrac{1}{2}\{r_{11} + r_{33} \pm \sqrt{(r_{11} - r_{33})^2 + 4r_{13}r_{31}}\} \tag{4.3}$$

taking the positive sign for λ_3 and the negative for λ_4. It then follows from equation (3.21) that

$$\bar{n}_i(T) = d_{i1} + c_{i3}e^{\lambda_3 T} + c_{i4}e^{\lambda_4 T} \quad (i = 1, 2, 3, 4). \tag{4.4}$$

The next step is to set down and solve the simultaneous equations for the coefficients. We first put $i = 1$ and let h take the values 2, 3 and 4, thus obtaining

$$\left.\begin{array}{l} r_{11}d_{11} + r_{31}d_{31} = 0 \\ r_{11}c_{13} + r_{31}c_{33} = \lambda_3 c_{13} \\ r_{11}c_{14} + r_{31}c_{34} = \lambda_4 c_{14} \end{array}\right\} \tag{4.5}$$

Three further sets of equations are obtained for $i = 2$, 3 and 4 as follows:

$i = 2$
$$\left.\begin{array}{l} r_{12}d_{11} = 0 \\ r_{12}c_{13} = \lambda_3 c_{23} \\ r_{12}c_{14} = \lambda_4 c_{24} \end{array}\right\} \tag{4.6}$$

$i = 3$
$$\left.\begin{array}{l} r_{13}d_{11} + r_{33}d_{31} = 0 \\ r_{13}c_{13} + r_{33}c_{33} = \lambda_3 c_{33} \\ r_{13}c_{14} + r_{33}c_{34} = \lambda_4 c_{34} \end{array}\right\} \tag{4.7}$$

$i = 4$
$$\left.\begin{array}{l} r_{34}d_{31} = 0 \\ r_{34}c_{33} = \lambda_3 c_{43} \\ r_{34}c_{34} = \lambda_4 c_{44} \end{array}\right\} \tag{4.8}$$

It follows at once that $d_{11} = d_{31} = 0$ and hence the first equation in each group can be ignored in what follows. The initial conditions require that all members of the system are in S_1 at time zero. Let us suppose therefore that $n_1(0) = 1$, $n_i(0) = 0$, $i > 1$. If $n_1(0) = N$ the appropriate values of $\bar{n}_i(T)$ can be obtained simply by multiplying by N those obtained assuming $n_1(0) = 1$. In addition to the equations listed above we now have

$$\left. \begin{aligned} d_{11} + c_{13} + c_{14} &= 1 \\ d_{21} + c_{23} + c_{24} &= 0 \\ d_{31} + c_{33} + c_{34} &= 0 \\ d_{41} + c_{43} + c_{44} &= 0 \end{aligned} \right\} \tag{4.9}$$

To solve the equations we proceed as follows. Adding both sides of equation (4.5) and using the initial conditions we obtain

$$\lambda_3 c_{13} + \lambda_4 c_{14} = r_{11}. \tag{4.10}$$

A similar operation on equation (4.6) yields

$$\lambda_3 c_{23} + \lambda_4 c_{24} = r_{12}. \tag{4.11}$$

But this equation can be expressed in terms of c_{13} and c_{14} from equation (4.6) to give

$$c_{13} + c_{14} = 1. \tag{4.12}$$

The pair of simultaneous equations (4.10) and (4.12) may then be solved, giving

$$c_{13} = \frac{\lambda_4 - r_{11}}{(\lambda_4 - \lambda_3)} \qquad c_{14} = \frac{r_{11} - \lambda_3}{(\lambda_4 - \lambda_3)} \tag{4.13}$$

and hence,

$$c_{23} = \frac{r_{12}(\lambda_4 - r_{11})}{\lambda_3(\lambda_4 - \lambda_3)} \qquad c_{24} = \frac{r_{12}(r_{11} - \lambda_3)}{\lambda_4(\lambda_4 - \lambda_3)}. \tag{4.14}$$

If this whole procedure is repeated on equations (4.7) and (4.8), we obtain

$$\left. \begin{aligned} c_{33} &= \frac{-r_{13}}{(\lambda_4 - \lambda_3)} & c_{34} &= \frac{r_{13}}{(\lambda_4 - \lambda_3)} \\ c_{43} &= \frac{-r_{13}r_{34}}{\lambda_3(\lambda_4 - \lambda_3)} & c_{44} &= \frac{r_{13}r_{34}}{\lambda_4(\lambda_4 - \lambda_3)} \end{aligned} \right\} \tag{4.15}$$

Only two constants remain to be determined; these are d_{21} and d_{41}. Using the initial conditions we find

$$d_{21} = -c_{23} - c_{24} = -r_{12}r_{33}/\lambda_3\lambda_4 \tag{4.16}$$

$$d_{41} = -c_{42} - c_{43} = r_{13}r_{34}/\lambda_3\lambda_4. \tag{4.17}$$

We now turn to consider how these results may be used to make valid comparison of survival rates. When $N = 1$, $\bar{n}_i(T)$ may be regarded as the probability of being in S_i at time T. Thus $\bar{n}_2(T)$ and $\bar{n}_4(T)$ may be interpreted as the crude risks of death from cancer and natural causes respectively. However $\bar{n}_4(T)$ also depends on the force of natural mortality, and, as we pointed out in Section 2, this reduces its value as a measure of risk. We really require a net measure of risk from which the effect of natural mortality is eliminated. The actuarial approach to the problem defines a net rate of mortality due to cancer by the formula

$$_A\bar{n}_2(T) = \bar{n}_2(T)/\{1 - \tfrac{1}{2}\bar{n}_4(T)\}. \tag{4.18}$$

This measure purports to give the expected number of cancer deaths that would occur in $(0, T)$ if natural mortality did not exist. The derivation of equation (4.18), will be clearer if we write it in the form

$$\bar{n}_2(T) = {}_A\bar{n}_2(T) - \tfrac{1}{2}\bar{n}_4(T){}_A\bar{n}_2(T). \tag{4.19}$$

The second term on the right-hand side of equation (4.19) is an estimate of the number of people who would have died from cancer in the period had they not in fact died from natural causes. It is obtained by assuming that the probability of death from cancer being preceded by death from natural causes is one half. Our model provides an alternative method of estimating net rates. We can eliminate the effect of natural mortality by putting $r_{34} = 0$ in the model. The net risk may then be written

$$\bar{n}_2^0(T) = \frac{r_{12}r_{31}}{\lambda_3^0\lambda_4^0} + \frac{r_{12}(\lambda_4^0 - r_{11})}{\lambda_3^0(\lambda_4^0 - \lambda_3^0)}\, e^{\lambda_3^0 T} + \frac{r_{12}(r\sqrt{11} - \lambda_3^0)}{\lambda_4^0(\lambda_4^0 - \lambda_3^0)}\, e^{\lambda_4^0 T}, \tag{4.20}$$

where the superfix on $\bar{n}_2(T)$, λ_3 and λ_4 denotes that r_{34} has been set equal to zero.

The use of these results may be illustrated by two numerical examples. We assume the following transition intensities

	r_{12}	r_{13}	r_{31}	r_{34}
Example 1	1.0	2.0	0.5	0.2
Example 2	0.5	0.5	0.5	0.5

Substituting these values in equation (4.3), we find for Example 1:

$$\left.\begin{array}{l} \bar{n}_2(T) = 0.6364 - 0.3764e^{-0.3260T} - 0.2600e^{-3.3740T} \\ \bar{n}_2^0(T) = 1 - 0.7344e^{-0.1492T} - 0.2657e^{-3.3508T} \end{array}\right\} \tag{4.21}$$

4

and for Example 2:

$$\left.\begin{array}{l} \bar{n}_2(T) = \frac{2}{3} - \frac{1}{2}e^{-\frac{1}{2}T} - \frac{1}{6}e^{-(3/2)T} \\ \bar{n}_2^0(T) = 1 - 0.7236e^{-0.1910T} - 0.2764e^{-1.3090T} \end{array}\right\}. \qquad (4.22)$$

One unsatisfactory feature of the actuarial risk is seen from its limiting behaviour as $T \to \infty$. Instead of approaching one, as we would expect a reasonable measure to do, it tends to a limit less than one in both cases. Inspection of equation (4.18), shows that this result always holds. It also appears to be generally true that $_A\bar{n}_2(T) < \bar{n}_2^0(T)$ if T is sufficiently large. Some numerical values are given in the following table.

TABLE 4.1

A comparison of net risks of cancer death calculated by (a) the actuarial method and (b) using the stochastic model.

T		0.5	1	2	5	∞
Example 1	$\bar{n}_2(T)$	0.269	0.356	0.440	0.563	0.636
	$\bar{n}_2^0(T)$	0.269	0.358	0.455	0.652	1.000
	$_A\bar{n}_2(T)$	0.272	0.370	0.477	0.656	0.778
Example 2	$\bar{n}_2(T)$	0.199	0.326	0.474	0.626	0.667
	$\bar{n}_2^0(T)$	0.199	0.328	0.486	0.721	1.000
	$_A\bar{n}_2(T)$	0.201	0.338	0.515	0.733	0.800

This example provides a good illustration of the use of a stochastic model for measuring a social phenomenon. It also shows that the use of 'common-sense' corrections to crude measures may seriously underestimate the quantity being measured. These arguments pre-suppose that the model used provides an adequate description of the phenomenon. If, in fact, the transition intensities are not constant the simpler actuarial estimate may be preferable because it is 'distribution-free'. As we show below, rough methods are available for testing the adequacy of the model.

We have conducted the foregoing discussion as if the transition rates were known. In practice they will not be known and must therefore be estimated from the data. A general method for estimating the intensities was proposed by Zahl (1955). For our present purposes the simpler method of Fix and Neyman will suffice. At time T we can observe the numbers of original patients in each of the four states. These numbers may be treated as estimates of the $\bar{n}_i(T)$'s which in turn are functions of the unknown parameters. In the present case this method would yield four equations for estimating the four unknown parameters. Unfortunately the equations are not linearly independent because

$$\sum_{i=1}^{4} \bar{n}_i(T) = N,$$

the total number observed. The situation would be even worse if there were other non-zero intensities in **R**. The difficulty can be overcome if the state of the system can be observed at several points in time. An alternative method is to observe some additional feature of the system by, for example, adopting the proposal of Fix and Neyman to count the number of returns to S_1 in $(0, T)$. If sufficient observational material is available it will not only be possible to estimate all the parameters but also to test the fit of the model. A preliminary discussion of the estimation problem was given by Fix and Neyman but this is an area which requires further investigation.

The limiting structure, $\bar{\mathbf{n}}(\infty)$, can be derived directly without recourse to the full treatment just described. However, the method is more simply explained with reference to Herbst's application so we defer it until Section 4.2.

From equations (4.16) and (4.17), we have

$$\left.\begin{array}{l} \bar{n}_2(\infty) = d_{21} = r_{12}(r_{31} + r_{34})/\lambda_3\lambda_4 \\ \bar{n}_4(\infty) = d_{41} = r_{13}r_{34}/\lambda_3\lambda_4. \end{array}\right\} \tag{4.23}$$

The remaining limiting expectations are zero. The relative values of $\bar{n}_2(\infty)$ and $\bar{n}_4(\infty)$ thus depend in a simple way on the transition rates. The form of this dependence can be most clearly seen by writing the ratio as follows,

$$\frac{n_2(\infty)}{n_4(\infty)} = \frac{r_{12}}{r_{13}}\left(1 + \frac{r_{31}}{r_{34}}\right), \tag{4.24}$$

in which r_{12}/r_{13} is the ratio of the intensities out of the state 'diagnosed as suffering from cancer' and r_{31}/r_{34} is the ratio of intensities out of the state 'recovery'. A high recovery rate r_{13} tends to increase the proportion of patients who die of 'other causes' but this effect will be counteracted to some extent if there is also a high rate of relapse, r_{31}.

We have already pointed out that the model was originally developed to provide a basis for measuring the effect of a treatment. One such measure is provided by $\bar{n}_2^0(T)$, the net proportion who would die of cancer if death from other causes was eliminated. Fix and Neyman argue that $\bar{n}_2^0(T)$ is not the only nor necessarily the most appropriate measure of survival. A discussion of this point would be outside the scope of the book but we mention it in order to observe that the quantities $\bar{n}_2(T)$ or $\bar{n}_2^0(T)$ are likely to be useful in constructing alternative measures. For example, Fix and

Neyman suggest the use of the expected normal life in a period $(0, T)$ if cancer were the only risk of death. Since $\bar{n}_2^0(T)$ is the distribution function of 'normal' life in the absence of other risks the expectation may be written

$$e_2 = T\{1 - \bar{n}_2^0(T)\} + \int_0^T x \frac{d\bar{n}_2^0(x)}{dx} \, dx$$

or

$$e_2 = \int_0^T \{1 - \bar{n}_2^0(x)\} dx. \tag{4.25}$$

4.2. Labour Turnover

The matrix of transition rates for Herbst's application discussed in Section 2.2 has the following form

$$\mathbf{R} = \begin{vmatrix} r_{11} & 0 & 0 & 0 & 0 \\ r_{12} & r_{22} & 0 & 0 & 0 \\ r_{13} & r_{23} & r_{33} & 0 & 0 \\ 0 & r_{24} & 0 & 0 & 0 \\ 0 & 0 & r_{35} & 0 & 0 \end{vmatrix} \tag{4.26}$$

where $r_{11} = -r_{12} - r_{13}$, $r_{22} = -r_{23} - r_{24}$ and $r_{33} = -r_{35}$. Because of the triangular form, the eigen values of $\mathbf{R}$ are equal to the diagonal elements. In order to conform to our earlier notation we shall label them as follows:

$$\lambda_1 = 0, \quad \lambda_2 = 0, \quad \lambda_3 = r_{11}, \quad \lambda_4 = r_{22}, \quad \lambda_5 = r_{33}.$$

We again begin by supposing that we have one member of the system which is in state S_1 at time zero. The expected number in state S_i at time T is then

$$\bar{n}_i(T) = d_{i1} + c_{i3}e^{\lambda_3 T} + c_{i4}e^{\lambda_4 T} + c_{i5}e^{\lambda_4 T} \quad (i = 1, 2, \ldots, k). \tag{4.27}$$

The coefficients are obtained, as before, from equation (3.15), with the following result

$$\left.\begin{array}{l} d_{11} = 0 \quad c_{13} = 1, \quad c_{14} = c_{15} = 0 \\[2mm] d_{21} = 0 \quad c_{23} = -c_{24} = r_{12}/(r_{11} - r_{22}), \quad c_{25} = 0 \\[2mm] d_{31} = 0 \quad c_{33} = \dfrac{r_{13}}{(r_{11} - r_{33})} + \dfrac{r_{12}r_{23}}{(r_{11} - r_{22})(r_{11} - r_{33})} \\[4mm] c_{34} = \dfrac{-r_{12}r_{23}}{(r_{11} - r_{22})(r_{22} - r_{33})} \end{array}\right\} \tag{4.28}$$

$$c_{35} = \frac{-r_{13}}{r_{11} - r_{33}} + \frac{r_{12}r_{23}}{(r_{11} - r_{33})(r_{22} - r_{33})}$$

$$d_{41} = \frac{r_{12}r_{24}}{r_{11}r_{22}} \qquad c_{43} = \frac{r_{12}r_{24}}{r_{11}(r_{11} - r_{22})}$$

$$c_{44} = \frac{-r_{12}r_{24}}{r_{22}(r_{11} - r_{22})} \qquad c_{45} = 0$$

$$d_{51} = 1 - \frac{r_{12}r_{24}}{r_{11}r_{22}} \qquad c_{53} = \frac{-r_{33}}{r_{11}} \left\{ \frac{r_{13}(r_{11} - r_{22}) + r_{12}r_{23}}{(r_{11} - r_{22})(r_{11} - r_{33})} \right\}$$

$$c_{54} = \frac{r_{33}r_{12}r_{23}}{r_{22}(r_{22} - r_{33})(r_{11} - r_{22})}$$

$$c_{55} = \frac{r_{13}}{r_{11} - r_{33}} - \frac{r_{12}r_{23}}{(r_{11} - r_{33})(r_{22} - r_{33})}.$$

$$\left.\begin{array}{c}\\\\\\\\\\\\\\\\\\\\\\\end{array}\right\} \quad \begin{array}{c}(4.28)\\(contd.)\end{array}$$

The values of some of these coefficients could have been found by simple direct argument. For example, it is clear that $d_{11} = d_{21} = d_{31} = 0$ because these are the expected numbers in S_1, S_2 and S_3 after an infinitely long period of time. Similarly an elementary probability approach gives

$$\bar{n}_1(T) = e^{r_{11}T}$$

because all members of S_1 are subject to a constant transition intensity equal to $-r_{11}$. Less obviously, but without the need of the general theory, we can find $\bar{n}_4(\infty) = d_{41}$ and $\bar{n}_5(\infty) = d_{51}$. We have already pointed out in Section 4.1 that there are advantages in being able to determine the limiting distribution directly. Since $d_{11} = d_{21} = d_{31} = 0$ it follows that $d_{41} = 1 - d_{51}$ so we only need to consider d_{41}. This is the expected proportion of those who, starting in S_1, eventually reach S_4. Referring back to the diagram in Section 2.2 we see that this can only be achieved if the first transition is to S_2 and the next, and last, from S_2 to S_4. The joint probability of these two transitions can be found from the following lemma, which holds for Markov processes in continuous time.

LEMMA. *If, from a state S_1, direct transitions are possible to any one of the states $S_2, S_3, \ldots, S_k$ with transition intensities $r_{12}, r_{13}, \ldots, r_{1k}$ respectively, then*

$$Pr\{S_1 \to S_i \text{ in one step}\} = r_1 \Big/ \sum_{j=2}^{k} r_{1j} \quad (i = 1, 2, \ldots, k).$$

PROOF. Suppose that the transition to S_i takes place in $(T, T + \delta T)$. The probability is then

$$r_{1i}\delta T \, Pr\{\text{no transition has taken place in } (0, T)\}.$$

The probability of no transitions in $(0, T)$ is

$$\exp\left(-\sum_{j=2}^{k} r_{1j}T\right).$$

The total probability of the transition $S_1 \to S_i$ is then obtained by integrating over T giving

$$Pr\{S_1 \to S_i \text{ in one step}\} = \int_0^\infty r_{1i}e^{-T\sum_{j} r_{1j}}\,dT = r_{1i}\bigg/\sum_{j=2}^{k} r_{1j}$$

$$(i = 2, 3, \ldots, k),$$

which was to be proved.

Using this result and the fact that the two transitions are independent by the Markov property,

$$Pr\{S_1 \to S_2, S_2 \to S_4\} = \frac{r_{12}}{r_{12} + r_{13}} \times \frac{r_{24}}{r_{23} + r_{24}} = \frac{r_{12}r_{24}}{r_{11}r_{22}}$$

as we found before. The reader should be able to find d_{41} in the application of Section 4.1 by this method. The calculation is more complicated than here because there are infinitely many paths which terminate in S_4. Nevertheless the probabilities form a geometric progression which is easily summed to give the required answer.

Herbst was interested in discovering whether the model provides an adequate description of organizational commitment. He therefore found it necessary to compare the predictions of the theory with actual data. This comparison has to be somewhat indirect because, as we pointed out earlier, only S_5 is directly observable. Nevertheless the theory predicts that the expected proportion remaining with the organization at time T after joining will be of the form

$$1 - \bar{n}_5(T) = d_{51} + c_{53}e^{r_{11}T} + c_{54}e^{r_{22}T} + c_{55}e^{r_{33}T}. \qquad (4.29)$$

Herbst fitted this equation to length of service distributions obtained from two firms by Hedberg (1960). Firm A had a high loss of entrants and Firm B a low loss. The curves were fitted by equating percentage points and yielded for

Firm A

$$1 - \bar{n}_5(T) = 0.1493 + 0.4544e^{-0.4720T} + 0.4194e^{-0.0966T}$$
$$- 0.0231e^{-10.15T} \qquad (4.30)$$

and for

Firm B

$$1 - \bar{n}_5(T) = 0.4700 + 0.1274e^{-0.3680T} + 0.4025e^{-0.1142T}. \qquad (4.31)$$

In the second case $-r_{33}$ was effectively infinite. The observed and fitted values of $1 - \bar{n}_5(T)$ are given below in Table 4.2.

TABLE 4.2

Observed and estimated values of $100\{1 - \bar{n}_5(T)\}$, for Hedberg's data.

Month	Firm A 7628 entrants		Firm B 968 entrants	
	Actual	Theoretical	Actual	Theoretical
0	100.00	100.00	100.0	100.0
1	82.66	82.66	91.7	91.7
2	68.85	68.85	85.1	85.1
3	58.95	58.94	79.8	79.8
4	52.10	51.66	75.6	75.4
5	46.61	46.17	71.7	71.8
6	42.32	41.92	67.7	68.7
7	38.73	38.53	64.9	66.1
8	35.74	35.77	63.0	63.8
9	33.52	33.46	61.3	61.9
10	31.78	31.56	59.5	60.2
11	30.19	29.81	58.5	58.7
12	28.46	28.33	57.2	57.4
13	27.20	27.03	55.9	56.2
14	25.85	25.87	55.4	55.2
15	24.79	24.83	54.8	54.3
18	22.25	22.30	53.1	52.2
21	20.36	20.43	51.4	50.7
24	19.06	19.04	49.7	49.6
27	18.01	18.00	48.8	48.9
30	17.31	17.23	48.2	48.3
36	16.45	16.22	47.7	47.7
42	15.77	15.65	47.4	47.3
48	15.35	15.33	47.2	47.2
54	15.18	15.16	47.1	47.1
60	15.05	15.06	—	—
66	15.00	15.00	—	—

The closeness of the fit with such large samples is remarkable and seems to provide strong evidence in favour of Herbst's theory. However, as we shall see in Chapter 7, other models lead to similar mathematical functions for describing length of service distributions. A further test of the model, in this case, can be made by estimating the transition intensities. There are five of these and they may be estimated from the coefficients in equation (4.29) which are functions of the intensities. Five of the seven equations can be used to provide estimating equations. The estimates of the r_{ij}'s so obtained are then used to predict the remaining two coefficients. Once again the agreement between the prediction and the actual values of the coefficient is extremely good. The estimated rates are given in the following diagrams.

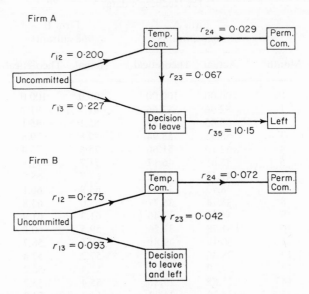

In the high loss firm there is greater 'relative pressure towards leaving' at both the uncommitted and temporarily committed stages. This tends to strengthen our belief in the consistency and appropriateness of the model.

CHAPTER 5

CONTINUOUS TIME MODELS FOR GRADED SOCIAL SYSTEMS

1. INTRODUCTION

The theory of closed systems in continuous time can easily be extended to cover open systems. In making this extension we shall follow the pattern of Chapter 3. First, in Section 2, we shall develop the continuous time analogue of the model with given input. This work has much in common with theory developed by Seal (1945) and Vajda (1947) for hierarchical organizations. Secondly we shall construct a continuous time version of Young's model for an expanding organization. This development is believed to be new but it has very close links with renewal theory.

One of the main fields of application of these models is to the study of manpower movements in hierarchical organizations. The models as described in Sections 2 and 3 of this chapter suffer from two serious limitations when used for this purpose. They both involve the assumption that the loss rate for all members of the system is constant. There is a growing body of empirical evidence, some of which is summarized in Chapter 6, which shows that loss rates are decreasing functions of length of service. Secondly, both models require that the promotion rates shall be constants also. This might be plausible in some cases but it would seem more realistic to make the promotion chances depend upon total length of service or seniority in the present grade. One of the principal advantages of the continuous time formulation is that it allows us to relax these restrictive assumptions, at least in special cases.

In Section 4, therefore, we shall remove the requirement that the loss rates must be constants. This can be done without sacrificing the Markov property of the process; hence it will be possible to obtain complete solutions. The Markov property is lost as soon as we make the promotion, or loss, rates depend on seniority within the grade. Nevertheless it is still possible to obtain results in special cases which are sufficient to justify a number of general remarks about the robustness of the assumption of constant rates. The discussion of this question is given in Section 5.

93

2. MARKOV SYSTEMS WITH GIVEN INPUT

2.1. General Theory and an Illustration

Let the expected number of entrants to the system in $(x, x + \delta x)$ be $R(x)\delta x$. As in Chapter 3, suppose that the proportion of recruits allocated to grade i is p_{0i} $(i = 1, 2, \ldots, k)$. The expected number of those entering the system at time x who will be in grade j at time T $(T > x)$ is then

$$\sum_{i=1}^{k} p_{0i} p_{ij}(T - x) R(x)\delta x.$$

The total expected number in the jth grade at time T is then obtained by integrating this expression with respect to x and adding the contribution from those who were in the system at $T = 0$. Thus we have

$$\bar{n}_j(T) = \sum_{i=1}^{k} \left\{ p_{0i} \int_0^T p_{ij}(T - x) R(x)\mathrm{d}x + n_i(0) p_{ij}(T) \right\}$$
$$(j = 1, 2, \ldots, k + 1). \quad (2.1)$$

The expected number who will have left is denoted by $\bar{n}_{k+1}(T)$ and equation (2.1) includes this case also. If input occurs at discrete points in time, equation (2.1) is easily modified by replacing the integral by a sum. For convenience we shall treat the case where input occurs continuously. Equation (2.1) is the continuous analogue of the equation numbered (2.1) in Chapter 3.

In this section we shall suppose that $R(x)$ is a given function. We first use equation (2.1) to continue our study of Herbst's model for organizational commitment and then, in Section 2.2 we shall introduce Seal and Vajda's work on hierarchical organizations. Let us assume that all entrants and original members begin in the uncommitted state S_1, then $p_{0i} = 0$ if $i \geq 2$ and $p_{01} = 1$. With this assumption all terms but the first in equation (2.1) are zero and hence the only transition probabilities required are $p_{1j}(T)$ for $j = 1, 2, \ldots, k$. These probabilities were found in the previous chapter where we showed in equation (4.27) that they had the form

$$p_{1j}(T) = d_{j1} + c_{j3}\mathrm{e}^{r_{11}T} + c_{j4}\mathrm{e}^{r_{22}T} + c_{j5}\mathrm{e}^{r_{33}T} \quad (j = 1, 2, \ldots, 5). \quad (2.2)$$

The expected size of the jth grade may thus be written,

$$\bar{n}_j(T) = d_{j1} \int_0^T R(x)\mathrm{d}x + \sum_{i=j}^{3} c_{j,i+2} \int_0^T \mathrm{e}^{r_{ii}(T-x)} R(x)\mathrm{d}x$$
$$+ n_1(0)\{d_{j1} + \sum_{i=1}^{3} c_{j,i+2}\mathrm{e}^{r_{ii}T}\} \quad (j = 1, 2, \ldots, 5). \quad (2.3)$$

To illustrate the dependence of $\bar{n}_j(T)$ on $R(x)$ let us consider the case $R(x) = Re^{\alpha x}$ $(R > 0)$. The integration in equation (2.3) is straightforward and yields

$$\bar{n}_j(T) = d_{j1}R\left(\frac{e^{\alpha T} - 1}{\alpha}\right) + R\sum_{i=1}^{3}c_{j,i+2}\left(\frac{e^{\alpha T} - e^{r_{ii}T}}{\alpha - r_{ii}}\right)$$

$$+ n_1(0)\{d_{j1} + \sum_{i=1}^{3}c_{j,i+2}e^{r_{ii}T}\}. \quad (2.4)$$

The result is what we might have anticipated from our studies of geometric input in discrete time in Chapter 3. If $\alpha > 0$ the expected grade sizes increase exponentially with time. If $\alpha < 0$, they tend to zero with increasing T if $d_{j1} = 0$ and to a limit $d_{j1}\{n_1(0) - \alpha^{-1}\}$ otherwise. In this application $d_{j1} \neq 0$ for $j = 4$ and 5 which are the terminal states representing loss or permanent attachment. The case $\alpha = 0$ gives a constant rate of input and the expected values become, when T is large,

$$\bar{n}_j(T) \sim Rd_{j1}T + R\sum_{i=1}^{3}\frac{c_{ji+2}}{(-r_{ii})} + n_1(0)d_{j1} \quad (j = 1, 2, \ldots, 5). \quad (2.5)$$

The size of the two terminal states will thus grow linearly with T and the sizes of the remainder will approach limits given by the second term in equation (2.5). The behaviour for other functions of $R(x)$ can be investigated in a similar manner. We now use these results to make calculations of limiting state sizes for the two firms considered by Herbst. These will show us how the members would be distributed among the various psychological states when the system had reached equilibrium. This will only happen for the transient states S_1, S_2 and S_3 for which we find, using equation (4.28) of Chapter 4

$$\bar{n}_1(\infty) = R/(-r_{11}), \quad \bar{n}_2(\infty) = Rr_{12}/r_{11}r_{22},$$

$$\bar{n}_3(\infty) = R(r_{13}/r_{11}r_{33} + r_{12}r_{23}/r_{11}r_{22}r_{33}). \quad (2.6)$$

For the 'high loss' factory (*Firm A*) we found

$$r_{12} = 0.200, \quad r_{13} = 0.227, \quad r_{23} = 0.067, \quad r_{24} = 0.029,$$

$$r_{35} = 10.15, \quad -r_{11} = 0.427, \quad -r_{22} = 0.096, \quad -r_{33} = r_{35}$$

which gives

$$\bar{n}_1(\infty) = 2.34R, \quad \bar{n}_2(\infty) = 4.88R, \quad \bar{n}_3(\infty) = 0.09R.$$

For *Firm B*, the 'low loss' factory the corresponding figures are

$$r_{12} = 0.275, \quad r_{13} = 0.093, \quad r_{23} = 0.042, \quad r_{24} = 0.072, \quad r_{35} = \infty$$

and

$$\bar{n}_1(\infty) = 2.72R, \quad \bar{n}_2(\infty) = 6.56R, \quad \bar{n}_3(\infty) = 0.$$

Both firms would be expected to have about the same number of workers in the state of indecision but the real difference between the firms appears when we consider $\bar{n}_2(\infty)$. The 'low loss' firm has substantially more members in the temporarily committed state than does the 'high loss' firm. This is a prediction of Herbst's theory which it might be possible to test in practice either for constant input or for any other prescribed pattern.

Herbst tested his model using what is sometimes called a 'cohort' method of analysis. That is he used data obtained by following each entrant through his subsequent history with the firm. The model predicts the length of service distribution which should be observed. The comparison of this with actual distributions enabled Herbst to estimate the parameters of his model and to test its validity. In many cases the statistician has to be satisfied with what is known as 'census' data. Such data give information about employees who are with the firm at one or more given points in time. The theory of closed systems is sufficient for a cohort analysis but we shall see that the theory of open systems is needed if data of the census type are all that is available. Inspection of equation (2.1) reminds us that prediction of $\bar{n}_j(T)$ requires a knowledge of the recruitment history of the firm through the function $R(x)$. Fortunately this information is usually much easier to obtain than the length of service of individual employees.

Suppose, for simplicity, that new entrants have been recruited at a constant rate throughout the history of the firm. If the numbers in each state at any time could be observed equation (2.4) would provide five estimating equations for any given value of T. In this application we have assumed that it is only possible to observe the number who have left at any time. Thus observations of the system at a minimum of five points in time would be needed to estimate the five parameters of the model. Observations at further points would be necessary to test its predictions. This method will not be satisfactory if our observations are confined to large values of T. In this case

$$\bar{n}_5(T) \sim RT(1 - r_{12}r_{24}/r_{11}r_{22}).$$

Observation at a single value of T will only permit us to estimate the ratio $r_{12}r_{24}/r_{11}r_{22}$. Repeated observation of the number who have left will not provide additional equations for estimating the individual parameters.

It will merely serve to verify that $\bar{n}_5(T)$ is, in fact, linear in T. In a census analysis it is therefore very important to observe the system at well-separated points in time before equilibrium has been reached.

The census approach, using the open model, may be more appropriate than the cohort method in the kind of application envisaged by Fix and Neyman. Instead of following the post-treatment history of each patient it might be necessary to use data giving the state of each patient at selected points in time. A very special case of our general model with only two states, alive and dead, has been discussed by Littell (1952) and Armitage (1959) in this context.

Although our discussion has centred upon the particular application to labour turnover it can be adopted to cover the general case with recruitment to each of k stages. For example, when investigating the limiting forms of $\{\bar{n}_j(T)\}$, we shall have to deal with expressions similar to those given in equation (2.3). The limiting behaviour is determined by the integrals of the form

$$\text{(a)} \quad \int_0^T R(x)\mathrm{d}x \quad \text{and} \quad \text{(b)} \quad \int_0^T R(x)e^{\lambda_h(T-x)}\,\mathrm{d}x,$$

where λ_h (<0) is an eigen value of the matrix of transition intensities. If $\int_0^\infty R(x)\mathrm{d}x$ converges, the total input is finite and $\bar{n}_j(T)$ approaches a limit for all j. It may be shown that this limit is zero for all transient (non-terminal) states. The more usual case will be the one where the integral diverges. The terminal states then grow with T and are ultimately proportional in size to the total input given by (a). In this case the transient states may or may not increase indefinitely. For these states $d_{ij} = 0$ for all i and j so that the behaviour of $\bar{n}_j(T)$ for large T is governed by the integrals of the form (b). The condition for the expectations of the transient states to tend to finite limits is that the integral

$$\int_0^T R(x)e^{\lambda\max(T-x)}\,\mathrm{d}x \tag{2.7}$$

converges as $T \to \infty$. The limit need only be investigated for the largest eigen value because if the integral (2.7) converges in that case it will certainly do so in the remaining cases.

2.2. Application to Hierarchical Systems

The Markov model may be used for hierarchical systems in which loss and promotion can occur at any time. Continuous time models for such systems have been given by Seal (1945) and Vajda (1947). Their models were non-Markovian but both authors discussed some special cases which coincide with those derived from our general theory. We consider a system which can be represented diagrammatically as follows.

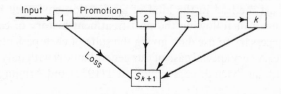

This system has one terminal state which we have labelled S_{k+1}. Promotion takes place only from one grade to the one above it and new entrants all go into grade 1. The matrix of transition intensities for the system we have described has the form

$$\mathbf{R} = \begin{pmatrix} r_{11} & 0 & 0 & \cdots & 0 & 0 & 0 \\ r_{12} & r_{22} & 0 & & 0 & 0 & 0 \\ 0 & r_{23} & r_{33} & & 0 & 0 & 0 \\ \cdot & \cdot & \cdot & & \cdot & \cdot & \cdot \\ \cdot & \cdot & \cdot & & \cdot & \cdot & \cdot \\ \cdot & \cdot & \cdot & & \cdot & \cdot & \cdot \\ 0 & 0 & 0 & & r_{k-l,k} & r_{kk} & 0 \\ r_{1,k+1} & r_{2,k+1} & r_{3,k+1} & \cdots & r_{k-1,k+1} & r_{k,k+1} & r_{k+1,k-1} \end{pmatrix} \quad (2.8)$$

where

$$r_{ii} = -(r_{i,i+1} + r_{i,k+1}), \quad i < k$$

$$r_{kk} = -r_{k,k+1}, \quad r_{k+1,k+1} = 0.$$

The simple triangular structure of $\mathbf{R}$ enables us to obtain explicit formulae for the eigen values and the coefficients $\{c_{ij}\}$ which appear in the expressions for the transition probabilities $\{p_{ij}(T)\}$. We find at once that $\lambda_i = r_{ii}$ $(i = 1, 2, \ldots, k + 1)$. The equations which determine the c's obtained from equation (3.16) of Chapter 4 are

and

$$\left. \begin{array}{c} r_{i-1,i}c_{i-1,h} + r_{ii}c_{ij} = r_{hh}c_{ih} \quad (i, h = 1, 2, \ldots, k + 1) \\[2mm] \displaystyle\sum_{h=1}^{k+1} c_{ih} = 1 \text{ if } i = 1 \\[2mm] = 0 \text{ if } i > 1. \end{array} \right\} \quad (2.9)$$

The initial conditions represented by this last pair of equations follow from the fact that all new entrants begin their careers in grade 1. The set of equations (2.9) may be solved to give

$$\left.\begin{array}{l} c_{1h} = \prod_{j=1}^{i-1} r_{j,j+1} \Big/ \prod_{\substack{j=1 \\ j \neq h}}^{i} (r_{jj} - r_{hh}) \quad \left(\begin{array}{l} i = 2, 3, \ldots, k+1 \\ h = 1, 2, \ldots, i \end{array} \right) \\[2ex] c_{11} = 1 \\[1ex] c_{ih} = 0 \text{ otherwise.} \end{array}\right\} \quad (2.10)$$

We shall be interested only in $\bar{n}_j(T)$ for $j \leq k$, in which case

$$\bar{n}_j(T) = \int_0^T R(x) p_{1j}(T - x)\mathrm{d}x + \sum_{i=0}^{j} n_i(0) p_{ij}(T) \quad (j = 1, 2, \ldots, k). \quad (2.11)$$

The coefficients obtained from equation (2.9) give

$$p_{1j}(T) = \sum_{h=1}^{k} c_{jh} e^{r_{hh} T} \quad (2.12)$$

and this may be substituted in equation (2.11). A similar expression can be found for $p_{ij}(T)$, $i > 1$ and all j, using the appropriate initial conditions but they can easily be deduced from those for $p_{1j}(T)$ when we have a simple hierarchy. An entrant who starts his career in grade i of a k-stage system is in the same position as one who starts in grade 1 in a $(k - (i - 1))$-stage system. By replacing k by $k - i + 1$ and relabelling the transition intensities the required expressions are obtained. We give an example below. It is obvious that $p_{ij}(T) = 0$ if $i > j$ which is why the upper limit of summation in the last term of equation (2.11) is j.

The model which we have described is slightly more general than the Markov version of Vajda's (1945) model. He assumed a constant rate of input to the system and a constant loss rate; his results may thus be obtained from ours by putting $R(x) = R$ and $r_{i,k+1} = r_{k+1}$ say, for $i \leq k$. We have also given the expected grade sizes for all T, whereas Vajda discussed only the limiting case.

As we have pointed out on several occasions the theory which we have used above requires that the quantities r_{ii} ($i = 1, 2, \ldots, k + 1$) are all distinct. In the case we are discussing $r_{ii} = -(r_{i,i+1} + r_{i,k+1})$ for $i \leq k$ so that equalities between the r_{ii} would occur if the total loss rates for certain grades were equal. A case of particular interest in which this happens occurs if $r_{i,i+1} = r$ and if $r_{i,k+1} = r_{k+1}$ for $i < k$. This corresponds to a situation in which promotion rates and loss rates are the same for all grades except the last. The appropriate modifications to the theory may be obtained by allowing the eigen values r_{ii}, $i < k$, to approach one another in equation (2.12). The resulting expression for $p_{1j}(T)$ is then

$$p_{1j}(T) = \frac{r^{j-1}}{(j-1)!} T^{j-1} e^{-(r+r_{k+1})T} \quad (j = 1, 2, \ldots, k-1). \tag{2.13}$$

If $j = k$ the expression is slightly more complicated but we shall see below that it is not needed. For $p_{ij}(T)$ we use the device mentioned above and find that

$$p_{ij}(T) = \frac{r^{j-i}}{(j-i)!} T^{j-i} e^{-(r+r_{k+1})T} \quad (k > j \geq i). \tag{2.14}$$

Using equations (2.13) and (2.14) we may determine $\bar{n}_j(T)$ for $j < k$ by substitution in equation (2.11); $\bar{n}_k(T)$ is then obtained from

$$\bar{n}_k(T) = \sum_{j=1}^{k} \bar{n}_j(T) - \sum_{j=1}^{k-1} \bar{n}_j(T). \tag{2.15}$$

The total size at time T is obtained by summing both sides of equation (2.11) over j and using the fact that

$$\sum_{j=1}^{k} p_{ij}(x) = 1 - p_{i,k+1}(x) = 1 - e^{-r_{k+1}x}.$$

This then gives

$$\sum_{j=1}^{k} \bar{n}_j(T) = \int_0^T R(x) e^{-r_{k+1}(T-x)} dx + N(0) e^{-r_{k+1}T}, \tag{2.16}$$

where

$$N(0) = \sum_{j=1}^{k} n_i(0).$$

We illustrate the theory by taking $k = 3$,

$$r_{i,i+1} = 1, \quad (i = 1, 2, \ldots), \quad r_{i,4} = 2 \quad (i = 1, 2, 3)$$

for which

$$p_{ij}(T) = \frac{1}{(j-i)!} T^{j-i} e^{-3T} \quad \left(\begin{matrix} i = 1, 2, 3 \\ i < j < 3 \end{matrix} \right). \tag{2.17}$$

Let the input be an exponential function of time with $R(x) = 100 e^{\alpha x}$ and let $n_1(0) = 100$, $n_2(0) = 50$, $n_3(0) = 20$. We leave the parameter α unspecified in order to examine the effect which it has on the solution. Equation (2.11) yields

$$\bar{n}_1(T) = \frac{100}{3 + \alpha} e^{\alpha T} + 100 e^{-3T} \left\{ \frac{2 + \alpha}{3 + \alpha} \right\}$$

$$\bar{n}_2(T) = \frac{100}{(3 + \alpha)^2} e^{\alpha T} + 100 e^{-3T} \left\{ T + \frac{1}{2} - \frac{T}{3 + \alpha} - \frac{1}{(3 + \alpha)^2} \right\}. \tag{2.18}$$

The expectation $\bar{n}_3(T)$ is now obtained by subtracting $\bar{n}_1(T) + \bar{n}_2(T)$ from

$$\sum_{j=1}^{3} \bar{n}_j(T) = \frac{100e^{\alpha T}}{(2 + \alpha)} + 100e^{-2T}\left\{1.7 - \frac{1}{2 + \alpha}\right\}. \quad (2.19)$$

The crucial dependence of $\bar{n}_j(T)$ on α is evident from these formulae. If $\alpha > 0$ the input increases exponentially with time and so do the expected sizes of the grades. If $\alpha < 0$ the expected grade sizes tend to zero with increasing time. The reader should compare these results with those obtained in Chapter 3 for the discrete time model with geometric input. In the case of constant input, obtained by putting $\alpha = 0$, the $\bar{n}_j(T)$'s approach finite limits as $T \to \infty$. These limits are

$$\bar{n}_1(\infty) = 33.3, \quad \bar{n}_2(\infty) = 11.1, \quad \bar{n}_3(\infty) = 5.6$$

the overall size being 50. This last result could have been found directly from the fact that the average time spent in the system is $r_{i4}^{-1} = \frac{1}{2}$ ($i = 1$, 2, 3) and that the input is 100 per unit time. The limiting size is, of course, independent of the initial size and the parameter values we have chosen bring about a reduction in overall total size from 170 to 50. Inspection of equation (2.18) shows that the lowest grade reaches its limit more rapidly than the middle and highest grades. We observed the same phenomenon with the discrete time model.

It is interesting to observe that the *relative* sizes of the $\bar{n}_j(T)$'s for large T depend upon α in a simple fashion. If $\alpha > -2$ then

$$\left. \begin{array}{c} \bar{n}_1(T) \sim \dfrac{100}{3 + \alpha} e^{\alpha T} \quad \bar{n}_2(T) \sim \dfrac{100}{(3 + \alpha)^2} e^{\alpha T} \\[2mm] \bar{n}_3(T) \sim \dfrac{100}{(2 + \alpha)(3 + \alpha)^2} e^{\alpha T}. \end{array} \right\} \quad (2.20)$$

The effect of increasing the rate of input is to increase the sizes of the lower two grades relative to the highest. Conversely a decreasing rate of input leads to a concentration at the upper end of the hierarchy. Had we repeated the calculation with larger values of k we should have found that, for large T, the grade sizes were in geometric progression except for the kth grade. In particular, this result holds for the case of constant input obtained by putting $\alpha = 0$. In this case we find

$$\left. \begin{array}{c} \bar{n}_j(\infty) = \dfrac{R}{r}\left(\dfrac{r}{r + r_{k+1}}\right)^j \quad (j = 1, 2, \ldots, k - 1) \\[3mm] \bar{n}_k(\infty) = \dfrac{R}{r_{k+1}} - \displaystyle\sum_{j=1}^{k-1} \bar{n}_j(\infty) = \dfrac{R}{r_{k+1}}\left(\dfrac{r}{r + r_{k+1}}\right)^{k-1} \end{array} \right\} \quad (2.21)$$

where R is the rate of input to the system. It thus follows that *a hierarchical system with constant promotion rates throughout, a constant loss rate and a constant input rate will tend to a geometric structure.* The exception to this general rule is that the kth grade will be larger than the term in the geometric series corresponding to $j = k$. A system of the kind that we have discussed will thus have a tendency to become 'top-heavy'. If $R(x)$ has the exponential form considered earlier the same result holds for the relative expected grade sizes as we have already noted in our example. Later in this chapter we shall consider how far this general conclusion remains true when the rather special assumptions of the present model are relaxed.

3. STOCHASTIC VARIATION OF THE GRADE SIZES

Our analysis so far has been wholly concerned with the expected values of the grade sizes. Clearly it is also desirable to have information about the distribution of the grade sizes and, in particular about their variances and covariances. Unfortunately the theory used for the discrete time model in Chapter 3 has not yet been extended to cover the continuous case. In principle the joint distribution of the grade sizes could be obtained from the theory of multi-variable Markov processes but no results covering cases of interest to us appear to have been published. However, insofar as the discrete time model approximates the continuous time version we may use the results of Section 2.4 in Chapter 3 as a general guide to behaviour in the continuous case. In particular we recall that when the input is a Poisson variable and when recruits are allocated to grade j with probability p_{0j} ($j = 1, 2, \ldots, k$) then the grade sizes are asymptotically and independently distributed in the Poisson form. We conjecture that this result holds also in continuous time if the input is a Poisson process. This conjecture is supported by the following two exact results which can be obtained for this case under the further assumption that the loss rate is the same for each grade.

The first result concerns the total size. If we exclude the state S_{k+1} the system may be regarded as a birth and death process in which the 'births' are new entrants and the 'deaths' are losses. Adopting the notation of Feller (1950) (Vol. I, p. 377), the parameters of the process are $\lambda_n = R$, $\mu_n = n r_{k+1}$. Under these circumstances Feller showed that the distribution of total size has, asymptotically, a Poisson distribution with mean R/r_{k+1}.

A similar result holds for the lowest grade. In this case we must also assume that there are no demotions into grade 1. If this is so the input to this grade is Poisson with parameter $R p_{01}$. The 'death' rate is now $\mu_n = n(r_{12} + r_{1,k+1})$. Hence the number in the lowest grade has, in the limit, a Poisson distribution with parameter $R p_{01}/(r_{12} + r_{1,k+1})$. This agrees, of course, with the expression for the mean obtained in Section 5.2. This argument cannot be extended to grade 2, or higher grades, because the input to them is not fixed but depends on sizes of other grades.

4. CONTINUOUS TIME THEORY FOR AN EXPANDING ORGANIZATION

4.1. General Theory

The theory in this case may be derived from the basic equation (2.1). Instead of being given the input function $R(x)$ we now start from a function which specifies the rate of expansion. Let us suppose that the organization is to be increased in size by an amount $M(T)\delta T$ between time T and $T + \delta T$. (The increase in size cannot, of course, be a continuous variable but it is convenient to treat it as such. If the increases are realizations of a stochastic process $M(T)\delta T$ would be interpreted as the expected increase.) The input function is thus determined by the need to replace losses and to provide for the increase in overall size. Thus we have

$$R(T)\delta T = M(T)\delta T + \bar{n}_{k+1}(T + \delta T) - \bar{n}_{k+1}(T)$$

or, as $\delta T \to 0$

$$R(T) = M(T) + \frac{d\bar{n}_{k+1}(T)}{dT}. \tag{4.1}$$

Using this relationship we may eliminate $R(T)$ from equation (2.1) and obtain a set of equations for the expected grade sizes which depend only on known functions as follows

$$\bar{n}_j(T) = \sum_{i=1}^{k} p_{0i} \left\{ \int_0^T p_{ij}(T - x)M(x)dx + \int_0^T p_{ij}(T - x)\frac{d\bar{n}_{k+1}(x)}{dx} dx \right\}$$
$$+ \sum_{i=1}^{k} n_i(0)p_{ij}(T) \quad (j = 1, 2, \ldots, k + 1). \tag{4.2}$$

By putting $j = k + 1$ in equation (4.2) we have an integral equation for $\bar{n}_{k+1}(T)$. Substitution of this in equation (4.2) for $j = 1, 2, \ldots, k$ then gives expressions for the remaining grade sizes. This procedure is facilitated by the introduction of Laplace transforms. The Laplace transform of a continuous function $f(x)$, defined for $x \geq 0$, is as follows:

$$f^*(s) = \int_0^\infty f(x)e^{-sx}dx. \tag{4.3}$$

We shall also require the following well-known results about transforms.

(a) If $h(T) = \int_0^T f(t - x)g(x)dx$

then
$$h^*(s) = f^*(s)g^*(s).$$

(b) The transform of the derivative of $f(x)$ is $sf^*(s) - f(0)$.

Using these definitions and results we take the Laplace transform of each side of equation (4.2) and obtain

$$\bar{n}_j^*(s) = \sum_{i=1}^{k} p_{0i}\{p_{ij}^*(s)M^*(s) + s\bar{n}_{k+1}^*(s)p_{ij}^*(s)\} + \sum_{i=1}^{k} n_i(0)p_{ij}^*(s)$$

$$= \{M^*(s) + s\bar{n}_{k+1}^*(s)\}\sum_{i=1}^{k} p_{0i}p_{ij}^*(s) + \sum_{i=1}^{k} n_i(0)p_{ij}^*(s)$$

$$(j = 1, 2, \ldots, k + 1). \qquad (4.4)$$

Setting $j = k + 1$ gives

$$n_{k+1}^*(s) = \frac{\{M^*(s)\sum_{i=1}^{k} p_{0i}p_{i,k+1}^*(s) + \sum_{i=1}^{k} n_i(0)p_{i,k+1}^*(s)\}}{1 - s\sum_{i=1}^{k} p_{0i}p_{i,k+1}^*(s)}. \qquad (4.5)$$

This expression may now be substituted in equation (4.4) to give

$$\bar{n}_j^*(s) = \frac{\{\sum_{i=1}^{k} n_i(0)p_{i,k+1}^*(s) + M^*(s)\}\sum_{i=1}^{k} p_{0i}p_{ij}^*(s)}{1 - s\sum_{i=1}^{k} p_{0i}p_{i,k+1}^*(s)} + \sum_{i=1}^{k} n_i(0)p_{ij}^*(s)$$

$$(j = 1, 2, \ldots, k). \qquad (4.6)$$

This formula appears to be rather formidable, especially since it has to be inverted before yielding what we require. However, some simplifications may be possible in particular applications. For example, if demotions are ruled out then $p_{ij}(T)$, and hence $p_{ij}^*(s)$, are zero for $j < i$. If the loss rate is independent of the grade, $p_{i,k+1}^*(s) = p_{k+1}^*(s)$, say, and the denominator simplifies to $1 - sp_{k+1}^*(s)$. Finally, if $p_{01} = 1$, $p_{0i} = 0 \, (i > 1)$, each sum in equation (4.6) is replaced by its first term.

Even without these simplifications the problem of inversion is not intractable. The form of $p_{ij}(T)$ makes its transform $p_{ij}^*(s)$ a rational algebraic fraction. If $M^*(s)$ has this form also, $\bar{n}_j^*(s)$ can be inverted by general methods described, for example, in Feller (1950) (Vol. I, Chapter 11). As we shall see in Section 4.3 it is possible to determine the limiting behaviour of the system from equation (4.6), without inverting the transform.

4.2. An Illustration

Consider a system with $k = 3$, $p_{01} = 1$, $p_{02} = p_{03} = 0$, $r_{12} = r_{23} = r$ and $r_{14} = r_{24} = r_{34} = r_4$, say. Assume also that $n_1(0) = N$, $n_2(0) = n_3(0) = 0$. The Laplace transform of $\bar{n}_j(T)$ is then, from equation (4.6),

$$\bar{n}_j^*(s) = \frac{\{Nsp_4^*(s) + M^*(s)\}p_{1j}^*(s)}{1 - sp_4^*(s)} + Np_{1j}^*(s)$$

$$= \{N + M^*(s)\}p_{1j}^*(s)/(1 - sp_4^*(s)) \quad (j = 1, 2, 3).$$

The probabilities $\{p_{1j}(T)\}$ are given, under the above assumptions, by equation (2.13) for $j = 1$ and 2 hence

$$p_{1j}^*(s) = \frac{r^{j-1}}{(r + r_4 + s)^j} \quad (j = 1, 2). \tag{4.7}$$

Under the assumption of a constant loss rate

$$p_{1,4}(T) = 1/s - 1/(s + r_4). \tag{4.8}$$

At this point we must specify the function $M(T)$; we shall again assume exponential growth, setting $M(T) = Me^{\alpha T}$ $(M > 0)$. On this assumption $M^*(s) = M/(s - \alpha)$ if $s > \alpha$, otherwise the transform does not exist.

Taking first $j = 1$ we find

$$\bar{n}_1^*(s) = (s + r_4)(Ns - N\alpha + M)/s(s - \alpha)(r + r_4 + s). \tag{4.9}$$

Resolution into partial fractions gives

$$\bar{n}_1^*(s) = \frac{A_1}{s} + \frac{B_1}{s - \alpha} + \frac{C_1}{s + r + r_4} \tag{4.10}$$

provided that $\alpha \neq 0$. The coefficients in the expansion are

$$A_1 = \left(\frac{N\alpha - M}{\alpha}\right)\left(\frac{r_4}{r + r_4}\right)$$

$$B_1 = \frac{M}{\alpha}\frac{(r_4 + \alpha)}{(r + r_4 + \alpha)}$$

$$C_1 = \frac{r\{N(r + r_4) + N\alpha - M\}}{(r + r_4)(r + r_4 + \alpha)}.$$

We may note that $A_1 + B_1 + C_1 = N$. If $\alpha = 0$ the partial fraction representation is

$$\bar{n}_1^*(s) = \frac{A_1'}{s} + \frac{B_1'}{s^2} + \frac{C_1'}{(s + r + r_4)} \tag{4.11}$$

where

$$A_1' = \frac{Mr}{(r + r_4)^2} + \frac{Nr_4}{(r + r_4)}$$

$$B_1' = \frac{Mr_4}{(r + r_4)}$$

$$C_1' = \frac{r\{N(r + r_4) - M\}}{(r + r_4)^2}.$$

Inverting the leading expressions in equations (4.10) and (4.11), we find

$$\left.\begin{aligned}
\bar{n}_1(T) &= A_1 + B_1 e^{\alpha T} + C_1 e^{-(r + r_4)T} \quad \alpha \neq 0 \\
&= A_1' + B_1' T + C_1 e^{-(r + r_4)T} \quad \alpha = 0.
\end{aligned}\right\} \tag{4.12}$$

The last term in each part of the right-hand side of equation (4.12) tends to zero as T increases. For large values of T the behaviour of $\bar{n}_1(T)$ depends critically on the value of α. Three cases must be distinguished as follows:

$$\bar{n}_1(T) \sim B_1 e^{\alpha T} \quad \text{if } \alpha > 0$$

$$\sim B_1' T \quad \text{if } \alpha = 0$$

$$\sim A_1 \quad \text{if } \alpha < 0.$$

The determination of $\bar{n}_2(T)$ follows similar lines to that of $\bar{n}_1(T)$ and yields a solution of the form

$$\bar{n}_2(T) = A_2 + B_2 e^{\alpha T} + C_2 e^{-(r + r_4)T} + DTe^{-(r + r_4)T} \quad (\alpha \neq 0). \tag{4.13}$$

If $\alpha = 0$ the second term in equation (4.13) is replaced by one which is linear in T and the coefficients have different values. Their determination is left to the reader. The approach to the limit is somewhat slower for $\bar{n}_2(T)$ than for $\bar{n}_1(T)$ because of the factor T which is present in the last term. The general form of $\bar{n}_3(T)$ is identical with equation (4.13) and a similar remark about the rate of approach to the limit applies. We take up the general question of limiting behaviour in this model in the following section.

4.3. Limiting Behaviour of $\bar{n}(T)$

The limit of $\bar{n}(T)$ can be found from equation (4.6) without inverting the transform. This follows from the fact that

$$\lim_{T \to \infty} \bar{n}_j(T) = \lim_{s \to 0} s\bar{n}_j^*(s) \quad (j = 1, 2, \ldots, k) \tag{4.14}$$

if $\bar{n}_j^*(s)$ exists for all $s > 0$. In order to evaluate the limit we need the following results about the behaviour of the Laplace transforms of the transition probabilities near the origin $s = 0$.

(a) $$p_{ij}^*(s) = \int_0^\infty p_{ij}(T)\mathrm{d}T + O(s) \quad (j \le k)$$

(b) $$p_{i,k+1}^*(s) = s^{-1} + O(1).$$

(4.15)

These results are a consequence of the fact that the transition probabilities are finite series of exponential terms. It now follows from equation (4.14) that

$$\lim_{T \to \infty} \bar{n}_j(T) = C\{N + \lim_{s \to 0} M^*(s)\} \sum_{i=1}^k p_{0i} \int_0^\infty p_{ij}(T)\mathrm{d}T. \quad (4.16)$$

The value of C is most easily found using the result

$$\sum_{j=1}^k \bar{n}_j^*(s) = \frac{N}{s} + \frac{M^*(s)}{s}. \quad (4.17)$$

Thus summing both sides of equation (4.16) over j we find

$$C = \left\{ \sum_{i=1}^k p_{0i} \int_0^\infty \sum_{j=1}^k p_{ij}(T)\mathrm{d}T \right\}^{-1}.$$

The limit given by equation (4.16) will be finite if

$$\lim_{s \to 0} M^*(s) = \int_0^\infty M(T)\mathrm{d}T$$

is finite; that is if the total increase in size is finite. In practice this must always be so but it is instructive, nevertheless, to consider infinite increases as we did in Section 4.2. However, whether or not the total increase is finite the relative expected grade sizes are given by

$$a_j(\infty) = \sum_{i=1}^k p_{0i} \int_0^\infty p_{ij}(T)\mathrm{d}T \bigg/ \sum_{i=1}^k p_{0i} \int_0^\infty \sum_{j=1}^k p_{ij}(T)\mathrm{d}T$$

$$(j = 1, 2, \ldots, k) \quad (4.18)$$

where the sum

$$\sum_{j=1}^k p_{ij}(T) = 1 - p_{i,k+1}(T).$$

If the loss rate is constant and independent of the grade, with intensity r_{k+1}, we have

$$1 - p_{i,k+1}(T) = \mathrm{e}^{-r_{k+1}T}$$

and hence

$$\int_0^\infty \{1 - p_{i,k+1}(T)\}\mathrm{d}T = \frac{1}{r_{k+1}}.$$

The denominator of equation (4.18) may thus be replaced by r_{k+1}^{-1}.

The foregoing argument rests on the assumption that $M^*(s)$ exists for all $s > 0$. It therefore fails, for example, if $M(T) = Me^{\alpha T}$ with $\alpha > 0$ since the transform exists only for $s > \alpha$. We shall pursue this point further in the next section. For the present we state the important conclusion that: *if $M^*(s)$ exists for all $s > 0$, then the relative expected grade sizes approach limits, independent of $M(T)$, given by equation* (4.18). The condition that $M^*(s)$ exist for $s > 0$ imposes a restriction on the rate of growth comparable to condition A of Chapter 3. This is not immediately obvious since the condition is stated in terms of the Laplace transform. We therefore proceed to express it in an alternative form which makes its nature clearer.

Reference to the standard works on the Laplace transform, for example, Widder (1946) (Theorem 2.2a), shows that the existence of $M^*(s)$ for all $s > 0$ implies that

$$\lim_{T \to \infty} e^{-\beta T} \int_0^T M(x)\mathrm{d}x = 0 \tag{4.19}$$

for all $\beta > 0$. The condition will certainly be satisfied if $M(T)$ is proportional to any power of T but not if it increases exponentially with time. The similarity between equation (4.19) and condition A of Chapter 3 becomes evident if we note that equation (4.19) is equivalent to

$$\lim_{T \to \infty} \left\{ -\beta T + \log \int_0^T M(x)\mathrm{d}x \right\} = -\infty \tag{4.20}$$

for all $\beta > 0$ which holds if, and only if,

$$\lim_{T \to \infty} \frac{\mathrm{d}}{\mathrm{d}T} \left\{ \log \int_0^T M(x)\mathrm{d}x \right\} < \beta \text{ for all } \beta > 0. \tag{4.21}$$

The left-hand side of equation (4.21) may be expressed as

$$\lim_{T \to \infty} M(T) \Big/ \int_0^T M(x)\mathrm{d}x$$

and hence for the condition to hold we must have

$$\lim_{T \to \infty} \frac{M(T)}{\displaystyle\int_0^T M(x)\mathrm{d}x} = 0; \tag{4.22}$$

this should be compared with condition A. We shall call equation (4.22) condition A'.

4.4. Illustration of Limiting Behaviour

We illustrate the foregoing theory by applying it to the example discussed in Section 4.2. The expression for $\bar{n}_1(T)$ is given in equation (4.12). If

$\alpha < 0$ condition A' is satisfied and we find from equation (4.16), or directly from equation (4.12), that

$$\bar{n}_1(\infty) = A_1 = \left(\frac{M - N\alpha}{-\alpha}\right)\frac{r_4}{(r + r_4)}.$$

In a similar manner we obtain

$$\bar{n}_2(\infty) = \left(\frac{M - N\alpha}{-\alpha}\right)\frac{rr_4}{(r + r_4)^2}$$

and

$$\bar{n}_3(\infty) = \left(\frac{M - N\alpha}{-\alpha}\right)\frac{r^2}{(r + r_4)^2}.$$

$$(4.23)$$

The relative grade sizes can be obtained from equation (4.23) by omitting the factor $(M - N\alpha)/(-\alpha)$.

If $\alpha = 0$ the grade sizes increase without limit and we find, for large values of T that

$$\begin{aligned}\bar{n}_1(T) &\sim TMr_4/(r + r_4) \\ n_2(T) &\sim TMrr_4/(r + r_4)^2 \\ \bar{n}_3(T) &\sim TMr^2/(r + r_4)^2.\end{aligned}$$

$$(4.24)$$

It should be noted that the relative expectations are the same for $\alpha = 0$ as when $\alpha < 0$; this is as it should be since condition A' is satisfied in both cases.

The case $\alpha > 0$ is particularly interesting because the rate of growth is then too rapid for condition A' to hold. Referring again to equations (4.12) and (4.13), we see that the term in $e^{\alpha T}$ will become dominant and hence that

$$\bar{n}_j(T) \sim B_j e^{\alpha T} \quad (j = 1, 2, 3) \tag{4.25}$$

as $T \to \infty$. The relative expectations $\{a_j(\infty)\}$ are thus given by,

$$\begin{aligned}a_1(\infty) &= (r_4 + \alpha)/(r + r_4 + \alpha) \\ a_2(\infty) &= r(r_4 + \alpha)/(r + r_4 + \alpha)^2 \\ a_3(\infty) &= r^2/(r + r_4 + \alpha)^2.\end{aligned}$$

$$(4.26)$$

These expressions should be compared with those derived from equations (4.23), (4.24) and (4.25); the latter are obtained from equation (4.26) by deleting α. *The effect of the rapid rate of growth is to increase the relative size of the lowest grade and decrease that of the highest.* In fact if α is very large the lowest grade becomes dominant as we observed with the discrete time model. In the limit as $\alpha \to \infty$, $\mathbf{a}(\infty) \to \mathbf{p}_0$ which, in the present example is $(1, 0, 0)'$.

5. GENERALIZATION TO THE CASE WHERE THE LOSS RATE IS A FUNCTION OF LENGTH OF SERVICE

5.1. Basic Theory

In the theory of continuous Markov processes which we formulated in Chapter 4, the transition intensities were functions of time. The basic equations for the transition probabilities and the expected grade sizes for the general case were given in equations (3.5) and (3.6) of Chapter 4. In the remainder of that chapter we considered only the special case where the transition intensities were constant. This assumption appeared to be sufficient for the applications which were made there. In the context of the hierarchical systems considered here the time parameter refers to the length of service or seniority of an individual member. In assuming that the transition intensities are constant we are supposing that promotion policies and decisions to leave an organization are independent of length of service. Both assumptions seem implausible but there is little firm evidence on the way in which promotion rates depend on seniority. On the other hand, there is a large body of data to show (see Chapter 6) that the leaving intensity is not constant but decreases as length of service increases. We therefore proceed to investigate the effect of relaxing the assumption of a constant loss rate.

General methods are available for the solution of the basic equations of the Markov process. It is easy to obtain an explicit solution in one case which is of particular interest to us. To do this we restrict attention to systems in which there are no demotions. The matrix $\mathbf{R}(T)$ is then triangular. The next step is to consider an organization of k grades; those who leave the system are considered, as before, to be in state S_{k+1}. Finally we suppose that all transition intensities are constants except for those into S_{k+1}. The latter intensities are supposed to depend only on length of service and not on the grade of the individual. The matrix of transition intensities thus has the following form:

$$\mathbf{R}(T) = \begin{pmatrix} r_{11}(T) & 0 & . & . & . & . & . & 0 & 0 \\ r_{12} & r_{22}(T) & & & & & & & . \\ . & . & . & & & & & & . \\ . & & . & . & & & & & . \\ . & & & . & . & & & & . \\ . & & & & . & . & & & . \\ . & & & & & . & . & & . \\ r_{1k} & r_{2k} & . & . & . & . & . & r_{kk}(T) & 0 \\ r_{k+1}(T) & r_{k+1}(T) & . & . & . & . & r_{k+1}(T) & 0 \end{pmatrix} \quad (5.1)$$

The differential equations for the transition probabilities $\{p_{ij}(T)\}$ are thus

$$\frac{dp_{ij}(T)}{dT} = \sum_{h=1}^{j-1} r_{hj}p_{ih}(T) + r_{jj}(T)p_{ij}(T) \quad \begin{pmatrix} i = 1, 2, \ldots, k \\ j = 1, 2, \ldots, k \end{pmatrix} \quad (5.2)$$

$$\frac{dp_{i,k+1}(T)}{dT} = \sum_{h=1}^{k} r_{k+1}(T)p_{ih}(T)$$

$$= r_{k+1}(T)(1 - p_{i,k+1}(T)) \quad (i = 1, 2, \ldots, k). \quad (5.3)$$

The set of equations given by equation (5.3) can be solved immediately, using the initial condition $p_{i,k+1}(0) = 0$, to give

$$p_{i,k+1}(T) = 1 - \exp\left\{-\int_0^T r_{k+1}(x)dx\right\} \quad (i = 1, 2, \ldots, k). \quad (5.4)$$

This probability is, of course, the distribution function of completed length of service and it could have been found directly. In fact the appropriate choice of $r_{k+1}(T)$ for a given problem would usually be made on the basis of the observed distribution $p_{i,k+1}(T)$.

The system of equations (5.2) cannot be solved in the manner of Chapter 4 because some of its coefficients are not constants. It can, however, be transformed into a set which has constant coefficients as follows. Let

$$\left.\begin{aligned} r'_{ij} &= r_{ij} \quad (i \neq j) \\ r'_{jj} &= r_{jj}(T) + r_{k+1}(T) \quad (j = 1, 2, \ldots, k). \end{aligned}\right\} \quad (5.5)$$

Note that r'_{jj} is a constant for all j in consequence of the definition of $r_{jj}(T)$. We introduce a new set of probabilities, denoted by $\{p'_{ij}(T)\}$, as follows

$$p_{ij}(T) = p'_{ij}(T)\{1 - p_{i,k+1}(T)\} \quad (i, j = 1, 2, \ldots, k). \quad (5.6)$$

The probability $p'_{ij}(T)$ defined in equation (5.6) is the conditional probability of the transition from grade i to grade j in $(0, T)$ given that no loss occurs in the same interval. Substituting from equation (5.6) into equation (5.2), we obtain

$$\frac{dp'_{ij}(T)}{dT} = \sum_{h=1}^{j} r'_{hj}p'_{ih}(T) \quad (i, j = 1, 2, \ldots, k). \quad (5.7)$$

This system of equations can be solved by the methods of the last chapter. By first finding $p'_{ij}(T)$ from equation (5.7) we are able to determine $p_{ij}(T)$ from equation (5.6).

If the probabilities $\{p_{ij}(T)\}$ have been computed for the system on the assumption of a constant loss rate it is a simple matter to obtain the

probabilities for a time-dependent loss rate. To illustrate the procedure
let $i = 1$. Then we may write

$$p'_{1j}(T) = \sum_{h=1}^{k} c'_{jh} e^{r'_{hh}T} \quad (j = 1, 2, \ldots, k). \tag{5.8}$$

Reference to equation (2.10) shows that the coefficients $\{c'_{jh}\}$ are the same
as those for the system with constant loss rate because $r_{jj} - r_{hh} = r'_{jj} - r'_{hh}$
and $r_{j,j+1} = r'_{j,j+1}$. Using equation (5.6) we then have

$$p_{1j}(T) = \sum_{h=1}^{k} c_{jh} \exp \left\{ r'_{hh}T - \int_{0}^{T} r_{k+1}(x)\mathrm{d}x \right\} \tag{5.9}$$

where the coefficients $\{c_{jh}\}$ are those previously computed on the basis of a
constant loss rate. The only alteration required by our generalization is in
the form of the exponent where $r_{hh}T$ is replaced by

$$r'_{hh}T - \int_{0}^{T} r_{k+1}(x)\mathrm{d}x.$$

5.2. Illustration of the Theory

We are now in a position to assess the likely consequences of erroneously
assuming the loss rate to be constant. We shall illustrate the procedure
using the example first introduced in Section 2.2. In that case we took
$k = 3$, $r_{12} = r_{23} = r = 1$ and $r_{14} = r_{24} = r_{34} = r_4 = 2$. The discussion
will be confined to the case of a constant rate of input with $R = 100$ and
will be concerned solely with the limiting grade structure $\bar{n}(\infty)$. We first
note that the expected total size of the system depends only on the mean of
the distribution of completed length of service. We shall therefore choose
$r_4(T)$ to be such that the mean length of stay in the system is $\frac{1}{2}$ as before.
In the case of a constant loss rate the length of stay has an exponential
distribution. In our examples below we shall consider two extreme departures from this form.

Consider first a mixed exponential distribution with density function

$$f(T) = \tfrac{1}{2}\{\lambda_1 e^{-\lambda_1 T} + \lambda_2 e^{-\lambda_2 T}\}. \tag{5.10}$$

In order that this shall give the same mean length of service as the earlier
example we must choose λ_1 and λ_2 to satisfy

$$\lambda_1^{-1} + \lambda_2^{-1} = 1. \tag{5.11}$$

To obtain the transition probabilities from those already found for a constant loss rate we require the result that, for the distribution of equation (5.10),

$$\exp\left\{-\int_0^T r_{k+1}(x)dx\right\} = \tfrac{1}{2}\{e^{-\lambda_1 T} + e^{-\lambda_2 T}\}.$$

The case $\lambda_1 = \lambda_2 = 2$ yields the formulae for the exponential distribution of length of stay. Making the necessary substitutions in equation (5.9), we find

$$\left.\begin{aligned}
\bar{n}_1(\infty) &= 50\left\{\frac{1}{\lambda_1 + 1} + \frac{\lambda_1 - 1}{2\lambda_1 - 1}\right\} \\
\bar{n}_2(\infty) &= 50\left\{\frac{1}{(\lambda_1 + 1)^2} + \frac{(\lambda_1 - 1)^2}{(2\lambda_1 - 1)^2}\right\} \\
\bar{n}_3(\infty) &= 50 - \bar{n}_1(\infty) - \bar{n}_2(\infty)
\end{aligned}\right\} \qquad (5.12)$$

where λ_2 has been eliminated using equation (5.11) and $\lambda_1 \geq 1$. As λ_1 varies between 1 and infinity, $\bar{\mathbf{n}}(\infty)$ takes on all its possible values. It may readily be shown that the expected grade sizes given in equation (5.12) have extreme values at $\lambda_1 = 2$, which is the exponential case at $\lambda_1 = 1$ and at $\lambda_1 = \infty$. The last two cases are equivalent because $f(T)$ is symmetrical in λ_1 and λ_2. The extreme structures attainable are given in the first two columns of Table 5.1. We shall discuss the results below.

At the opposite extreme to that considered in the last paragraph we may suppose that the length of stay is a constant. That is we take

$$\left.\begin{aligned}
r_4(T) &= 0, \quad T \leq r_4^{-1} \\
&= \infty, \quad T > r_4^{-1}.
\end{aligned}\right\} \qquad (5.13)$$

In this case, with $r_4 = 2$, the limiting grade sizes will be given by

$$\bar{n}_j(\infty) = 100\int_0^{\frac{1}{2}} p_{1j}^0(x)dx \quad (j = 1, 2, 3), \qquad (5.14)$$

where $p_{1j}^0(x)$ is obtained from equation (2.13) by setting $r_{k+1} = 0$. The range of integration is restricted because

$$\exp\left\{-\int_0^T r_4(x)dx\right\} = 0 \quad \text{for } T > \tfrac{1}{2}.$$

Substituting the numerical values for r we obtain

$$\left.\begin{aligned}
\bar{n}_1(\infty) &= 100(1 - e^{-\frac{1}{2}}) = 39.4 \\
\bar{n}_2(\infty) &= 100(1 - \tfrac{3}{2}\,e^{-\frac{1}{2}}) = 9.0 \\
\bar{n}_3(\infty) &= 50 - \bar{n}_1(\infty) - \bar{n}_2(\infty) = 1.6.
\end{aligned}\right\} \qquad (5.15)$$

The foregoing results are brought together in the following table.

TABLE 5.1

Grade structures for the example under various
extreme assumptions about the loss intensity.

	$\lambda_1 \to 1$ or ∞	$\lambda_1 = 2$	Fixed length of stay
$\bar{n}_1(\infty)$	25.0	33.3	39.4
$\bar{n}_2(\infty)$	12.5	11.1	9.0
$\bar{n}_3(\infty)$	12.5	5.6	1.5
$N(\infty)$	50.0	50.0	50.0

The figures in Table 5.1 represent, in a certain sense, the greatest variation in structure that can occur. They relate only to one particular example
but calculations for other cases suggest that the general pattern revealed
here is typical. It can be seen from the table that the greater the variability of the length of service distribution the greater the size of the
highest grade. In absolute terms, the change in the highest grade is roughly
balanced by that in the lowest, but in relative terms, the highest grade
depends most critically on the assumption of constant loss rate. In practice,
length of service distributions have been found to be highly skew and they
have been successfully graduated by mixed exponential distributions.
With constant promotion rates we would therefore expect the limiting
structure to be more like that in the first column of the table with a relatively large number of members in the highest grade. *Any factor which
tends to increase the variability of length of service with the mean held
constant is therefore likely to increase the size of the higher grades at the
expense of the lower.*

In the preceding discussion we have considered a constant rate of input.
We would have reached similar conclusions had we dealt with expanding
organizations with rate of growth satisfying condition A', because the
limiting structures are the same in both cases. A fuller generalization
allowing the promotion rates to depend on length of stay would be of
great interest.

6. GENERALIZATION TO THE CASE WHERE THE PROMOTION RATE DEPENDS ON SENIORITY WITHIN THE GRADE

6.1. A Direct Approach

All of our conclusions so far in this chapter rest on the assumption of
constant promotion rates. Common knowledge about the way in which
large organizations operate suggests that this is an oversimplification. Of

the many variables which may influence a person's chance of promotion the length of service in his current grade is perhaps the most important. We shall therefore abandon the assumption of constant promotion intensities in favour of one which makes them depend upon seniority within the grade.

Our general line of approach in this chapter has been to solve the equations of the associated closed system to obtain the transition probabilities and these have then been substituted in equation (2.1) or equation (4.2), to obtain the expected grade sizes. The mathematics have been relatively simple because the closed system possessed the Markov property. This remained true under the generalization discussed in Section 5. Once the transition intensities are made to depend on seniority within the grade the future of the system no longer depends only on its present state but also requires a knowledge of the seniority structure of the grades. This feature greatly increases the mathematical complexity of the problem but some useful results can be obtained using a direct approach.

We consider initially a closed system of hierarchical form in which promotion is into the next highest grade and recruitment is into the lowest. The only transition probabilities that we require are then $p_{1j}(T)$ ($j = 1, 2, \ldots, k$), where k is the number of grades. When these have been found we can go back to equation (2.1) or equation (4.2), as the case may be, and obtain the expected grade sizes for the open system in which we are interested. Let $r_{j,j+1}(\tau)$ ($j = 1, 2, \ldots, k - 1$) denote the promotion intensity from grade j to grade $j + 1$ for a person who entered grade j a time τ ago. As before $r_{j,k+1}(T)$ is the intensity of loss for an individual with present length of service T. It is now possible to set up an integral equation for $p_{1j}(T)$ as follows. Consider first the case $j = 1$; $p_{11}(T)$ is the probability that an entrant to grade 1 has neither been promoted or lost in time T. The total intensity acting on a member of grade 1 at time T is $r_{12}(T) + r_{1,k+1}(T)$ and hence

$$p_{11}(T) = \exp\left\{-\int_0^T (r_{12}(x) + r_{1,k+1}(x))\mathrm{d}x\right\}. \tag{6.1}$$

The case $j = 2$ is now approached by observing that $p_{12}(T)$ may be written

$$p_{12}(T) = \int_0^T p_{11}(x)r_{12}(x)p_{22}(T - x)\mathrm{d}x. \tag{6.2}$$

We obtain this expression by first computing the probability conditional upon x, the time of transfer to grade 2, and then integrating over x from 0 to T. The probability $p_{22}(T - x)$ is obtained in a manner similar to that used for $p_{11}(T)$. The total intensity at time T acting on a person who entered grade 2 at time $T - \tau$ is $r_{2,k+1}(T) + r_{23}(\tau)$ and hence

$$p_{22}(T - x) = \exp\left\{-\int_{T-\tau}^{T} (r_{2,k+1}(y) + r_{23}(y - T + \tau))dy\right\}. \qquad (6.3)$$

In general we have

$$p_{1j}(T) = \int_{0}^{T} p_{11}(x)r_{12}(x)p_{2j}(T - x)dx \quad (j = 2, 3, \ldots, k). \qquad (6.4)$$

The probabilities $\{p_{1j}(T)\}$ may be obtained recursively since $p_{2j}(T - x)$ can obviously be found from $p_{1,j-1}(T)$ as in the case $j = 2$ above.

Equations (6.1) and (6.4) provide, in principle, the means of obtaining a complete solution to the problem. In practice it is not easy to obtain explicit solutions especially for large values of j. Since we shall present an alternative method which is sufficiently general for most purposes a detailed discussion of these integral equations will not be necessary. The chief value of the direct approach is that it easily yields a general solution for $j = 1$ which, in turn, leads to $\bar{n}_1(T)$. We shall now use it for that purpose.

Suppose that there is a maximum time that may be spent in the lowest grade. If promotion or loss has not occurred by that time then promotion follows automatically. Such an assumption requires that the promotion intensity $r_{12}(\tau)$ becomes infinite at $\tau = b$, where b is the maximum length of service in the grade. A simple, increasing function of length of service having this property was suggested by Vajda (1947) who took

$$r_{12}(\tau) = c/(b - \tau) \quad (0 \le \tau < b; c > 0). \qquad (6.5)$$

We shall assume that the loss intensity has a similar form with

$$r_{1,k+1}(\tau) = u/(v - \tau) \quad (0 \le \tau < v; u > 0), \qquad (6.6)$$

where v is the maximum time that can be spent in the organization. (In grade 1 total length of service and seniority within the grade are synonymous. Hence we may use either T or τ to denote it.) If equation (6.6) obtains, the length of completed service distribution associated with this loss rate has density function

$$f(\tau) = \frac{u}{v}\left(1 - \frac{\tau}{v}\right)^{u-1} \quad 0 \le \tau < v \qquad (6.7)$$

and the mean length of service is

$$\mu = v/(u + 1). \qquad (6.8)$$

Under the foregoing assumptions we find from equation (6.1) that

$$p_{11}(T) = \left(\frac{b - T}{b}\right)^{c}\left(\frac{v - T}{v}\right)^{u} \quad (0 \le T < \min(b, v)). \qquad (6.9)$$

The expected size of the lowest grade may now be found by substituting from equation (6.9) into equation (2.1). Assuming a constant rate of input we have, for the kind of hierarchy being considered in this section,

$$
\begin{aligned}
\bar{n}_1(T) &= R \int_0^T \left(1 - \frac{x}{b}\right)^c \left(1 - \frac{x}{v}\right)^u dx + n_1(0) \left(1 - \frac{T}{b}\right)^c \left(1 - \frac{T}{v}\right)^u \\
&\hspace{4cm} (0 \le T < \min(b, v)) \\
&= R \int_0^{\min(b,v)} \left(1 - \frac{x}{b}\right)^c \left(1 - \frac{x}{v}\right)^u dx \quad (\min(b, v) \le T < \infty).
\end{aligned}
\right\} \quad (6.10)
$$

It is obvious from equation (6.10) that the limiting value of $\bar{n}_1(T)$ is attained at $T = \min(b, v)$ and is given by the second of the two integrals.

We may now compare these results with those obtained when we assumed constant promotion and loss rates. To do this meaningfully we must arrange that the Markov system has the same average length of stay as the one considered above. This is achieved by taking

$$r_{1,k+1} = (u + 1)/v, \quad r_{12} = (c + 1)/b. \tag{6.11}$$

If we restrict the comparison to the limiting case we have shown that, for the Markov system, $\bar{n}_1(\infty) = R/(r_{12} + r_{1,k+1})$. This has to be compared with the second expression in equation (6.10), which may now be written

$$\bar{n}_1(\infty) = \int_0^{\min(b,v)} \left(1 - \frac{x}{b}\right)^{r_{12}b-1} \left(1 - \frac{x}{v}\right)^{r_{1,k+1}v-1} dx. \tag{6.12}$$

If both v and b tend to infinity

$$\bar{n}_1(\infty) \to R \int_0^\infty e^{-x(r_{12}+r_{1,k+1})} dx = R/(r_{12} + r_{1,k+1})$$

which agrees with the known result for constant transition rates. The greatest divergence between the two assumptions will occur when b and v are both small. The extreme case occurs when

$$b = r_{12}^{-1} \quad \text{and} \quad v = r_{1,k+1}^{-1}$$

(smaller values of b or v would make u or c negative). In this case

$$\bar{n}_1(\infty) = R \min(r_{12}^{-1}, r_{1,k+1}^{-1}). \tag{6.13}$$

It thus follows that, for any system with transition rates given by equations (6.5) and (6.6),

$$R/(r_{12} + r_{1,k+1}) \le \bar{n}_1(\infty) \le R \min(r_{12}^{-1}, r_{1,k+1}^{-1}). \tag{6.14}$$

The effect of making promotion chances increase with length of service is thus to increase the expected size of the lowest grade. Since the total

5

expected size does not depend on the form of the promotion intensity we further conclude that the *relative* expected size of the lowest grade will also be increased.

As b and v increase, the approach to the lower bound of the inequalities (6.14) is quite rapid as may be seen from the fact that when $b = v$

$$\bar{n}_1(\infty) = R/(r_{12} + r_{1,k+1} - v^{-1}). \tag{6.15}$$

We may therefore conclude that the assumption of a constant promotion intensity may not be crucial at least for the lowest grade. This investigation could be pursued for the second lowest grade but we shall use an alternative method.

6.2. A Method Involving Hypothetical Grades

This method has been widely adopted in the theory of queues for dealing with non-Markovian systems. In essence it involves the replacement of the actual system by a Markov system of greater complexity. It depends on the following argument. Suppose that we have two grades in series with constant promotion rates as shown in the diagram and that there are no losses.

The lengths of stay in stages I and II will be exponential with means $1/r'_{12}$ and $1/r'_{23}$ respectively. Suppose now that the transitions between I and II are not observable and that the members of the two grades cannot be distinguished. The distribution of length of stay for the combined grade is thus the sum of two independent exponential variates. There is little loss in generality if we assume that $r'_{12} = r'_{23} = r$, say, in which case the length of service in the combined grade has density function

$$f(T) = r^2 T e^{-rT} \quad (T \geq 0). \tag{6.16}$$

Promotions from the combined grade will now appear *as if* the promotion rate was

$$r_{12}(T) = f(T) \bigg/ \int_T^\infty f(x)\mathrm{d}x = r\left(\frac{rT}{rT + 1}\right)$$

$$= 2r_{12}\left(\frac{r_{12}T}{r_{12}T + \frac{1}{2}}\right) \tag{6.17}$$

where r_{12} is the constant rate which would lead to the same mean length of stay. We have thus produced a Markov system which behaves, when viewed in a particular way, as a non-Markov system with $r_{12}(T)$ given by equation (6.17).

The argument just given may be generalized. Instead of two stages we may consider g stages for which we find

$$f(T) = \frac{r^g}{(g-1)!} T^{g-1} e^{-rT} \quad T \geq 0. \tag{6.18}$$

Under these circumstances $r_{12}(T)$ is always an increasing function of T with rate of increase depending on g and it always tends to a limit as $T \to \infty$.

The method we adopt is to replace each grade of the actual system by an appropriate number, g, of what will be termed sub-grades. The loss rates must be the same for each sub-grade within a given grade. The expected sizes of the sub-grades are determined by the standard theory for Markov processes. Those for the actual grades are then simply obtained by summation over the relevant sub-grades. We illustrate the method on the kind of simple hierarchy discussed in Section 2.2 for the case of constant transition rates. Again we restrict attention to the limiting behaviour. Let us assume that the loss rate is the same for all grades and denoted by r_{k+1} and that there is a constant rate of input R. Although not necessary, it is convenient to assume that the same value of g is appropriate for each grade. Our system is to be replaced by one of gk grades with constant and equal promotion intensities. To facilitate comparison with the results given in equation (2.21) we denote these intensities by gr. Let $\bar{z}_j(\infty)$ denote the limiting expected size of the jth sub-grade; it may be obtained from equation (2.21) by replacing r by rg, and k by gk, thus

$$\left. \begin{aligned} \bar{z}_j(\infty) &= \frac{R}{gr} \left(\frac{gr}{gr + r_{k+1}} \right)^j \quad (j = 1, 2, \ldots, gk - 1) \\ \bar{z}_{gk}(\infty) &= \frac{R}{r_{k+1}} \left(\frac{gr}{gr + rk} \right)^{gk-1}. \end{aligned} \right\} \tag{6.19}$$

The expected number in the jth grade of the original organization is then

$$\left. \begin{aligned} \bar{n}_j(\infty) &= \frac{R}{gr} \sum_{i=g(j-1)+1}^{gj} \left(\frac{gr}{gr + r_{k+1}} \right)^i \\ &= \frac{R}{r_{k+1}} \left(\frac{gr}{gr + r_{k+1}} \right)^{g(j-1)} \left\{ 1 - \left(\frac{gr}{gr + r_{k+1}} \right)^g \right\} \\ &\qquad\qquad (j = 1, 2, \ldots, k - 1). \end{aligned} \right\} \tag{6.20}$$

If $g = 1$, equation (6.20) reduces to the expression given in equation (2.21) for constant promotion rates. By increasing g we increase the dependence of promotion on length of service in the grade. In the extreme case as $g \to \infty$ all promotions take place after a fixed length of service r^{-1} when we find

$$\left.\begin{aligned}
\bar{n}_j(\infty) &= \frac{R}{r_{k+1}} \exp\left\{-\frac{r_{k+1}}{r}(j-1)\right\}\left[1 - \exp\left\{-\frac{r_{k+1}}{r}\right\}\right] \\
&\hspace{4cm} (j = 1, 2, \ldots, k-1) \\
\bar{n}_k(\infty) &= R/r_{k+1} - \sum_{j=1}^{k-1} \bar{n}_j(\infty).
\end{aligned}\right\} \quad (6.21)$$

An interesting feature revealed by equations (6.20) and (6.21) is that the relative expected grade sizes, except the last, form a geometric progression whatever g. The constant factor of the progression varies between $(1 + r_{k+1}/r)$ for the constant promotion intensity and $\exp(-r_{k+1}/r)$ for promotion after fixed length of service. Some numerical values are given in Table 5.2.

TABLE 5.2

Comparison of the constant factors appropriate for the
two extreme promotion rules.

r_{k+1}/r	2	1	$\frac{1}{2}$	$\frac{1}{5}$	0
$\left(1 + \dfrac{r_{k+1}}{r}\right)^{-1}$	0.333	0.500	0.667	0.833	1.000
$\exp\left\{-\dfrac{r_{k+1}}{r}\right\}$	0.135	0.368	0.607	0.819	1.000

The importance of the assumption about the promotion rates thus depends upon the ratio r_{k+1}/r. If the ratio is small, meaning that promotion is much more likely than loss, the assumption is not critical. On the other hand, if r_{k+1}/r is large the kind of assumption we make will be much more important. This point is illustrated by Table 5.3 where we have compared grade structures for high and low values of the ratio.

The effect of making the promotion intensities increasing functions of seniority is to increase the relative sizes of the lower groups at the expense of the higher. A similar result was obtained when we allowed the loss rate to depend on total length of service. Another similarity between the two cases is that the size of the higher grades depends more critically on the assumptions. In general, therefore, we may expect the Markov model to over-estimate the sizes of the higher grades and under-estimate the lower.

TABLE 5.3

The relative grade structures $\mathbf{a}(\infty)$ for promotion after a
fixed or random length of stay when $k = 4$.

	Grade	1	2	3	4
$\dfrac{r_{k+1}}{r} = 2$	Random	0.667	0.222	0.074	0.037
	Fixed	0.865	0.117	0.016	0.002
$\dfrac{r_{k+1}}{r} = \frac{1}{2}$	Random	0.333	0.222	0.148	0.296
	Fixed	0.393	0.239	0.145	0.223

Although it seems more realistic to suppose that promotion rates are
increasing functions of seniority the method of sub-stages can be adapted
for use when they are decreasing functions. One way of doing this is to
set up Markov systems with grades in *parallel*.† The idea can be demonstrated on the following system with two stages in parallel and constant
transition intensities.

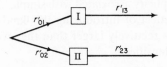

The length of stay of those members passing through I will be exponential
with parameter r'_{13}. Those who pass through II will have an exponential
length of stay distribution with parameter r'_{23}. If we are unable to distinguish
the two stages the apparent density function of length of stay will be a mixture of the two exponential densities. More precisely, using the lemma
given in Section 4.2 of Chapter 4, the density function will be

$$f(T) = \left(\frac{r'_{01}}{r'_{01} + r'_{02}}\right) r'_{13} e^{-r'_{13}T} + \left(\frac{r'_{02}}{r'_{01} + r'_{02}}\right) r'_{23} e^{-r'_{23}T}, \quad (T \geq 0). \quad (6.22)$$

It can easily be shown that

$$f(T) \bigg/ \int_T^\infty f(x)\,\mathrm{d}x$$

is a strictly decreasing function of T for this distribution and it is the
apparent intensity of loss for the combined grades.

† Another way, suggested by Professor Coleman, is to replace the single stage by a
'well' or 'cul-de-sac' of sub-grades. An individual enters the well, executes a random
walk within it until he returns to the entrance and leaves. The possibilities of this method
remain to be explored.

We now show how this result may be used to study a three-grade hierarchy with promotion intensities of the kind leading to the density function of equation (6.22). Consider the following Markov system with possible routes of transfer indicated by arrows.

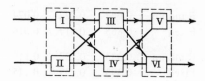

Each pair of grades within the dotted rectangles is assumed to have the same loss rate. If the rectangles represent the grades of the actual system, the Markov system sketched above will have decreasing promotion intensities when its sub-grades are combined. The transition rates can be chosen to give the required average throughputs both for the individual grades and for the system as a whole. It should be noticed that the matrix of transition intensities arising from the system described above is triangular so that much of the simplicity associated with simple hierarchical systems is retained. The general effect of introducing this kind of dependence is to make the higher grades relatively larger than they would have been with constant promotion intensities.

CHAPTER 6

RECRUITMENT AND WASTAGE IN
SYSTEMS WITH GIVEN
TOTAL SIZE

1. INTRODUCTION

In Chapters 3 and 5 we have given models for organizations whose present and future size is fixed in advance. To solve those models we had to determine the number of recruits required to achieve the target size. This, however, was merely an intermediate step on the way to finding the expected grade sizes which were our main interest. In the present chapter we shall consider the recruitment and loss aspects of these systems in more detail. Our main object now is to provide formulae for predicting recruitment needs and wastage under a variety of assumptions about the behaviour of the system. We shall assume throughout the chapter that the loss intensities are independent of the grades. This assumption enables us to ignore internal movements when calculating overall figures of gain and loss.

In addition to their use for prediction, our results have important implications for the interpretation of crude labour wastage, or turnover, figures. Labour wastage figures are calculated in many organizations and they are often regarded as a barometer of morale or stability within the organization. A high wastage figure is interpreted as a symptom of low morale and, conversely, a low wastage figure is taken to be a favourable sign. The renewal theory model will be used in this chapter to demonstrate the limitations of the crude index of turnover and to direct attention to more adequate measures based on the length of service distribution.

The two fundamental factors on which the recruitment and wastage figures depend are the changes in the total size of the organization and the loss intensities of its members. We have already seen that an individual's completed length of service distribution is an alternative, but equivalent way of expressing his loss intensity. In this chapter we shall find it to be the more convenient representation. For brevity we shall refer to this distribution as the *CLS distribution*. In Section 2 we shall present some empirical CLS distributions and describe the probability models which have been used to account for them. The most striking feature of these distributions is their high degree of positive skewness. Later in the chapter we shall see that this feature is responsible for the slow rate at which our

123

models reach their equilibrium states. Hence it will be necessary to concentrate attention on the transient, rather than the equilibrium, state of the system.

In Section 3 we shall examine the relationship between the CLS distribution and the crude figures of wastage and recruitment. We shall begin by supposing that the size of the organization is fixed because under these circumstances the wastage and recruitment figures in any period will be the same. Exact and approximate formulae will be given for the expectations, and in some cases the variances of the number of recruits required. Initially, it will be assumed that the CLS distribution is unchanging in form but, at a later stage, we shall allow its parameters to be functions of the age of the system. A case of special interest arises when an abrupt change occurs in the form of the CLS distribution as a result of a new recruitment policy.

When the total size remains constant, the system is equivalent to the so-called 'self-renewing aggregate' of renewal theory. Not surprisingly the relevant theory developed in Chapter 5 reduces, in this case, to well-known results of renewal theory. These, in turn, will form the basis of the models of Chapter 7 where we shall consider hierarchical organizations with *fixed* grade sizes. Thus this chapter forms a link between the models of Chapter 5 in which the promotion rates were fixed and those of Chapter 7 where the grade sizes will be fixed. Provided that we are interested only in the total input or output the present model is applicable in either situation.

The effect of growth or contraction of the system on the recruitment and wastage rates will be explored in Section 4. The analysis of an expanding organization, begun in Chapter 5, will be continued. We shall also extend the theory of that chapter to the case of a contracting organization. One interesting problem which then arises is to find the conditions under which natural wastage is sufficient to achieve the required rate of run-down.

It is possible to develop the theory in either discrete or continuous time. The continuous version is easier to handle analytically and it leads on naturally to the more elaborate models of the next chapter. Hence, apart from one brief digression, our treatment will be wholly in terms of the continuous time model.

2. MODELS FOR THE LEAVING PROCESS

On various occasions in the course of the last three chapters we have had to specify the form of loss intensities or probabilities. Since these quantities play a fundamental role in this and the following chapter it will be convenient at this point to review the probability models which have been proposed for the leaving process.

Rice, Hill and Trist (1950) published several empirical CLS distributions obtained in their studies at the Glacier Metal Company. They observed that the distributions could be graduated by smooth J-shaped curves but they did not put forward any theoretical model to account for this phenomenon. Silcock (1954) reviewed the literature on turnover up to that date and proposed two models to account for observed CLS distributions. His first model was suggested by a remark of Rice and others (1950) to the effect that they had found a regularity in the turnover pattern which appeared to be characteristic of the firm and independent of economic and social forces operating outside the firm. Silcock interpreted this as implying a constant 'force of separation' or loss intensity. If this were the case the CLS distribution would, of course, be exponential as we have already seen. Although it seems doubtful whether such a strong interpretation is justified it does provide a testable hypothesis about the nature of the leaving process. The exponential distribution was fitted by Silcock to several CLS distributions and, in every case, the fit was very poor. Two examples are given in Table 6.1 from which it can be seen that the observed distribution is always more skew than the fitted exponential.

The truncation of the distribution at 21 months makes it impossible to investigate the form of the upper tail but it is clear from the data available that the exponential hypothesis is not tenable.

The second model proposed by Silcock (1954) is a generalization of the first. The assumption of a constant loss rate for each individual is retained but the rate is supposed to vary in the population from which employees are drawn. This seems a very plausible hypothesis in view of the individual differences which manifest themselves in almost all aspects of human behaviour. Let us denote the loss intensity by λ so that, for any individual, the CLS distribution has density function

$$f(T) = \lambda e^{-\lambda T} \quad (\lambda > 0, \, T \geq 0).$$

We now treat λ as a random variable and denote its distribution function by $H(\lambda)$. The observed CLS distribution will therefore have the density function

$$f(T) = \int_0^\infty \lambda e^{-\lambda T} dH(\lambda) \quad (T \geq 0). \tag{2.1}$$

This distribution is always more skew than the exponential distribution with the same mean and it therefore has the main characteristic demanded by our data. A partial justification of this conclusion is obtained by considering the value of the density at the origin. From equation (2.1),

$$f(0) = \int_0^\infty \lambda dH(\lambda) \tag{2.2}$$

TABLE 6.1

Observed and fitted CLS distributions for two firms.

Length of Completed Service	Glacier Metal Co. (1944–1947)				J. Bibby & Sons Ltd. (Males, 1950)			
	Actual Number of Leavers	Exponential Fit	Type XI Fit	Mixed Exponential Fit	Actual Number of Leavers	Exponential Fit	Type XI Fit	Mixed Exponential Fit
Under 3 months	242	160.2	242.0	242.0†	182	103.9	195.4	182.0†
3 months	152	138.9	150.3	152.0†	103	86.8	87.5	103.0†
6 months	104	120.4	103.8	101.4	60	72.4	51.8	60.7
9 months	73	104.5	76.5	72.7	29	60.5	35.0	38.0
12 months	52	90.6	59.2	55.8	31	50.5	25.6	25.5
15 months	47	78.5	47.4	45.7	23	42.1	19.7	18.6
18 months	49	68.1	38.8	39.2	10	35.2	15.8	14.7
21 months and over	487	444.8	488.0	497.2	191	177.6	198.2	186.5
Total	1206	1206.0	1206.0	1206.0	629	629.0	629.0	629.0

† These figures agree exactly with those observed because the distribution was fitted by equating percentage points. For further details see Bartholomew (1959).

which is the arithmetic mean of $H(\lambda)$. The mean of the distribution given in equation (2.1) is easily shown to be

$$\mu = \int_0^\infty \lambda^{-1} dH(\lambda). \tag{2.3}$$

The zero ordinate of the exponential distribution having mean λ as given by equation (2.3) is μ^{-1} which is the harmonic mean of $H(\lambda)$. Since the arithmetic mean is never less than the harmonic mean it follows that the density function of equation (2.1) has the greater zero ordinate.

In order to fit the distribution we must specify $H(\lambda)$. Silcock (1954) chose a gamma distribution with density function

$$\frac{dH(\lambda)}{d\lambda} = \frac{c^\nu}{\Gamma(\nu)} \lambda^{\nu-1} e^{-c\lambda} \quad (\nu > 0, \, c > 0, \, \lambda \geq 0) \tag{2.4}$$

and hence showed that

$$f(T) = \frac{\nu}{c} \left(1 + \frac{T}{c}\right)^{-(\nu+1)} \quad (T \geq 0). \tag{2.5}$$

This is a J-shaped distribution of the Pearson family in which it is classified as Type XI. When Silcock (1954) fitted this distribution to his data the agreement with the empirical distribution was much improved. Some of Silcock's calculations are given in Table 6.1 under the heading 'Type XI' fit.

The gamma distribution for λ used above is quite flexible depending as it does on two parameters. Its main advantage in the present context is its mathematical tractability. However, the particular functional form which we adopt is not crucial. For some purposes it is simpler to suppose that λ can take only two values which we will denote by λ_1 and λ_2. If the associated probabilities are p and $1 - p$ respectively the overall CLS distribution will be

$$f(T) = p\lambda_1 e^{-\lambda_1 T} + (1 - p)\lambda_2 e^{-\lambda_2 T} \quad (0 < p < 1, \, \lambda_1, \, \lambda_2 > 0; \, T \geq 0). \tag{2.6}$$

This is the mixed exponential distribution used in earlier chapters. It was fitted by Bartholomew (1959) to the data used by Silcock and some of the results are given in Table 6.1. There is very little to choose between the Type XI and mixed exponential distributions in these examples in spite of the radical difference in form of $H(\lambda)$ in the two cases.

It cannot be concluded from the foregoing analysis that the 'mixture' models proposed by Silcock (1954) give a true explanation of the situation. There are other models which give equally good agreement with the data and at least one of them gives the same functional form for $f(T)$.

An example of the latter is provided by the decision process model for organizational commitment of Herbst (1963) which was discussed in Chapter 4. According to that model there is no difference between individuals. Instead, the loss intensity for each person changes as he moves from one psychological state to another. Assuming constant transition rates we saw that the CLS distribution for the whole system had the form

$$f(T) = \sum_{i=1}^{k} p_i \lambda_i e^{-\lambda_i T} \quad (T \geq 0), \qquad (2.7)$$

where $\sum_{i=1}^{k} p_i = 1$.

This distribution belongs to the family given by equation (2.1) if the p's are non-negative. In general, this need not be so. Herbst (1963) showed that the density given by equation (2.6) could arise as a special case of his model. As we saw in Table 4.2, Herbst's model provides an excellent fit to Hedberg's (1961) data. There is no statistical means of discriminating between the models of Silcock and Herbst if we only have data on length of service.

A third type of distribution has been extensively used to graduate CLS distributions. This work originated in a paper by Lane and Andrew (1955) who demonstrated that the lognormal distribution provided a good fit to their data. On this hypothesis $\log T_e$ is normally distributed with mean which we will denote by ω and variance σ^2. This distribution has several practical advantages. The chief of these is that it brings the statistical analysis of data within the province of 'normal theory'. It appears that σ is usually in the neighbourhood of 2 and hence many questions can be expressed in terms of the single parameter ω. This parameter has a simple interpretation because e^{ω} is the median or 'half-life' of the distribution. A second advantage of the lognormal form is that it can accommodate a feature of many observed distributions which is not explained by the Silcock model. When lengths of service are recorded with high accuracy it often happens that the histogram of CLS rises steeply to a peak before beginning its characteristic decline. This feature is often obscured by coarse grouping of the data and has, therefore, sometimes been overlooked. Apart from its behaviour near the origin and in the extreme upper tail the lognormal distribution $\sigma = 2$ is not easily distinguishable from members of the mixed exponential family.

Apart from its descriptive value the lognormal distribution can be shown to arise from a plausible model of the leaving process. Aitchison (1955) pointed out that it was a consequence of Kapteyn's law of proportionate effect. In the present context this law implies that the length of time which a person spends in his present job will be a random multiple of the time he spent in his previous job. That is if T_j denotes a man's CLS in his jth job then

$$T_{j+1} = T_j u_{j+1} \quad (j = 1, 2, 3, \ldots), \tag{2.8}$$

where $\{u_2, u_3, \ldots\}$ is a sequence of random variables with known joint distribution. An immediate consequence of equation (2.8) is that

$$\left.\begin{aligned} T_{j+1} &= T_1 \prod_{i=2}^{j+1} u_i \quad (j \geq 1) \\ \log_e T_{j+1} &= \log_e T_1 + \sum_{i=2}^{j+1} \log_e u_i. \end{aligned}\right\} \tag{2.9}$$

or

Provided that the joint distribution of the u's is such that the central limit theorem applies to the sum of their logarithms it follows that, for moderate j, $\log_e T_{j+1}$ is approximately normally distributed. Thus the model predicts that a new recruit who has had several previous jobs will have a CLS distribution which is approximately lognormal.

If the u's have the same joint distribution for all members of the population from which recruits come an important conclusion can be drawn. Suppose that we classify all recruits according to the number of previous jobs that they have had, then within these groups σ, the standard deviation of $\log_e T$, should be constant. On the other hand, the parameter ω, which is the expectation of $\log_e T$, depends on the characteristics of the individual through $\log_e T_1$. Thus if we compare homogenous groups of recruits we would expect any differences between their distributions to show up in the parameter ω. This is precisely what Lane and Andrew (1955) found. The parameter σ was constant and near to 2 for almost all of the groups which they considered but there were subtantial differences in the ω's. In reaching this conclusion we have ignored the fact that the observed distributions have not, in fact, been classified by the number of previous jobs. This omission is less serious than might appear at first sight. We might reasonably expect $E(\log_e u_i)$ to be in the neighbourhood of zero, meaning that u_i has its mean value near to 1, so that ω will depend only slightly upon n. Provided also that n does not vary very much, the shape of the lognormal curve is not likely to be seriously distorted by the heterogeneity introduced through σ.

The lognormal model is like Silcock's in that it incorporates a feature allowing for individual differences in the propensity to leave. In the former model these are reflected in the quantities T_1 which may vary between individuals. The lognormal theory, however, goes further by supposing that these initial characteristics can be modified by subsequent job experience. Even if this model is only approximately true certain important practical consequences follow. Equation (2.9) shows the important role played by length of service in the first job on subsequent lengths of stay. This suggests *that if particular care is taken to ensure satisfaction in a person's first job then their subsequent rate of turnover will be reduced.* We have noted that existing data are compatible with this hypothesis but they do not provide enough information to enable a satisfactory test to be made. Support for the lognormal hypothesis must be sought by classifying leavers by their number of previous jobs. If the model is correct we should find that σ increased with j, the number of jobs held before the present one. If the u's are independent we should find that σ^2 was proportional to j.

The various models for the leaving process which we have described are of considerable interest in themselves and more empirical research is needed to enable us to discriminate between them. For most purposes in the remainder of this chapter the origin of the model is not important. All that we require is an adequate description of the CLS distribution. For this reason we shall use whichever of the various forms offers the greatest mathematical advantage.

3. RECRUITMENT AND WASTAGE IN ORGANIZATIONS OF CONSTANT SIZE

3.1. The Renewal Model

In an organization of constant size each loss must be associated with a gain. The recruitment and wastage processes are therefore essentially the same. In this section we shall use the notation and terminology appropriate to the former but our results will, where necessary, be translated into wastage terms. If each entrant has the same CLS distribution the behaviour of the process can be studied using the techniques of renewal theory. As we have already remarked the formulae for predicting recruitment needs can be deduced either from the results of Chapter 5, or by a direct appeal to renewal theory. In order to emphasize the continuity of our development we shall adopt the first course.

In the notation of Chapter 5 the expected number of recruits required in the interval $(0, T)$ is $\bar{n}_{k+1}(T)$. This quantity is obtained by setting $j = k + 1$ in equation (2.1) of that chapter. Our assumption that the loss intensity is independent of the grade means that $p_{i,k+1}(T)$ is equal to

$$F(T) = \int_0^T f(t)\,dt$$

for all i. Making this change of notation and writing N for the total size of the organization the integral equation for $\bar{n}_{k+1}(T)$ becomes

$$\bar{n}_{k+1}(T) = NF(T) + \int_0^T F(T - x)\frac{d\bar{n}_{k+1}(x)}{dx}\,dx. \tag{3.1}$$

The quantity $\bar{n}_{k+1}(T)$ is related to the more familiar renewal density, which we denote by $h(T)$, and the recruitment rate $R(T)$ by the equations

$$\bar{n}_{k+1}(T) = N \int_0^T h(x)dx = \int_0^T R(x)dx. \qquad (3.2)$$

Differentiating both sides of equation (3.1) with respect to T and using equation (3.2) we find

$$\left. \begin{aligned} h(T) &= f(T) + \int_0^T h(x)f(T-x)dx \\ &= f(T) + \int_0^T h(T-x)f(x)dx \end{aligned} \right\} \qquad (3.3)$$

which is the well-known integral equation for the renewal density. Under very general conditions it is known that

$$\lim_{T \to \infty} h(T) = \mu^{-1},$$

where μ is the mean of the CLS distribution.

As a consequence of equation (3.2), either of the equations (3.1) or (3.3) may be used to predict recruitment needs. We prefer to work with the renewal density rather than the expected number of losses in $(0, T)$ because the former provides the best starting point for the development of the approximations discussed in the next section. It is important to notice that we have assumed that the origin of our time scale corresponds to an initial state of the organization when all employees had zero length of service. This case is of particular importance but a more general assumption will be made in Section 3.5.

The integral equation for the renewal density can sometimes be solved by taking the Laplace transform of both sides. This gives

$$h^*(s) = f^*(s) + h^*(s)f^*(s)$$

whence

$$h^*(s) = f^*(s)/\{1 - f^*(s)\}. \qquad (3.4)$$

The usefulness of this technique depends upon whether or not the right-hand side of equation (3.4) can be inverted. Unfortunately this does not appear to be possible either for the Type XI or lognormal CLS distributions so we shall have to rely on approximate methods. In the case of the mixed exponential distribution the solution of the equation by the Laplace transform is straightforward and is given in the following section.

3.2. Solution of the Renewal Equation for the Mixed Exponential CLS Distribution

When the CLS distribution has the form

$$f(T) = p\lambda_1 e^{-\lambda_1 T} + (1 - p)\lambda_2 e^{-\lambda_2 T}$$

its Laplace transform is

$$f^*(s) = p\left(\frac{\lambda_1}{\lambda_1 + s}\right) + (1 - p)\left(\frac{\lambda_2}{\lambda_2 + s}\right). \tag{3.5}$$

When this expression is substituted in equation (3.4), $h^*(s)$ may be inverted by standard methods, as in Bartholomew (1959), to give

$$h(T) = \mu^{-1} + \{p\lambda_1 + (1 - p)\lambda_2 - \mu^{-1}\} \exp\{-(p\lambda_2 + (1 - p)\lambda_1)T\} \tag{3.6}$$

where $\mu = p/\lambda_1 + (1 - p)/\lambda_2$ is the mean of $f(T)$. This formula shows that $h(T)$ approaches its limit in an exponential curve. Further, since $p\lambda_1 + (1 - p)\lambda_2 \geq \mu^{-1}$, it follows that the number of recruits required will always be in excess of the number predicted by equilibrium theory. The expected number of recruits needed in any time interval can be found by integrating $h(T)$. Some illustrative calculations are given in Table 6.2 using two of the mixed exponential distributions fitted in Table 6.1.

TABLE 6.2

Percentage recruitment (wastage) figures in successive quarters for a new firm with mixed exponential CLS distribution.

	Recruitment using the CLS distributions fitted to data from:	
Quarter	Glacier Metal Co.	J. Bibby & Sons (Males)
1	22.6 ⎫	34.6 ⎫
2	18.2 ⎬ 69.5	28.6 ⎬ 108.3
3	15.3 ⎪	24.2 ⎪
4	13.4 ⎭	20.9 ⎭
5	12.1 ⎫	18.5 ⎫
6	11.3 ⎬ 44.6	16.8 ⎬ 65.4
7	10.8 ⎪	15.5 ⎪
8	10.4 ⎭	14.6 ⎭

We have not carried the calculations beyond the end of the second year because it is doubtful whether the fit of the mixed exponential distribution is adequate in the upper tail. This remark is based on the results of a comparison of the mixed exponential with the lognormal distribution using Lane and Andrew's (1955) data. These give estimates of the CLS distribution over the range 0 to 40 or 50 years. The lognormal distribution is much more successful in graduating the long upper tail than is the mixed exponential.

The figures in Table 6.2 show, in a striking fashion, the rapid decline in recruitment which can occur in a new organization. In the examples we have chosen, the figure is roughly half in the second year what it was in the first. This conclusion has obvious implications both for recruitment planning and the interpretation of wastage figures. It suggests that the high initial wastage might be reduced by careful selection of employees with a view to rejecting those with short service prospects. It must be emphasized that we have assumed that the CLS distribution does not change with time. This would be a questionable assumption under the conditions likely to exist when a new organization is established.

For the purpose of interpreting crude wastage figures† the meaning of Table 6.2 is clear. *A change in the wastage rate does not necessarily indicate a change in those factors which precipitate leaving.* It may simply reflect a change in the length of service structure. This fact makes it quite meaningless, for example, to compare the crude wastage rate of a new firm with that of an old one. Other things being equal the older one will have the lower wastage. An even more extreme example is given by Lane and Andrew (1955) who cited two firms for which the members of the high wastage firm actually had a greater expectation of service than those in the low wastage firm. Considerations of this kind show that crude wastage figures should be used with great circumspection. It is far safer to base the measurement of the leaving process on some characteristic of the CLS distribution. Lane and Andrew (1955) suggested using the estimated expectation of service. For the lognormal distribution the mean is given by $\exp\{\omega + \frac{1}{2}\sigma^2\}$. In view of our earlier remarks about the near constancy of σ we might equally take the median of the distribution which is e^ω. Apart from the fact that this measure is easily interpretable as the 'half-life' it has the added advantage of being easy to estimate from observed distributions which are usually truncated.

3.3. An Approximate Solution of the Renewal Equation

We have seen that some empirical CLS distributions can be satisfactorily graduated by a mixed exponential curve—at least in the interval 0 to 21

---

† Crude wastage is defined as the number of leavers in the period divided by the average number of employees during the same period.

months. However, we have also pointed out that, over longer periods, the lognormal is more satisfactory because it has a longer upper tail. The same is true of the Type XI distribution obtained from Silcock's model. Unfortunately it is not possible to obtain a simple explicit expression for $h(T)$ for either of these distributions. In order to investigate the form of $h(T)$ over longer periods we therefore require an approximate method for obtaining a solution to the renewal equation.

The approximation which we will use was derived by Bartholomew (1963b). It was intended for use when the CLS distribution is extremely skew and has the following form

$$h^0(T) = f(T) + F^2(T) \Big/ \int_0^T G(x)\mathrm{d}x, \qquad (3.7)$$

where $G(T) = 1 - F(T)$. The approximation has the following properties in common with the exact solution of the renewal equation.

(a) If $f(T) = \lambda e^{-\lambda T}$ then $h^0(T) = h(T) = \lambda$ for all T.

(b) $\lim_{T \to \infty} h^0(T) = \lim_{T \to \infty} h(T) = \mu^{-1}$.

(c) $h^0(0) = h(0) = f(0)$.

(d) $\left. \dfrac{\mathrm{d}^i h^0(T)}{\mathrm{d}T^i} \right|_{T=0} = \left. \dfrac{\mathrm{d}^i h(T)}{\mathrm{d}T^i} \right|_{T=0}$ $(i = 1, 2)$.

These properties suggest that the approximation is likely to be good everywhere if $f(T)$ is close to the exponential and will always be good near $T = 0$ and when T is large. The method of derivation used in Bartholomew (1963), given for a more general equation in Section 3.5, also suggests that the approximation will be good if $f(T)$ has a long upper tail. A further useful property of the approximation is that $h^0(T)$ is an upper bound for $h(T)$ if the loss intensity associated with $f(T)$ is non-increasing. We shall test the adequacy of the approximation in special cases after we have considered two examples.

The simplicity of the approximation is apparent when we consider its form for Silcock's model. In this case

$$f(T) = \frac{v}{c}\left(1 + \frac{T}{c}\right)^{-(v+1)} \qquad G(T) = \left(1 + \frac{T}{c}\right)^{-v}$$

and

$$\int_0^T G(x)\mathrm{d}x = \mu\left\{1 - \left(1 + \frac{T}{c}\right)^{-v+1}\right\}.$$

Hence, from equation (3.7),

$$h^0(T) = \frac{\nu}{c}\left(1 + \frac{T}{c}\right)^{-(\nu+1)} + \frac{\left\{1 - \left(1 + \frac{T}{c}\right)^{-\nu}\right\}^2}{\mu\left\{1 - \left(1 + \frac{T}{c}\right)^{-\nu+1}\right\}}$$

$$\sim \frac{1}{\mu}\left\{1 - \left(\frac{c}{T}\right)^{\nu-1}\right\} \quad \text{if } \nu > 1. \tag{3.8}$$

When ν is a little greater than 1, the approach to equilibrium is very slow. If $0 < \nu < 1$ the mean is infinite and $h(T)$ approaches zero like $T^{\nu-1}$. In the case $\nu = 1$ the zero limit is approached like $(\log T)^{-1}$. The calculations made by Silcock (1954) for 8 distributions gave 6 out of 8 values of v between 0.5 and 1. We would therefore expect the wastage rate to go on declining slowly over all periods likely to be of practical interest.

The approximation also takes a simple form for the lognormal CLS distribution. Thus we have

$$f(T) = \frac{1}{\sqrt{2\pi}\sigma T}\exp\left\{-\frac{1}{2}\left(\frac{\log_e T - \omega}{\sigma}\right)^2\right\}$$

$$F(T) = \Phi\left(\frac{\log_e T - \omega}{\sigma}\right)$$

and

$$\int_0^T G(x)dx = T\left\{1 - \Phi\left(\frac{\log_e T - \omega}{\sigma}\right)\right\} + \mu\Phi\left(\frac{\log_e T - \omega}{\sigma} - \sigma\right) \tag{3.9}$$

where $\mu = e^{\omega + \frac{1}{2}\sigma^2}$ and $\Phi(.)$ is the standard normal distribution function. The approximation can therefore be calculated using tables of the normal probability integral. It is clear from equation (3.9) that equilibrium will not be reached until $X = (\log_e T - \omega)/\sigma$ is large enough for $\Phi(X)$ to be negligible. To investigate this point in more detail let us examine the form of $h^0(T)$ for large T. If X is large we may write

$$\Phi(X) \sim 1 - \frac{1}{\sqrt{2\pi}X}e^{-\frac{1}{2}X^2}.$$

Straightforward manipulation then gives

$$h^0(T) \sim \mu^{-1}\left\{1 - \frac{1}{\sqrt{2\pi}}\frac{\sigma}{X(X - \sigma)}e^{-\frac{1}{2}(X - \sigma^2)}\right\}^{-1}. \tag{3.10}$$

If $\sigma = 2$ and $X = 4$, say, then

$$h^0(T)\big|_{X=4} = \frac{1.02}{\mu}.$$

When $X = 4$, $T = \mu e^\sigma \doteq 400\mu$. This means that it would take about 400 times the average CLS to get within 2 per cent of the equilibrium value. Bearing in mind that the lognormal distribution cannot represent the true state of affairs beyond about 40 or 45 years, it is clear that equilibrium behaviour will be of limited practical interest.

The transient behaviour of the renewal model is illustrated in Table 6.3, assuming a lognormal CLS distribution. Calculations have been made for a typical case by taking $\omega = 0$ and $\sigma = 2$. If the unit of time is one year then $\omega = 0$ corresponds to a 'half life' of one year. For this distribution $\mu = e^2 = 7.389$ so that $h(\infty) = 0.1353$.

TABLE 6.3

Approximation to the renewal density for a lognormal CLS distribution with parameters $\omega = 0$, $\sigma = 2$.

$\log_e T$	0	1	2	3	4	5	10	∞
T	1	2.71	7.39	20.1	54.6	148.4	22,026	∞
$h^0(T)$	0.574	0.424	0.318	0.244	0.194	0.194	0.125	0.135

The figures in this table show the extreme slowness with which $h^0(T)$ approaches its limit. Even after 20 years the renewal density is still roughly twice its equilibrium value. The fact that $h(T)$ for a comparable mixed exponential distribution reaches equilibrium in a matter of a few years serves to emphasize the need for accurate graduation of the tail of the distribution if long-term predictions are required.

We have assumed in the foregoing discussion that conclusions drawn from the behaviour of $h^0(T)$ can be applied to $h(T)$. This assumption can be tested in certain cases as we shall now show. Some comparisons of $h(T)$ and $h^0(T)$ were made in Bartholomew (1963b) for the discrete time version of the renewal equation. The CLS distribution which was used for these calculations was the discrete analogue of the Type XI curve. In all cases the agreement was good even for the most skew distributions considered. A comparison for the case of continuous time can be made for the mixed exponential CLS distribution. The results are given in Table 6.4 for the two CLS distributions which were used for the calculations given in Tables 6.1 and 6.2.

Table 6.4

Comparison of $h(T)$ and $h^0(T)$ for two mixed exponential distributions.

		T									
		0	0.2	0.4	0.6	0.8	1.0	1.5	2.0	10.0	∞
(Glacier Metal Co.) $p = 0.6513$ $\lambda_1 = 0.2684$ $\lambda_2 = 2.4228$	$h(T)$	1.020	0.840	0.712	0.620	0.555	0.508	0.440	0.411	0.389	0.389
	$h^0(T)$	1.020	0.841	0.715	0.628	0.567	0.525	0.466	0.439	0.392	0.389
(J. Bibby & Sons) $p = 0.4363$ $\lambda_1 = 0.2339$ $\lambda_2 = 2.5335$	$h(T)$	1.530	1.300	1.120	0.979	0.870	0.784	0.643	0.567	0.479	0.479
	$h^0(T)$	1.530	1.301	1.125	0.993	0.894	0.821	0.705	0.643	0.489	0.479

The agreement in this case is very good for the first six months but less good thereafter. However, $h^0(T)$ is an upper bound for $h(T)$ for all T and so statements about the rate of convergence to the limit can be based upon it. It thus appears from these calculations and those of Bartholomew (1963b) that $h^0(T)$ is limited in its ability to approximate to an exponential curve but that it is more satisfactory when the rate of approach to equilibrium is much slower. Any approximate solution can be improved by using $h^0(T)$ as a starting point for the iterative solution of the integral equation. Thus

$$h^{(1)}(T) = f(T) + \int_0^T h^0(T - x)f(x)\mathrm{d}x \qquad (3.11)$$

should be a better approximation than $h^0(T)$.

3.4. Distribution of the Number of Recruits

Standard renewal theory provides methods for finding the distribution of the number of recruits as well as its expectation. Let us begin by considering an organization with $N = 1$. The expected number of recruits required in the interval $(0, T)$ is then

$$\bar{n}_{k+1}(T) = \int_0^T h(x)\mathrm{d}x.$$

(The subscript $k + 1$ is not necessary in the present context so we shall omit it throughout the remainder of this section.) For large T it is known (see Cox 1962, p. 40) that $n(T)$ is approximately normally distributed with mean $T\mu^{-1}$ and variance $V^2 T\mu^{-1}$, where V^2 is the square of the coefficient of variation of the CLS distribution. For the lognormal distribution $V^2 = e^{\sigma^2} - 1$ which, for $\sigma = 2$, is equal to 53.6. Long-term predictions of recruiting needs are thus subject to a high degree of uncertainty. However, we have already seen in the case of the mean, that the limit is approached so slowly that asymptotic results are practically useless. The same is true of the variance so we must use exact results when dealing with this kind of CLS distribution.

The exact value of the variance of $n(T)$ can be found by using the following equation.

$$E\{n^2(T)\} = \bar{n}(T) + 2\int_0^T \bar{n}(T - x)h(x)\mathrm{d}x \qquad (3.12)$$

(see Parzen 1962, p. 179). Since we have the means of finding $\bar{n}(T)$ and $h(T)$ either exactly or approximately for any CLS distribution we can compute $E\{n^2(T)\}$ and hence the variance of $n(T)$. We illustrate the calculations using the mixed exponential distribution for which $h(T)$ was found in Section 3.2. If we let

$$a = p\lambda_1 + (1 - p)\lambda_2 - \mu^{-1}$$
$$b = p\lambda_2 + (1 - p)\lambda_1$$

then

and

$$h(T) = \mu^{-1} + ae^{-bT}$$

$$\bar{n}(T) = T\mu^{-1} + \frac{a}{b}(1 - e^{-bT}). \tag{3.13}$$

Making the necessary substitutions in equation (3.12) and subtracting $\bar{n}^2(T)$ we find the following expression for the variance

$$\text{var }\{n(T)\} = \frac{T}{\mu}\left\{1 + \frac{2a}{b}\right\} + \frac{a}{b}\left\{1 - \frac{4}{\mu b} + \frac{a}{b}\right\} + \frac{2a}{b}\left\{\frac{1}{\mu} - \frac{a}{b}\right\}Te^{-bT}$$

$$- \frac{a}{b}\left\{1 - \frac{4}{\mu b}\right\}e^{-bT} - \frac{a^2}{b^2}e^{-2bT}. \tag{3.14}$$

The corresponding results for an organization of size N are simply obtained by multiplying the mean and variance given above by N. Since $n(T)$ for a large organization can be regarded as the sum of the numbers for single member systems, the central limit theorem ensures its approximate normality. Some numerical values of expectations and standard errors are given in Table 6.5. For the purposes of this calculation we have considered two hypothetical firms with 1,000 employees. We assume the CLS distribution to be mixed exponential in both cases. In the first case we have used the parameter values obtained by fitting the curve to the Glacier Metal

TABLE 6.5

Expectations and standard errors of numbers of recruits required in various time intervals for two mixed exponential CLS distributions when $N = 1,000$

		Time interval			
		0–3 months	0–6 months	0–12 months	0–24 months
$p = 0.6513$	Mean	226	408	695	1,142
$\lambda_1 = 0.2684$	S.E.	16.2	21.8	29.0	39.2
$\lambda_2 = 2.4228$	Approx. S.E.	18.4	22.6	29.2	39.2
$p = 0.5377$	Mean	458	738	1,072	1,508
$\lambda_1 = 0.2187$	S.E.	27.0	34.3	41.8	52.5
$\lambda_2 = 4.8940$	Approx. S.E.	32.9	36.3	42.4	52.6

data; in the second we have used a more skew member of the mixed exponential family suggested by data relating to the United Steel Cos. given in Silcock (1954).

The rows labelled "Approx. S.E." were obtained using only the first two terms of the variance as given by equation (3.14). The approximation over-estimates the true value but the difference is negligible for all but the shortest time periods. It is clear from the table that predictions for even short periods are subject to considerable uncertainty.

3.5. Recruitment in an Organization of Constant Size but Changing CLS Distribution

The assumption that the CLS distribution is the same for all persons irrespective of when they join is unlikely to be true over long periods of time. Changes may occur gradually as a result of trends in economic or educational factors or abruptly because of the introduction of a new recruitment policy. There has been very little research on the effect of such changes so our account will necessarily be incomplete. We shall give some basic formulae which should be useful in a fuller investigation of the subject.

Let the density function of CLS for a person who joins the organization at time x after it was established be $f_x(T)$. We are assuming that this density has the same functional form for all x but that its parameters are continuous functions of x. The individual is thus characterized by the time at which he enters the organization. An integral equation for the renewal density can easily be constructed from first principles. The expected number of leavers in $(T, T + \delta T)$ from among those who joined in $(x, x + \delta x)$ is

$$h(x)\delta x f_x(T - x)\delta T.$$

Integrating with respect to x, adding in a term for the initial members and equating to $h(T)\delta T$ we find

$$h(T) = f_0(T) + \int_0^T h(x)f_x(T - x)\mathrm{d}x. \qquad (3.15)$$

This equation is not amenable to solution by taking Laplace transforms and we have not succeeded in finding a solution for any distributions of present interest. Even if we take $f_x(T)$ to be exponential with its parameter depending on x in a simple way no progress seems possible. The simplest way of investigating the solution would be to solve the discrete time version of equation (3.15) by numerical methods. In this case we have the following difference equation for $h(T)$:

$$h(T) = f_0(T) + \sum_{i=0}^{T-1} h(i)f_i(T - i) \quad (T = 1, 2, \ldots), \qquad (3.16)$$

where $f_i(T)$ is now a discrete probability distribution and $h(T)$ is the expected number of recruits needed at time T. In spite of the intractability of the generalized renewal equation it is possible to obtain an approximation to the solution similar to that given in equation (3.7). We shall give the argument in full and, in so doing, will justify the earlier approximation which is a special case.

In addition to satisfying equation (3.15), $h(T)$ is also the solution of the equation

$$F_0(T) = \int_0^T h(x)G_x(T - x)\mathrm{d}x \tag{3.17}$$

because both sides of this equation are alternative ways of expressing the expected proportion of initial members who have left at time T. It now follows that we may re-write equation (3.15) as

$$h(T) = f_0(T) + \frac{F_0(T)\displaystyle\int_0^T h(x)f_x(T - x)\mathrm{d}x}{\displaystyle\int_0^T h(x)G_x(T - x)\mathrm{d}x}. \tag{3.18}$$

The approximation consists of treating

$$\frac{\displaystyle\int_0^T h(x)f_x(T - x)\mathrm{d}x}{\displaystyle\int_0^T f_x(T - x)\mathrm{d}x} \quad \text{and} \quad \frac{\displaystyle\int_0^T h(x)G_x(T - x)\mathrm{d}x}{\displaystyle\int_0^T G_x(T - x)\mathrm{d}x}$$

as equal. The resulting approximation is then

$$h^0(T) = f_0(T) + \frac{F_0(T)\displaystyle\int_0^T f_x(T - x)\mathrm{d}x}{\displaystyle\int_0^T G_x(T - x)\mathrm{d}x}. \tag{3.19}$$

Each of the fractions following equation (3.18) is a weighted average of the renewal density. They will be close in value for any T either if the weight functions are similar or if $h(x)$ is nearly constant over the range of x for which the weights have appreciable density. The former situation occurs if $f_x(T)$ is close to the exponential with constant mean and the latter when $f_x(T)$ is highly skewed with slowly changing parameters. An investigation of the accuracy of the approximation in particular cases has yet to be undertaken.

So far we have assumed that the parameters of the CLS distribution are continuous functions of time. A case of considerable practical interest arises when there is an abrupt change from one set of parameter values to another. This could be a direct result of new selection methods or a new source of recruitment becoming available. In order to develop the theory for such a system let us take as our time origin the point at which the change in CLS distribution takes place. Let $f_1(T)$ be the density function of the CLS distribution for members recruited before the change and $f_2(T)$ the density function for those recruited afterwards. We shall denote by $d_1(T)$ the density function of the *residual CLS* distribution. This is the distribution of the remaining length of service of a member of the system selected at random at time zero. If we consider the process for $T \geq 0$ we have what Cox (1962, Chapter 2) has called a modified renewal process. The renewal density then satisfies the integral equation

$$h(T) = d_1(T) + \int_0^T h(T - x)f_2(x)dx. \tag{3.20}$$

On taking the Laplace transform of each side of equation (3.20) we find

$$h^*(s) = d_1^*(s)/\{1 - f_2^*(s)\}. \tag{3.21}$$

Whether or not this result is of value in solving the renewal equation will depend on the forms of $f_2(T)$ and $d_1(T)$. This last distribution will depend on the way in which the organization operated before time zero. In order to take the analysis further let us suppose that it started at time X with its members all having the same CLS distribution $f_1(T)$. Under these circumstances the residual CLS distribution at $T = 0$ is the same as the forward recurrence time and is thus given by

$$d_1(T) = f_1(X + T) + \int_0^X h(-x)f_1(x + T)dx, \tag{3.22}$$

where $h(-x)$ is the renewal density at time $X - x$ after the start of the initial process. In the limit as $X \to \infty$

$$d_1(T) \to \frac{1}{\mu_1} G_1(T) \tag{3.23}$$

where μ_1 is the mean of $f_1(T)$. In this case

$$d_1^*(s) = \frac{1}{\mu_1 s} \{1 - f_1^*(s)\}$$

so that equation (3.21) becomes

$$h^*(s) = \frac{1}{\mu_1 s} \frac{\{1 - f_1^*(s)\}}{\{1 - f_2^*(s)\}}. \tag{3.24}$$

As a simple illustration of this result let us suppose that

$$f_i(T) = \lambda_i e^{-\lambda_i T} \quad (i = 1, 2)$$

then

$$h^*(s) = \frac{\lambda_1(\lambda_2 + s)}{s(\lambda_1 + s)} = \frac{\lambda_2}{s} + \frac{\lambda_1 - \lambda_2}{\lambda_2 + s}.$$

This can easily be inverted to give

$$h(T) = \lambda_2 + (\lambda_1 - \lambda_2)e^{-\lambda_1 T}. \tag{3.25}$$

The new equilibrium is thus approached exponentially at a rate which depends on the initial renewal density λ_1. To take a more realistic example let

$$f_i(T) = p_i \lambda_{1i} e^{-\lambda_{1i} T} + (1 - p_i)\lambda_{2i} e^{-\lambda_{2i} T} \quad (i = 1, 2)$$

for which

$$h^*(s) = \frac{(s + \lambda_{12})(s + \lambda_{22})(s + \nu_1)}{\mu_1 s(s + \lambda_{11})(s + \lambda_{21})(s + \nu_2)} \tag{3.26}$$

where

$$\left. \begin{aligned} \nu_i &= \lambda_{1i}\lambda_{2i}/\mu_i \\ \mu_i &= p_i/\lambda_{1i} + (1 - p_i)/\lambda_{2i}. \end{aligned} \right\} (i = 1, 2)$$

By resolving equation (3.26) into partial fractions it is evident that $h(T)$ has the form

$$h(T) = A + Be^{-\nu_2 T} + Ce^{-\lambda_{11} T} + De^{-\lambda_2 T}. \tag{3.27}$$

Standard methods yield the following expressions for the coefficients:

$$A = \mu_2^{-1}$$

$$B = \frac{-(\nu_1 - \nu_2)(\lambda_{12} - \nu_2)(\lambda_{22} - \nu_2)}{\mu_1 \nu_2(\lambda_{11} - \nu_2)(\lambda_{21} - \nu_2)}$$

$$C = \frac{-(\lambda_{11} - \nu_1)(\lambda_{12} - \lambda_{11})(\lambda_{22} - \lambda_{11})}{\mu_1 \lambda_{11}(\lambda_{11} - \nu_2)(\lambda_{21} - \lambda_{11})}$$

$$D = \frac{(\lambda_{21} - \nu_1)(\lambda_{22} - \lambda_{11})(\lambda_{22} - \lambda_{21})}{\mu_1 \lambda_{21}(\lambda_{21} - \nu_2)(\lambda_{21} - \lambda_{11})}.$$

The implications of these formulae will be clearer if we consider a numerical example. Let

$$\left. \begin{aligned} \lambda_{11} &= 11.0 \\ \lambda_{21} &= 1.1 \end{aligned} \right\}, \quad \left. \begin{aligned} \lambda_{12} &= 5.5 \\ \lambda_{22} &= 0.55 \end{aligned} \right\}, \quad p_1 = p_2 = \tfrac{1}{2},$$

then

$$\mu_1 = 0.5, \quad \mu_2 = 1.0, \quad \nu_1 = 6.050 \quad \text{and} \quad \nu_2 = 3.025.$$

In this example the expected length of service for members recruited after time zero is twice that of the original members. Substitution of the numerical values in equation (3.27) gives, for the renewal density,

$$h(T) = 1 - 0.798e^{-3.025T} + 0.655e^{-11T} + 1.143e^{-1.1T}. \quad (3.28)$$

This function is plotted on figure 6.1 where it may be compared with the renewal density for the case when $f_1(T)$ and $f_2(T)$ are exponential with means 0.5 and 1.0 respectively. In the mixed exponential case the initial drop in recruitment is greater but the approach to the new equilibrium value is much slower. Over the period shown the total recruitment would need to be higher with the mixed exponential CLS distributions than with the exponential.

It is possible to find an approximation for $h(T)$ by the same method as before. By using the argument that led up to equation (3.17) we find that

$$D_1(T) = \int_0^T G_2(x)h(T - x)dx \quad (3.29)$$

where $D_1(T) = \int_0^T d_1(x)dx$. Hence we arrive at the approximation

$$h^0(T) = d_1(T) + \frac{D_1(T)F_2(T)}{\displaystyle\int_0^T G_2(x)dx}. \quad (3.30)$$

It may be verified that this expression gives the exact solution when the two distributions are exponential. The accuracy of the approximation for the numerical example discussed above can be judged from figure 6.1, where $h^0(T)$ is plotted as a broken line. For $T \leq 1$ the approximation is very close but it is less good thereafter. It should provide a useful guide in situations where the renewal equation (3.15) cannot be solved explicitly. An example of such a case arises when the CLS distribution is lognormal. Then we find that the functions

$$F_2(T) \quad \text{and} \quad \int_0^T G_2(x)dx$$

of equation (3.30) can be easily obtained as in Section 3.3. The same would be true of $d_1(T)$ and $D_1(T)$ if it were possible to assume that the system had reached equilibrium by time zero. However, our previous results show that this is a most unreasonable assumption. If X is known we could determine $d_1(T)$ from equation (3.22), but, in practice, it would be preferable to make a direct empirical estimate. This could be obtained from the length of service structure at $T = 0$ and the known CLS distribution, $f_1(T)$.

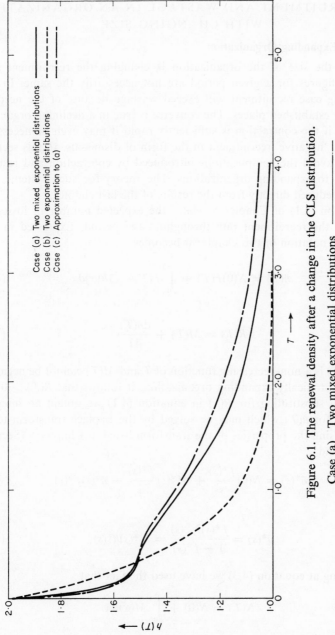

Figure 6.1. The renewal density after a change in the CLS distribution.

Case (a)   Two mixed exponential distributions
Case (b)   Two exponential distributions
Case (c)   Approximation to (a)

4. RECRUITMENT AND WASTAGE IN AN ORGANIZATION WITH CHANGING SIZE

4.1. An Expanding Organization

When the size of the organization is changing the recruitment and wastage figures for a given period are not necessarily the same. In the expanding case recruitment will exceed wastage because of the need to fill newly established places. The converse is true in a declining organization and if the contraction is sufficiently rapid it may even be necessary to have a 'negative' recruitment in the form of dismissals. In this section we shall avoid the complications introduced by contraction and restrict attention to expanding organizations. The theory for such systems can then be deduced directly from the results of the last chapter.

Equation (2.1) of Chapter 5 relates the expected number of losses in $(0, T)$ to the recruitment rate throughout the period. Expressed in the simplified notation of this chapter it becomes

$$\bar{n}(T) = N(0)F(T) + \int_0^T F(T - x)R(x)\mathrm{d}x \qquad (4.1)$$

where

$$R(T) = M(T) + \frac{\mathrm{d}\bar{n}(T)}{\mathrm{d}T}. \qquad (4.2)$$

Since $\bar{n}(T)$ is a non-decreasing function of T and $M(T)$ cannot be negative in a monotonically expanding organization, it follows that $R(T) \geq 0$ for all T. On substituting for $R(x)$ in equation (4.1) we obtain an integral equation for $\bar{n}(T)$ which may be solved by the Laplace transform technique. Using the properties of the transform listed in Chapter 5 (Section 4.1) we find

$$\bar{n}^*(s) = N(0)\frac{f^*(s)}{s} + M^*(s)\frac{f^*(s)}{s} + \bar{n}^*(s)f^*(s)$$

whence

$$\bar{n}^*(s) = \frac{f^*(s)N^*(s)}{1 - f^*(s)} = N^*(s)h^*(s). \qquad (4.3)$$

In arriving at equation (4.3) we have used the fact that

$$N(T) = N(0) + \int_0^T M(x)\mathrm{d}x$$

and hence that

$$N^*(s) = N(0)/s + M^*(s)/s.$$

On inverting each side of equation (4.3) we have

$$\bar{n}(T) = \int_0^T N(x)h(T - x)dx. \qquad (4.4)$$

Equations (4.3) and (4.4) show that the renewal density plays a fundamental role in the theory of expanding organizations. The methods and approximations of Section 3 can thus be used to find $h(T)$ and then $\bar{n}(T)$ can be determined from equation (4.4). Having found the expected number of losses, we can easily obtain the expected number of recruits by adding $N(T) - N(0)$ to $\bar{n}(T)$.

The foregoing theory can easily be adapted to cover the case of an organization which remains constant in size for a period and then enters on expansion. Let us transfer the time origin to the point at which the change takes place. Then the only modification required is the replacement of the term $N(0)F(T)$ in equation (4.1) by the expected number of those in the sytem at time zero who will have left at time T. If we denote the density function of residual CLS for members of the organization at time zero by $d(T)$, then the Laplace transform of $\bar{n}(T)$ is found to be

$$\bar{n}^*(s) = \left[f^*(s)N^*(s) + \frac{N(0)}{s} \{d^*(s) - f^*(s)\} \right]/\{1 - f^*(s)\}. \qquad (4.5)$$

If the system has reached equilibrium before expansion begins

$$d(T) = \frac{1}{\mu} G(T)$$

and

$$d^*(s) = \frac{1}{\mu} G^*(s) = \frac{1}{\mu s} \{1 - f^*(s)\}$$

so that

$$\bar{n}^*(s) = N^*(s)h^*(s) + \frac{N(0)}{\mu s^2} - \frac{N(0)}{s} h^*(s). \qquad (4.6)$$

This equation may be inverted term by term to give

$$\bar{n}(T) = \int_0^T N(x)h(T - x)dx + N(0)\left\{\frac{T}{\mu} - \int_0^T h(x)dx\right\}. \qquad (4.7)$$

The expected number of losses in this case differs from the earlier result of equation (4.4) by an amount equal to the last term of equation (4.7). It is known (see, for example, Cox 1962, Chapter 4) that

$$\lim_{T \to \infty} \left\{\frac{T}{\mu} - \int_0^T h(x)dx\right\} = -\tfrac{1}{2}(V^2 - 1)$$

where V is the coefficient of variation of the CLS distribution. Hence, for skew distributions with $V > 1$, there will be a smaller total loss when expansion is delayed until the system has reached equilibrium than when it takes place initially.

The statistics of recruitment and wastage are usually expressed, not in terms of total change, but as rates. Thus, for example, the crude wastage rate in the interval (T_1, T_2) is defined as

$$w(T_1, T_2) = \{n(T_2) - n(T_1)\} \Big/ \left\{ \frac{1}{(T_2 - T_1)} \int_{T_1}^{T_2} N(x)\mathrm{d}x \right\} \qquad (4.8)$$

where $n(T_1)$ and $n(T_2)$ are the observed numbers of losses at T_1 and T_2 respectively. If the function $N(T)$ is known only at the end-points of the interval, as in many published figures, the denominator in equation (4.8) is replaced by $\frac{1}{2}\{N(T_2) + N(T_1)\}$. For theoretical purposes it is useful to define an instantaneous wastage rate obtained by letting $T_2 \to T_1$ in equation (4.8) and replacing $n(T_1)$ and $n(T_2)$ by their expectations. Thus we let

$$w(T) = \frac{\mathrm{d}\bar{n}(T)}{\mathrm{d}T} \Big/ N(T). \qquad (4.9)$$

We shall make use of $w(T)$ in the following section but for present purposes we shall need $w(T_1, T_2)$.

In order to illustrate the effect of expansion on crude wastage we shall give two examples. Let us assume that the CLS distribution is mixed exponential then we have shown that

$$h(T) = \mu^{-1} + ae^{-bT}$$

where

$$a = p\lambda_1 + (1 - p)\lambda_2, \quad b = p\lambda_2 + (1 - p)\lambda_1$$

and

$$\mu = p/\lambda_1 + (1 - p)/\lambda_2.$$

In our first example we assume that the system is subject to a linear growth law of the form

$$N(T) = MT,$$

M being the rate of growth. The function $\bar{n}(T)$ can be obtained from equation (4.4) by straightforward integration. On substituting the result in equation (4.8) we find that

$$w(T_1, T_2) = \frac{T_2 - T_1}{\mu} + \frac{2a}{b(T_1 + T_2)} \left\{ T_2 - T_1 - \left(\frac{e^{-bT_1} - e^{-bT_2}}{b} \right) \right\}. \qquad (4.10)$$

Some calculations based on this formula are given in Table 6.6 for three CLS distributions of the mixed exponential family. The parameter values selected were those obtained by fitting the distribution to the data relating to the Glacier Metal Co., J. Bibby & Sons and the United Steel Cos. which have already been used in this chapter.

TABLE 6.6

Percentage wastage in successive quarters for a group
expanding at a constant rate.

Quarter	Glacier Metal Co.	J. Bibby & Sons	United Steel Cos.
1	23.5	35.8	49.6
2	21.3	32.9	40.5
3	19.5	30.2	33.5
4	18.0	28.0	28.6
5	16.8	26.2	25.2
6	15.9	24.6	22.7
7	15.1	23.3	20.9
8	14.5	22.2	19.4

A comparison of these figures with those in Table 6.2 shows that, although the wastage rate still decreases, it does not do so as rapidly as before. It can be seen from equation (4.10) that $w(T_1, T_2)$ does not depend on the value of M and hence the wastage approaches the same equilibrium value regardless of the rate of expansion.

The previous example is based on a continuous growth function. In our second example we shall suppose that $N(T)$ jumps from an initial value of $N(0)$ to a new value of $N(0) + N$ at $T = T_J$. The expected number of losses in this case is clearly

$$\bar{n}(T) = N(0) \int_0^T h(x)\mathrm{d}x \quad (T \le T_J)$$

$$= N(0) \int_0^T h(x)\mathrm{d}x + N \int_0^{T-T_J} h(x)\mathrm{d}x \quad (T > T_J).$$

Some quarterly wastage rates for this kind of growth are given in Table 6.7. Calculations are given for two values each of T_J and N assuming a CLS distribution like the one for the United Steel Cos.

The effect of an abrupt increase in size is to arrest the decreasing wastage rate. With a large increase in size there is a temporary increase in wastage but the effect is short-lived and after a year its influence has almost vanished.

TABLE 6.7

Percentage wastage in successive quarters for a firm expanded from size $N(0)$ to $N(0) + N$ at $T = T_J$ assuming the United Steel Cos. CLS distribution.

| | $T_J = \frac{1}{2}$ year | | $T_J = 1$ year | |
Quarter	$N = \frac{1}{2}N(0)$	$N = N(0)$	$N = \frac{1}{2}N(0)$	$N = N(0)$
1	45.8	45.8	45.8	45.8
2	28.0	28.0	28.0	28.0
3	27.9	32.4	19.0	19.0
4	18.9	21.2	14.4	14.4
5	14.4	15.6	23.3	29.0
6	12.1	12.7	16.7	19.5
7	11.0	11.3	13.3	14.7
8	10.4	10.6	11.5	12.3

4.2. A Contracting Organization

The theory which has been developed in Section 4.1 is not restricted in its application to expanding organizations. It applies whenever the recruitment rate $R(T)$ is non-negative for all T. The case of an organization which is being reduced in size may or may not fall into this category. If the desired rate of contraction is small the losses from the system may be more than sufficient to achieve it. New entrants will then be required to prevent the numbers from dropping too rapidly. On the other hand, if a rapid run-down is necessary natural wastage may not be enough to reach the target. In such cases it becomes necessary to introduce involuntary wastage by removing redundant members from the system. One important reason for studying contracting systems is to determine the conditions necessary to avoid redundancy. We shall therefore examine this question first.

The maximum rate of run-down which can be attained without redundancy is that which occurs when no recruits are admitted to the system. This will be called the *rate of natural contraction*. We can obtain this rate by putting $R(T) = 0$ for all T in equations (4.1) and (4.2). From the former we find that

$$\bar{n}(T) = N(0)F(T)$$

and from the latter that

$$M(T) = -\frac{\mathrm{d}\bar{n}(T)}{\mathrm{d}T}.$$

Eliminating $\bar{n}(T)$ between these equations we obtain

$$M(T) = -N(0)f(T)$$

and hence

$$N(T) = N(0)G(T). \tag{4.11}$$

Since this is the smallest size that can be achieved at time T without redundancy it is clear that any proposal calling for a greater reduction must involve some redundancy. The wastage rate (see equation 4.9) for an organization undergoing natural contraction is

$$w(T) = \frac{N(0)f(T)}{N(0)G(T)}$$

which is the same as the loss intensity of the CLS distribution $f(T)$. This loss intensity is usually a decreasing function and hence observed wastage rates will decline even though there has been no change in the leaving characteristics of the members. This example provides further evidence of the dangers of using crude wastage rates as indices of stability.

The above result has important practical implications but two words of caution should be added. We have assumed that the propensity to leave is unaffected by the decision to reduce the size of the organization. In practice the psychological effects of being in a declining firm might very well increase the tendency to leave. This would have the effect of making a faster run-down possible. Secondly, we have treated the organization as a whole but in practice some grades or divisions would have to be run-down more rapidly than others. It is perfectly possible to use the theory for sub-groups of a larger system and this should be done in preference to treating the system as a whole.

We shall continue the investigation by means of examples. Suppose first that the CLS distribution is exponential with parameter λ. As we have often pointed out, this assumption is not realistic but in the present instance it serves to expose another fallacy into which the naive interpretation of wastage figures can lead. Let the required size at time T be given by

$$N(T) = N(0)e^{-\alpha T} \quad (-\infty < \alpha < +\infty). \tag{4.12}$$

We shall be interested mainly in the case $\alpha > 0$ for which equation (4.12) implies a constant proportional reduction in size per unit time. Remembering that $h(T) = \lambda$ for the exponential distribution, it follows from equation (4.4) that

$$\bar{n}(T) = N(0)\lambda \int_0^T e^{-\alpha x}\, dx = \frac{\lambda N(0)}{\alpha}(1 - e^{-\alpha T}) \tag{4.13}$$

if $R(T)$ is non-negative for all T. But, from equation (4.2),

$$R(T) = N(0)e^{-\alpha T}(\lambda - \alpha) \qquad (4.14)$$

so that redundancy will be avoided completely if $\lambda \geq \alpha$. In words this means that the wastage rate must exceed the required rate of run-down. Therefore, if a firm had a steady wastage rate of 20 per cent, its size could be reduced by up to 20 per cent per year without causing redundancies. This seems to be intuitively obvious and might be supposed to hold under any circumstances. In fact it is true only when the CLS distribution is exponential which is probably never the case in practice. The extent to which this simple rule of thumb may err in practice will be examined by assuming the CLS distribution to be mixed exponential.

If

$$f(T) = p\lambda_1 e^{-\lambda_1 T} + (1 - p)\lambda_2 e^{-\lambda_2 T}$$

we have shown that

$$h(T) = \mu^{-1} + ae^{-bT}$$

where a, b and μ are as defined for this case in Section 4.1. Substitution in equation (4.4) gives

$$\bar{n}(T) = \frac{N(0)}{\mu}\left(\frac{1 - e^{-\alpha T}}{\alpha}\right) + N(0)a\left(\frac{e^{-bT} - e^{-\alpha T}}{\alpha - b}\right). \qquad (4.15)$$

The associated wastage rate is

$$w(T) = \frac{1}{\mu} + \frac{a}{\alpha - b}\{\alpha - be^{(\alpha - b)T}\} \qquad (4.16)$$

and the required rate of input is

$$R(T) = N(0)\left\{\left(\frac{1}{\mu} - \alpha + \frac{\alpha a}{\alpha - b}\right)e^{-\alpha T} - \frac{ab}{\alpha - b}e^{-bT}\right\}. \qquad (4.17)$$

Redundancies will thus be avoided if $R(T)$ is positive for all T; this will be so in the present example if

$$\left.\begin{array}{c}\alpha < b \\ \\ \dfrac{1}{\mu} - \alpha + \dfrac{\alpha a}{\alpha - b} > 0.\end{array}\right\} \qquad (4.18)$$

and

These conditions may be compared with $\mu^{-1} > \alpha$ for the case of the exponential CLS distribution obtained in equation (4.14).

As an illustration we shall use the Glacier Metal Co. data for which $a = 1.0196$, $b = 1.6716$ and $\mu^{-1} = 0.3890$. Using these figures we find that the inequalities (4.18) are both satisfied if $\alpha \leq 0.2280$. This upper limit for α corresponds to a reduction in size of $100(1 - e^{-0.2280})$ per cent $= 20.4$ per cent per annum which is thus the maximum annual rate of run-down if redundancy is to be avoided. Exponential theory would have predicted an upper limit for α of $\mu^{-1} = 0.3890$ with a maximum rate of run-down equal to $100(1 - e^{-0.3890})$ per cent $= 32.2$ per cent. Substitution of $\alpha = 0.3890$ in equation (4.17) shows that such a policy would lead to redundancies occurring after only

$$T = \frac{\log_e 1.6716 - \log_e 0.3890}{1.6716 - 0.3890} = \frac{1.4580}{1.2826} = 1.14 \text{ years.}$$

A similar analysis can be carried out for an organization which has reached equilibrium at a constant size before contraction, or expansion, begins. The expression for $\bar{n}(T)$ is obtained by adding the term

$$N(0) \left\{ \frac{T}{\mu} - \int_0^T h(x)\mathrm{d}x \right\}$$

to the right-hand side of equation (4.15). For the mixed exponential distribution

$$\frac{T}{\mu} - \int_0^T h(x)\mathrm{d}x = -\frac{a}{b}(1 - e^{-bT})$$

which leads to

$$R(T) = N(0) \left\{ \left(\frac{1}{\mu} - \alpha - \frac{\alpha a}{\alpha - b} \right) e^{-\alpha T} - \frac{\alpha a}{\alpha - b} e^{-bT} \right\} \qquad (4.19)$$

where time is now measured from the moment when the reduction in size began. The condition for $R(T)$ to be always positive is identical with that given by the inequalities (4.18). However, if $R(T)$ does become negative, the time at which it does so will not be the same in the two cases. In fact if we put $\alpha = \mu^{-1}$ in equation (4.19), it is clear that redundancies will occur from the outset.

The general conclusion of our analysis so far is *that it will not usually be possible to run-down an organization at a rate as high as the observed wastage rate without causing redundancies.* We must next consider the problem of how to estimate recruitment and wastage rates if redundancies occur.

When redundancies occur equation (4.1) is no longer valid but equation (4.20) continues to hold if we take $R(T) = 0$ whenever the right-hand side is negative. If this happens $\bar{n}(T)$ must be interpreted as the total expected loss—including dismissals. In order to determine $\bar{n}(T)$ and $R(T)$ in this case we must distinguish between those members who leave of their own choice and those who are dismissed. Let the dismissal rate at time T be $R_D(T)$ so that the expected number of dismissals in $(0, T)$ is

$$\bar{n}_D(T) = \int_0^T R_D(x)\mathrm{d}x. \qquad (4.20)$$

Also let $\bar{n}_L(T)$ denote the expected number of those who leave of their own accord in $(0, T)$. Then

$$\bar{n}(T) = \bar{n}_D(T) + \bar{n}_L(T)$$

and hence

$$\frac{\mathrm{d}\bar{n}(T)}{\mathrm{d}T} = \frac{\mathrm{d}\bar{n}_L(T)}{\mathrm{d}T} \quad \text{if } R_D(T) = 0$$

$$= \frac{\mathrm{d}\bar{n}_L(T)}{\mathrm{d}T} + R_D(T) \quad \text{if } R_D(T) > 0$$

for a given value of T. Now $R(T) = 0$ if and only if $R_D(T) > 0$ and, consequently, $R_D(T) = 0$ if and only if $R(T) > 0$. Therefore equation (4.2) must take one of the following forms:

$$\left. \begin{array}{c} R(T) = M(T) + \dfrac{\mathrm{d}\bar{n}_L(T)}{\mathrm{d}T} \\[4mm] 0 = M(T) + \dfrac{\mathrm{d}\bar{n}_L(T)}{\mathrm{d}T} + R_D(T). \end{array} \right\} \qquad (4.21)$$

or

It is clear that the first member of equation (4.21) will cover both cases if we define $R(T) = -R_D(T)$ whenever

$$M(T) + \frac{\mathrm{d}\bar{n}_L(T)}{\mathrm{d}T}$$

is negative. The final stage in the solution is to find an equation for $\bar{n}_L(T)$. This may be expressed as follows:

$$\bar{n}_L(T) = N(0)F(T) + \int_0^T F(T - x)\langle R(x)\rangle\mathrm{d}x$$

$$- \int_0^T J(T - x|x)\langle -R(x)\rangle\mathrm{d}x \qquad (4.22)$$

where

$$\langle X \rangle = X \text{ if } X > 0$$

$$= 0 \text{ if } X \leq 0.$$

In equation (4.22) the first two terms on the right-hand side give the expected number who would have left even if there had been no dismissals.

However, some of these potential leavers will have been dismissed so a term must be subtracted to allow for this. The third term is therefore the expected number of redundant members among the potential leavers. The function $J(T|x)$ is the probability that a person who is declared redundant at time x would have left voluntarily in the interval $(x, x + T)$. In general this probability will depend on how those to be dismissed are chosen. Three rules which suggest themselves for investigation are (a) 'last in first out,' (b) 'first in first out' and (c) 'selection at random.' No progress has been made on the general problem except when the CLS distribution is exponential. In that case the residual length of service distribution is exponential whichever rule is used for selecting those to be dismissed. We thus have $J(T|x) = F(T) = (1 - e^{-\lambda T})$ for all x and hence equation (4.22) takes the following form

$$\bar{n}_L(T) = N(0)F(T) + \int_0^T F(T - x)R(x)\mathrm{d}x. \qquad (4.23)$$

Recalling that the first part of equation (4.21) can be used regardless of the sign of $R(T)$ we have a pair of equations for finding $\bar{n}_L(T)$ and $R(T)$ which are identical in form to equations (4.1) and (4.2). With an exponential CLS distribution, and only in this case, it is possible to use the same method whether or not redundancies occur. The results which we obtained for this distribution which are given in equations (4.13) and (4.14) thus apply for all α and λ provided that $\bar{n}(T)$ is replaced by $\bar{n}_L(T)$ when $\lambda > \alpha$.

In the general case the solution is more difficult though straightforward in principle. We would first obtain $\bar{n}_L(T)$ by substituting for $R(x)$ in equation (4.22). Secondly we would find $R(T)$ from equation (4.21). When this was known we could calculate the expected number of dismissals from equation (4.20) and the expected number of recruits could be obtained as

$$\int_0^T \langle R(x) \rangle \mathrm{d}x.$$

CHAPTER 7

RENEWAL THEORY MODELS FOR GRADED SOCIAL SYSTEMS

1. INTRODUCTION

In this chapter we return to the study of graded social systems begun in Chapters 3 and 5. The distinguishing feature of the present models is that the grade sizes do not change with time. The models of the earlier chapters were based on the assumption that the transition intensities, or probabilities in the case of discrete time models, were given and hence that the grade sizes were random variables. In the present case the roles of the constants and random variables are reversed; it is the grade sizes which are fixed and the transition rates which are random variables. If the processes are viewed deterministically the two kinds of specification are equivalent as far as their equilibrium predictions are concerned. The differences emerge when we consider their transient and stochastic behaviour.

The assumption of fixed grade sizes is often more realistic than that of fixed promotion and loss rates. In many organizations there is a fixed establishment in each grade which is determined by the work available for its members to perform. This situation is found in many government organizations, notably the Civil Service, and in British universities where the proportion of senior non-professorial staff in teaching posts is limited to two-ninths of the total establishment. Our models are designed to describe the operation of such systems and, in particular, to show the effect of grade structure on promotion prospects and wastage rates. We shall restrict the discussion to models in continuous time but Section 3.5 of Chapter 3, contains some closely related results for a discrete time model.

The basic model has the same elements as before but its mode of operation is different. We suppose that the grades form a hierarchy as illustrated in the diagram in Section 2.2 of Chapter 5. Every movement connected with the system is assumed to arise from a loss. Suppose, for example, that a member of grade 2 leaves. The vacancy thus created must be filled at once in order to maintain the size of the grade. This may be done either by direct recruitment from outside or by transfer from within the organization. If the vacancy is filled by promotion from grade 1, a new vacancy is created in that grade and this in turn must be filled by outside recruitment or demotion. The operation of such a system depends upon two further factors. One is the stochastic mechanism governing losses from the system; the other is the procedure for filling vacancies. The latter factor includes the decision on whether or not to fill the vacancy from within the organization and, if so, how it is to be done.

The stochastic law governing loss from the system will be specified by a loss intensity as in Chapter 5. Two basic assumptions will be made and these will form the basis of one of our two main methods of classifying the models. In Sections 3 and 4 we shall assume that the loss intensity is a function of an individual's total length of service only. It follows from this assumption that other factors, such as the speed with which the individual has risen in the hierarchy, do not influence the likelihood of his leaving. In practice a man's decision to leave might very well result from his having been passed over for promotion. To accommodate this kind of effect we shall, in Sections 5 and 6, suppose that the loss intensity is a function only of length of service in the present grade. This can never be true exactly because, as a man approaches retirement, his age obviously becomes an important factor but we shall not incorporate this into the model.

Our second main classification of models is based on the promotion rule. A promotion rule specifies the way in which a person is selected to fill a vacancy from within the system. Again we shall concentrate on two extreme cases. The first rule says that a vacancy shall be filled by the most senior member of the grade below. If several members have the same seniority one of them is selected at random. When this rule is applied consistently, the length of sevice of the member promoted both within his grade and within the organization, is at least as great as that of any other person who is eligible. This rule, or something approximating to it, often operates when experience constitutes the main qualification for promotion. The second rule postulates that a man's chance of promotion shall be independent of his seniority or length of service. This would be appropriate when some kind of innate ability was the determining consideration in assessing suitability for promotion. In probabilistic language this rule says that the member to be promoted should be selected at random from among those eligible.

This four-fold classification of models includes a wide range of possibilities between the extremes which it encompasses. We are thus continuing our earlier policy of considering extreme situations which are relatively simple rather than typical cases which are highly complex.

2. NOTATION AND BASIC RELATIONS

All of our models may be regarded as generalizations of the simple renewal process which formed the basis of the analysis in the last chapter.

These processes are non-Markovian and their full mathematical analysis presents considerable difficulties. In order to make progress possible we shall impose two restrictions at the outset which were only introduced at a late stage in our previous discussion of hierarchical organizations. These are:

(a) That all recruits enter the lowest grade. Vacancies occurring in grade 1 must therefore be filled from outside and vacancies higher up must be filled internally.

(b) Demotions do not take place and promotions are always into the next highest grade. This means that a vacancy in grade 4, say, sets in train a succession of promotions ending with the entry of a new recruit to grade 1.

In particular cases we shall have to specialize still further by assuming that the grade sizes are large or that the system has reached equilibrium.

As far as possible we shall use the same notation and terminology as in previous chapters but some modifications will be necessary. The grade sizes are no longer functions of T so we shall drop the argument and write them as

$$n_1, n_2, \ldots, n_k \text{ with } N = \sum_{i=1}^{k} n_i.$$

To conform with the usage of Chapter 5 we should have to write the loss intensity for a member of grade j as $r_{j,k+1}(T)$. Since we shall be assuming that this intensity is independent of j and to avoid the need for subscripts we shall use the notation $\lambda(T)$ as in the last chapter. An extension of the notation of Chapter 6 will be introduced for the promotion rates between grades and the wastage rates from the grades. Let $n_j h_j(T)\delta T$ be the expected number of promotions from grade j to grade $j + 1$ in $(T, T + \delta T)$, $(j = 1, 2, \ldots, k - 1)$. We shall describe $h_j(T)$ as the *promotion density* from grade j. This is a natural extension of the notation $h(T)$ used for the input to the system as a whole. Similarly we shall write $n_j w_j(T)\delta T$ for the expected number of losses from grade j in $(T, T + \delta T)$, $(j = 1, 2, \ldots, k)$. When considering the limiting behaviour of the system we shall write

$$\lim_{T \to \infty} h_j(T) = h_j \quad \text{and} \quad \lim_{T \to \infty} w_j(T) = w_j.$$

The density $h_j(T)$ is the analogue of the promotion intensity $r_{j,j+1}(T)$ of Chapter 5. In fact it may be regarded as an 'average' intensity but it would be misleading to use the same notation and terminology.

The wastage and promotion densities are related because the number of entries into any grade during a given time interval must exactly balance the number of losses through promotion or wastage. This statement implies that

$$n_{j-1}h_{j-1}(T) = n_jh_j(T) + n_jw_j(T) \quad (j = 2, 3, \ldots, k-1). \quad (2.1)$$

When $j = 1$ this equation holds if we replace the left-hand side by $R(T)$ which is the rate of input to the system. It also holds with $j = k$ if we define $h_k(T) \equiv 0$. An equivalent way of expressing the result of equation (2.1) is to write

$$n_jh_j(T) = \sum_{i=j+1}^{k} n_iw_i(T) \quad (j = 0, 1, 2, \ldots, k-1). \quad (2.2)$$

where $n_0h_0(T)$ is read as $R(T)$ here and in the remainder of this chapter. This basic relationship holds for all our models and implies that it will be sufficient to find either the $h_j(T)$'s or the $w_j(T)$'s.

The above equations can be used to make certain simple but important deductions about the relationship between the grade structure and the promotion rates. For example, suppose that we wish to have a system which, in equilibrium, gives equal promotion chances at every level of the organization. Then setting $h_{j-1} = h_j = h$ the equilibrium form of equation (2.1) may be written

$$(n_{j-1} - n_j)h = n_jw_j \quad (j = 2, 3, \ldots, k-1). \quad (2.3)$$

Since n_jw_j must be non-negative for all j it follows from equation (2.3) that

$$n_{j-1} \geq n_j \quad (j = 2, 3, \ldots, k-1). \quad (2.4)$$

This means that the structure of the organization must, in general, taper towards the top with the exception that grade k may be larger than grade $k - 1$. In fact, we shall meet examples later in which it has to be very much larger. More generally, if $h_{j-1} \neq h_j$ the inequalities (2.4) must be replaced by

$$h_{j-1}n_{j-1} \geq h_jn_j \quad (j = 2, 3, \ldots, k). \quad (2.5)$$

Using these inequalities we can deduce that if $h_{j-1} \geq h_j$ ($j = 2, 3, \ldots, k - 1$), then the grade sizes may increase or decrease as we move up the hierarchy.

Further results for the equilibrium state can be obtained by using simple renewal-type arguments. If μ is the mean length of service then the equilibrium recruitment rate will be $R = N\mu^{-1}$ which must also satisfy the equation

$$\sum_{i=1}^{k} n_iw_i = N\mu^{-1}. \quad (2.6)$$

If μ_j denotes the average time spent in grade j then the expected through-put for that grade per unit time will be $n_j\mu_j^{-1}$. This is also equal to $n_{j-1}h_{j-1}$ and hence, from equation (2.1),

$$\frac{n_j}{\mu_j} = n_j(h_j + w_j) = n_{j-1}h_{j-1} \quad (j = 2, 3, \ldots, k-1). \tag{2.7}$$

Although these last equations do not lead to any immediate conclusions about the effect of structure on promotion chances they will be useful in the subsequent analysis.

3. A MODEL WITH LOSS RATE A FUNCTION OF TOTAL LENGTH OF SERVICE AND PROMOTION BY SENIORITY

3.1. General Theory

Our main objective in this section is to determine the promotion and wastage densities. We have seen from equation (2.2) that it is sufficient to determine one set of these quantities. In the present instance it happens to be more convenient to work with the wastage densities $\{w_j(T)\}$. The method which we shall use (see Bartholomew, 1963a), enables us to find

$$\sum_{i=1}^{j} n_i w_i(T)\delta T,$$

which is the expected number of losses from grades 1 to j inclusive in $(T, T + \delta T)$. The individual wastage densities are then obtained by differencing.

If $\lambda(T)$ denotes the loss intensity for members of the organization then the CLS distribution has density function

$$\left.\begin{aligned}
f(T) &= \lambda(T)\mathrm{e}^{-\int_0^T \lambda(x)dx} \\
\text{and} \\
G(T) &= 1 - F(T) = \mathrm{e}^{-\int_0^T \lambda(x)dx}.
\end{aligned}\right\} \tag{3.1}$$

We shall first calculate the required expectation conditional upon f, the number of original members of the organization who remain at time T. This is a random variable whose distribution depends upon T. Since we are assuming the behaviour of the members to be independent, f will have a binomial distribution with parameters N and $G(T)$.

Consider the probability that the individual with the ith longest service leaves the organization in $(T, T + \delta T)$. This probability takes one of two forms. If $i > N - f$ the member in question will be one who joined at the beginning having length of service T. Hence the required probability is

$\lambda(T)\delta T$. If $i \leq N - f$ the probability of the ith most senior member leaving in $(T, T + \delta T)$ may be written as

$$\delta T \int_0^T \lambda(x) A_i(x|T, f) dx, \qquad (3.2)$$

where $A_i(x|T, f)$ is the probability density function of that particular member's length of service. The determination of the probability of leaving thus depends on our being able to find the form of this distribution. It can be obtained directly because it is the ith order statistic from the length of service distribution of all present members of the organization who have joined since the process began. A standard result in renewal theory gives the density function of length of service as

$$\left. \begin{aligned} a(t|T) &= h(T - t)G(t) \quad 0 \leq t < T \\ Pr\{t = T\} &= G(T). \end{aligned} \right\} \qquad (3.3)$$

The density function for those recruited after $T = 0$ may thus be expressed as

$$a^\circ(t|T) = h(T - t)G(t)/F(T) \quad 0 \leq t < T, \qquad (3.4)$$

and hence

$$A_i(t|T, f) = (N - f) \binom{N - f - 1}{i - 1} a^\circ(t|T) \left\{ \int_0^t a^\circ(x|T) dx \right\}^{i-1}$$

$$\left\{ \int_0^t a^\circ(x|T) dx \right\}^{N - f - i} \quad (i - 1, 2, \ldots, N - f). \qquad (3.5)$$

The conditional expected number of losses in $(T, T + \delta T)$ from grades 1 to j is now obtained by summing the individual probabilities of leaving for all members in these grades. This is greatly facilitated by the following consequence of the promotion rule. The rule implies that no member of grades 1 to j can have longer service than any member of grades $j + 1$ to k. The summation is thus over values of i from 1 to N_j, where

$$N_j = \sum_{i=1}^{j} n_i.$$

Dropping the δT from both sides of the equation we thus obtain

$$\left. \begin{aligned} \sum_{i=1}^{j} n_i w_i(T|f) &= \sum_{i=1}^{N-f} \int_0^T \lambda(x) A_i(x|T, f) dx + (N_j - N + f)\lambda(T) \\ &\qquad\qquad\qquad\qquad (f \geq N - N_j) \\ &= \sum_{i=1}^{N_j} \int_0^T \lambda(x) A_i(x|T, f) dx \quad (f < N - N_j) \\ &\qquad\qquad\qquad\qquad (j = 1, 2, \ldots, k), \end{aligned} \right\} \qquad (3.6)$$

where $w_i(T|f)$ is the wastage density conditional upon f. Reversing the order of summation and integration in the first part of equation (3.6), we obtain a binomial series which may be summed to give

$$\sum_{i=1}^{N-f} A_i(x|T,f) = (N-f)a°(x|T).\tag{3.7}$$

The sum in the second part of equation (3.6) is an incomplete binomial series which can be expressed, using a well-known result, in terms of the Incomplete Beta-function. Thus

$$\sum_{i=1}^{N_j} A_i(x|T,f) = (N-f)a°(x|T)I_{y(x|T)}(N-N_j-f, N_j),\tag{3.8}$$

where

$$y(x|T) = \int_x^T a°(u|T)du\tag{3.9}$$

$$I_y(a,b) = \int_0^y u^{a-1}(1-u)^{b-1}du/B(a,b)$$

and

$$B(a,b) = \Gamma(a)\Gamma(b)/\Gamma(a+b).$$

Substituting these results in equation (3.6), using the expression for $a°(t|T)$ given in equation (3.4) and remembering that $\lambda(T)G(T) = f(T)$, we find

$$\begin{aligned}\sum_{i=1}^{j} n_i w_i(T|f) &= \frac{N-f}{F(T)}\int_0^T f(x)h(T-x)dx + (N_j-N+f)\lambda(T) \\ &\qquad\qquad\qquad\qquad\qquad\qquad (f \geq N-N_j) \\ &= \frac{N-f}{F(T)}\int_0^T f(x)h(T-x)I_{y(x|T)}(N-N_j-f, N_j)dx \\ &\qquad\qquad\qquad\qquad\qquad\qquad (f < N-N_j).\end{aligned}\tag{3.10}$$

The integral equation for the renewal density enables us to replace the integral in the first part of equation (3.10) by $h(T) - f(T)$. The final step in the determination is to find the unconditional expectations by averaging over f. This gives

$$\sum_{i=1}^{j} n_i w_i(T) = \sum_{f=0}^{N}\sum_{i=1}^{j} n_i w_i(T|f)\binom{N}{f}\{G(T)\}^f\{F(T)\}^{N-f} \quad (j=1,2,\ldots,k).\tag{3.11}$$

Inspection of the foregoing formulae shows that their evaluation requires the prior determination of the renewal density $h(T)$. This can be found either exactly or approximately by the methods of the previous chapter. There is therefore no obstacle, apart from the magnitude of the task, to finding numerical values for the wastage densities. However, this will seldom be necessary because the exact theory can be used to obtain much simpler approximations as we shall show later.

3.2. Exact Solution in Special Cases

The method of solution is most easily illustrated by assuming a constant loss intensity, λ. In this case

$$f(T) = \lambda e^{-\lambda T}$$

and

$$h(T) = \lambda.$$

Making this substitution in equation (3.10), we have

$$
\left.
\begin{aligned}
\sum_{i=1}^{j} n_i w_i(T|f) &= \frac{(N-f)}{1 - e^{-\lambda T}} \lambda(1 - e^{-\lambda T}) + \lambda(N_j - N + f) \\
&= N_j \lambda \quad (f \geq N - N_j) \\
&= (N-f)\lambda \left(1 - \frac{N - N_j - f}{N - f} \right) = N_j \lambda \\
&\quad (f < N - N_j) \quad (j = 1, 2, \ldots, k).
\end{aligned}
\right\}
\tag{3.12}
$$

These equations show that the wastage densities are independent of f, so that

$$\sum_{i=1}^{j} n_i w_i(T) = N_i \lambda \quad (j = 1, 2, \ldots, k).$$

Hence, for all j

$$w_j(T) = \lambda. \tag{3.13}$$

As we might have expected the wastage densities are constant in time and the same for all grades. The promotion densities can be obtained from equation (2.2), which gives

$$h_j(T) = (N - N_j)\lambda/n_j \quad (j = 1, 2, \ldots, k - 1). \tag{3.14}$$

These formulae show how the promotion prospects in the organization depend on the relative grade sizes. As an illustration of their use we return to a question raised earlier in the chapter and ask what structure would yield equal promotion prospects. In order to make the right-hand side of equation (3.14) independent of j we must have

$$n_j \propto N - N_j = \sum_{i=j+1}^{k} n_i \quad (j = 1, 2, \ldots, k - 1). \tag{3.15}$$

This condition implies that the grade sizes must decrease in geometric progression as we move up the hierarchy. The exception to this rule is that the size of the highest grade may be any multiple of the one below it. A similar result was obtained in Section 2.2 of Chapter 5, for a system with fixed input and random grade sizes. There we showed that, if the promotion rates were equal, then the expected grade sizes would form a geometric series. Here we have shown that if the grade sizes are in geometric progression then the *expected promotion rates* will be equal. This result illustrates a remark we made in Section 1, about the equivalence of the two kinds of model when interpreted deterministically.

The practical usefulness of the result for a constant loss rate is severely limited because we have seen in Chapter 6 that it has no empirical support. Nevertheless the extremely simple forms of the solution in this case provide a convenient base line from which to measure the consequences of introducing greater realism into the model.

A complete solution is difficult to obtain for any other loss intensity unless we consider special cases. One such case is obtained by taking $k = 2$, $n_1 = n_2 = 1$. This specialization yields a process of some intrinsic interest but of little practical relevance. The reason for introducing it at this stage is that it enables us to judge the adequacy of an approximation discussed in the next section.

If $n_1 = n_2 = 1$

$$Pr\{f = i\} = \binom{2}{i} \{G(T)\}^i \{F(T)\}^{2-i} \quad (i = 0, 1, 2).$$

The Incomplete Beta-function in equation (3.10) reduces to $y(x|T)$ when $j = 1$, so that equation (3.11) yields the following expression for $w_1(T)$

$$w_1(T) = 2h(T)G(T)$$
$$- f(T)G(T) + 2 \int_0^T f(t)h(T - t) \left\{ \int_t^T G(x)h(T - x)dx \right\} dt. \quad (3.16)$$

The effect of using a more realistic CLS distribution may be illustrated by taking

$$f(T) = \tfrac{1}{2}\{\lambda_1 e^{-\lambda_1 T} + \lambda_2 e^{-\lambda_2 T}\} \quad (T \geq 0).$$

We have already solved the renewal equation for this distribution and we found that

$$h(T) = \mu^{-1} + ae^{-bT},$$

where, with $p = \tfrac{1}{2}$,

$$a = \tfrac{1}{2}(\lambda_1 + \lambda_2) - \mu^{-1}, b = \tfrac{1}{2}(\lambda_1 + \lambda_2) \text{ and } \mu = \tfrac{1}{2}(\lambda_1^{-1} + \lambda_2^{-1}).$$

The evaluation of $w_1(T)$ from equation (3.16) is tedious but straightforward. Without loss of generality we may take $\mu = 1$ and then we find,

$$
\left.
\begin{aligned}
w_1(T) &= \frac{3}{2} - \frac{1}{2b} + \frac{2a^2}{b} \, e^{-bT} + \left(a^2 T - \frac{3a^2}{2b}\right) e^{-2bT} \\[6pt]
w_2(T) &= 2h(T) - w_1(T).
\end{aligned}
\right\}
\tag{3.17}
$$

Thus the wastage densities both approach their equilibrium values at a rate governed by the exponential factor e^{-bT}. Some illustrative calculations have been plotted on Figure 7.1, which appears later in the chapter. For these calculations we have taken $\lambda_1 = 10\lambda_2$ which, since $\mu = 1$, implies that

$$\lambda_1 = 5.5 \quad \lambda_2 = 0.55 \quad a = 2.025 \quad b = 3.025$$

and

$$
\left.
\begin{aligned}
w_1(T) &= 1.3347 + 2.7112e^{-3.025T} + \{4.1006T - 1.0209\}e^{-6.05T} \\[6pt]
w_2(T) &= 0.6653 + 1.3388e^{-3.025T} - \{4.1006T - 1.0209\}e^{-6.05T}.
\end{aligned}
\right\}
\tag{3.18}
$$

The wastage rate declines more rapidly in grade 2, than in grade 1, but both reach their equilibrium values after approximately the same length of time.

3.3. Solution when the Grade Sizes are Large

The general expressions for the wastage densities simplify considerably in two limiting cases which we shall consider in this and the following section. The first of these relates to the case when the grade sizes are large and the second to the equilibrium state reached as $T \to \infty$. Both cases are of interest in their own right but our more immediate concern is to see whether they will serve as approximations to the exact solution.

We shall examine the effect of allowing n_i $(i = 1, 2, \ldots, k)$ to tend to infinity with the ratios n_i/n_{i+1} $(i = 1, 2, \ldots, k - 1)$ held constant. The first step in the derivation is to note that, if the n_i's are large, we may replace

$$\sum_{i=1}^{j} n_i w_i(T) = E_f \sum_{i=1}^{j} n_i w_i(T|f)$$

by

$$\sum_{i=1}^{j} n_i w_i(T|E(f)).$$

The two expressions are asymptotically equal and we shall show that the latter will serve as a good approximation to the former for quite small values of the n_i's. In order to obtain the limiting forms for the wastage densities we must therefore replace f by its expectation $NG(T)$ in equation (3.10). The range of validity of each part of that equation requires careful consideration because it is defined in terms of f. An obvious way of dealing with the question is to replace f in the inequality $f \geq N - N_j$ by its expectation. This gives

$$NG(T) \geq N - N_j \quad \text{or} \quad NF(T) \leq N_j,$$

and so defines the range of validity of each part of equation (3.10) in terms of T. Let the critical value of T defined by this inequality be denoted by T'_j. The above step may then be justified by noting that

$$\lim_{\substack{N, N_j \to \infty \\ N_j/N \text{ fixed}}} Pr\{f \geq N - N_j | G(T)\} = 1 \text{ if } T < T'_j$$

$$= 0 \text{ if } T > T'_j.$$

Asymptotically, therefore, the inequalities in terms of f and T are equivalent. On making the necessary substitutions in equation (3.10) we find, for $T < T'_j$,

$$\sum_{i=1}^{j} n_i w_i(T) \doteq N\{h(T) - f(T)\} + N\lambda(T)\{G(T) - (N - N_j)/N\}$$

$$(j = 1, 2, \ldots, k)$$

which simplifies to give

$$\sum_{i=1}^{j} n_i w_i(T) \doteq Nh(T) - (N - N_j)\lambda(T). \tag{3.19}$$

Differencing the equation we finally obtain

$$\left.\begin{array}{l} n_1 w_1(T) \doteq Nh(T) - (N - n_1)\lambda(T) \\ w_j(T) \doteq \lambda(T) \quad (j = 2, 3, \ldots, k). \end{array}\right\} \tag{3.20}$$

For $T > T'_j$ the second part of equation (3.10) applies. After replacing f by its expectation the Incomplete Beta-function becomes

$$I_{y(x|T)}(NF(T) - N_j, N_j).$$

The limiting form of this function can be found by considering the behaviour of the Beta probability density function

$$\frac{1}{B(r, s)} u^{r-1}(1 - u)^{s-1}.$$

as r and $s \to \infty$ with their ratio remaining fixed. Under these conditions the density function becomes concentrated at the point $u = r/(r + s)$ and hence it follows that

$$I_y(r, s) \to 0 \text{ if } y < \frac{r}{r + s}$$

$$\to 1 \text{ if } y \geq \frac{r}{r + s}.$$

If we now apply this result to the second part of equation (3.10), we obtain

$$\sum_{i=1}^{j} n_i w_i(T) \doteq N \int_0^{x_j(T)} f(x) h(T - x) \mathrm{d}x \quad (T > T_j'), \tag{3.21}$$

where $x_j(T)$ satisfies

$$\int_0^{x_j(T)} G(x) h(T - x) \mathrm{d}x = N_j/N \quad (j = 1, 2, \ldots, k). \tag{3.22}$$

The last equation arises from the fact that $x_j(T)$ thus defined is the critical length of service at which the limiting value of the Incomplete Beta-function changes from 0 to 1.

The limiting form of the solution given by equations (3.20), (3.21) and (3.22) is much simpler than the exact form and again it depends only on the renewal density, $h(T)$. We shall illustrate these results and make some assessment of their suitability as approximations in the finite case by assuming that the CLS distribution is mixed exponential with parameters p, λ_1 and λ_2. For $T < T_j'$ the approximation can be written down at once from equation (3.20). When $T > T_j'$ we must use equations (3.21) and (3.22), remembering that the renewal density has the form

$$h(T) = \mu^{-1} + a e^{-bT}.$$

This gives

$$\sum_{i=1}^{j} n_i w_i(T) \doteq N \left(\frac{1}{\mu} \int_0^{x_j(T)} f(x) \mathrm{d}x + a e^{-bT} \int_0^{x_j(T)} e^{bx} f(x) \mathrm{d}x \right). \tag{3.23}$$

with $x_j(T)$ given by

$$\frac{1}{\mu} \int_0^{x_j(T)} G(x) \mathrm{d}x + a e^{-bT} \int_0^{x_j(T)} e^{bx} G(x) \mathrm{d}x = \frac{N_j}{N} \quad (j = 1, 2, \ldots, k). \tag{3.24}$$

We thus have a pair of parametric equations which can be used to plot the wastage densities as functions of time.

Some calculations have been made for the case $k = 2$, $n_1 = n_2$ using the same parameter values as for the exact solution obtained in Section 3.2.

The curves have been plotted on Figure 7.1, where they are labelled '$N = \infty$'. They may be compared with the exact solution for $N = 2$ found earlier which has been drawn on the same figure. In spite of the crudeness of the approximations which have been made it is clear that the magnitude of N has relatively little influence on the wastage densities. Further calculations are needed before this conclusion can be fully justified but this example suggests that little will be lost by using the formulae derived on the assumption of large grade sizes. Additional support for our conclusion is provided by the fact that the approximation yields the exact solution when the loss rate is constant.

In Sections 5 and 6 of the present chapter we shall assume that the loss intensity depends on seniority within the grade instead of on total length of service. Under this assumption we shall not be able to obtain the exact theory and shall have to be content with an approximation of the kind given above. Since it will be derived by a deterministic argument it is instructive to see how our present results could have been obtained without recourse to the exact solution.

If N is large the proportion of original members remaining at time T will be approximately equal to $G(T)$. By virtue of the promotion rule these members will occupy the upper part of the hierarchy. In fact, if $G(T) \geq 1 - N_j/N$, grades $j + 1$ to k will consist entirely of original members all with length of service T. These members are all subject to the loss intensity $\lambda(T)$ and hence the expected number of losses in $(T, T + \delta T)$ is $\lambda(T)(N - N_j)\delta T$. In consequence the expected number of losses from grades 1 to j inclusive is the difference between this number and the total number of losses from the whole system in the same interval. Thus we have

$$\sum_{i=1}^{j} n_i w_i(T) \doteq Nh(T) - \lambda(T)(N - N_j) \quad (j = 1, 2, \ldots, k).$$

as in equation (3.20). This result holds if $T < T_j'$. When $T > T_j'$ we proceed as follows. The length of service distribution for members at time T was given in equation (3.3), and hence we can easily calculate the proportion of members whose length of service is less than any given value. All members of grades 1 to j must have shorter lengths of service than any member of grades $j + 1$ to k. Hence promotion from grade j to grade $j + 1$ must take place after a length of service $x_j(T)$ which must be such that the proportion of persons whose service does not exceed this value is exactly equal to N_j/N. That is $x_j(T)$ must satisfy the equations

$$\int_0^{x_j(T)} G(x)h(T - x)\mathrm{d}x = \frac{N_j}{N} \quad (j = 1, 2, \ldots, k - 1),$$

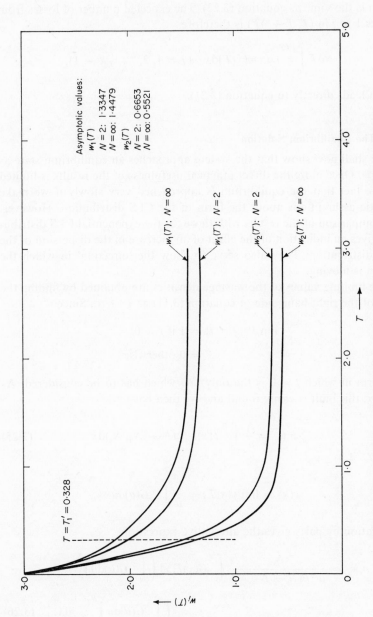

Figure 7.1. Graphs of $w_1(T)$ and $w_2(T)$ for $k = 2$, $n_1 = n_2$ and Promotion by Seniority

which is the same as equation (3.22). The expected number of losses from grades 1 to j in $(T, T + \delta T)$ is therefore

$$N\delta T \int_0^{x_j(T)} \lambda(x)a(x|T)dx \quad (j = 1, 2, \ldots, k - 1),$$

which leads directly to equation (3.21).

3.4. The Equilibrium Solution

We shall now show that the system approaches an equilibrium state as $T \to \infty$. Once more the direct practical usefulness of the results is limited by the fact that the equilibrium is approached very slowly if we make realistic assumptions about the form of the CLS distribution. However, the comparison of the results with those for the exponential CLS distribution gives an indication of the effect of an increase in the dispersion of the CLS distribution. They also serve to show the 'direction' in which the system is moving.

The limiting values of the wastage densities are obtained by finding the limit of the right-hand side of equation (3.11) as $T \to \infty$. Since

$$\lim_{T \to \infty} Pr\{f = i\} = 1 \text{ if } i = 0$$
$$= 0 \text{ otherwise}$$

the term in which $f = 0$ is the only one which has to be considered. As $T \to \infty$ this limit is easily found and we then have

$$\sum_{i=1}^{j} n_i w_i = \frac{N}{\mu} \int_0^\infty f(x) I_{y(x)}(N - N_j, N_j)dx \tag{3.25}$$

where

$$y(x) = \lim_{T \to \infty} y(x|T) = \frac{1}{\mu} \int_x^\infty G(u)du.$$

Integration by parts gives the alternative expression

$$\sum_{i=1}^{j} n_i w_i = \frac{N}{\mu^N B(N - N_j, N_j)} \int_0^\infty G(x)F(x) \left(\int_x^\infty G(u)du \right)^{N-N_j-1}$$
$$\left(\int_0^x G(u)du \right)^{N_j-1} dx. \tag{3.26}$$

These equations show that the equilibrium wastage densities can always be obtained either explicitly or by numerical integration.

An explicit solution can easily be obtained if the CLS distribution has the Type XI form. In this case

$$f(T) = \frac{v}{c}\left(1 + \frac{T}{c}\right)^{-(v+1)}$$

$$\mu = c/(v - 1)$$

$$G(T) = (1 + T/c)^{-v}$$

and

$$\int_T^\infty G(x)\mathrm{d}x = \mu\left(1 + \frac{T}{c}\right)^{-v+1}.$$

On substituting these expressions in equation (3.26) and evaluating the integral we find that

$$\sum_{i=1}^{j} n_i w_i = \frac{N}{\mu}\left\{1 - \frac{B\left(N, \dfrac{v}{v-1}\right)}{B\left(N - N_j, \dfrac{v}{v-1}\right)}\right\} \qquad (j = 1, 2, \ldots, k). \qquad (3.27)$$

If N, N_j and $N - N_j$ are all large, Stirling's approximation to the gamma function gives

$$\sum_{i=1}^{j} n_i w_i \sim \frac{N}{\mu}\left\{1 - \left(\frac{N - N_j}{N}\right)^{v/(v-1)}\right\} \qquad (j = 1, 2, \ldots, k). \qquad (3.28)$$

By allowing v to tend to infinity in either of equations (3.27) or (3.28) we recover the solution for the exponential distribution.

To illustrate the equilibrium theory we have given in Table 7.1 some values of w_1 when $k = 2$ for a Type XI CLS distribution with $\mu = 1$. The variance of the distribution is given in the last row of the table; it does not exist for $v \le 2$. These calculations suggest two general conclusions. First, *the effect of increasing the dispersion of the CLS distribution is to increase the wastage rate of the lowest grade relative to that of the system as a whole.* This implies a decrease in w_2 and hence a reduction in the promotion rate between grades 1 and 2. The amount of this change depends upon the structure of the organization, being greatest when the higher grade is larger than the lower. Put the other way round this conclusion states that the equilibrium promotion chances would be increased if the variability in completed length of service could be decreased. In a sense this is the converse of the conclusion reached in Chapter 5, Section 5.2. There we found that a decrease in the variability of CLS would tend to reduce the relative size of the lowest grade. The second conclusion is that the total size of the organization is relatively unimportant as far as its effect on w_1 is concerned. It is the relative rather than the absolute values of the grade sizes which are important. This supports our earlier conclusion based on the transient behaviour of the two-grade system with mixed exponential CLS distribution.

TABLE 7.1

Values of w_1 when $k = 2$ for a Type XI CLS
distribution with shape parameter ν.

				ν		
Structure	N	Limit as $\nu \to 1$	2	3	11	∞
	3	1.50	1.25	1.16	1.04	1.00
$n_1 = 2n_2$	18	1.50	1.32	1.20	1.05	1.00
	∞	1.50	1.33	1.21	1.05	1.00
	3	2.00	1.33	1.20	1.05	1.00
$n_1 = n_2$	18	2.00	1.47	1.28	1.07	1.00
	∞	2.00	1.50	1.29	1.07	1.00
	3	3.00	1.50	1.29	1.06	1.00
$n_1 = 2n_2$	18	3.00	1.63	1.35	1.08	1.00
	∞	3.00	1.67	1.37	1.08	1.00
Variance $(\nu/(\nu - 2))$		—	—	3.00	1.22	1.00

A full investigation of the dependence of the promotion and wastage densities on the structure for larger values of k would require extensive calculations but some further light can be thrown on the question by calculating the structure needed for the promotion rates to be equal. We have already solved this problem for the exponential CLS distributions. For any other distribution the promotion rates change with time and so the question can only be answered for the equilibrium state. We shall assume that the grade sizes are large enough to justify using the approximation given in equation (3.28). If we express this in terms of the h_j's by means of equation (2.2), it becomes

$$\frac{n_j}{N} = \frac{1}{\mu h_j} \left(1 - \frac{N_j}{N}\right)^{\nu/(\nu-1)} \qquad (j = 1, 2, \ldots, k-1). \qquad (3.29)$$

These equations enable us to determine the relative grade sizes necessary to attain any desired set of promotion densities. They have been solved for the case $k = 5$ and $h_1 = h_2 = h_3 = h_4$ and the results are given in

Table 7.2 for two values of v. For the purposes of this calculation we have supposed that the common promotion density is $2/\mu$.

TABLE 7.2

Relative grade sizes necessary to give equal promotion densities, in equilibrium, for $k = 5$, $\mu h = 2$ and a Type XI CLS distribution.

			j		
v	1	2	3	4	5
2	0.268	0.162	0.107	0.075	0.388
∞ (exponential)	0.333	0.222	0.148	0.099	0.198

The distribution with $v = 2$ has a much greater degree of skewness than the exponential distribution which has $v = \infty$. These calculations show that the structure has to be even more top-heavy when $v = 2$ than when $v = \infty$ in order to offer equal promotion chances at every level. The values of v which Silcock (1954) obtained by fitting the Type XI curve to his data were all smaller than 2. *It thus appears that the attainment of equal promotion prospects is an impossible goal in a pyramidical structure with typical wastage patterns.*

The limiting solution given by equation (3.25) is valid for all grade sizes. An equilibrium solution valid when the grade sizes are large can be found in two ways. One is to find the limiting form of equations (3.23) and (3.24) as $T \to \infty$. The other is to apply a limiting operation to equation (3.25) in which the grade sizes become large. In each one we reach the following approximate solution

$$\sum_{i=1}^{j} n_i w_i \doteq \frac{N}{\mu} \int_0^{x_j} f(x)\mathrm{d}x = \frac{N}{\mu} F(x_j), \tag{3.30}$$

where x_j satisfies

$$\frac{1}{\mu} \int_0^{x_j} G(x)\mathrm{d}x = N_j/N \quad (j = 1, 2, \ldots, k). \tag{3.31}$$

When the CLS distribution has the Type XI form these equations lead to the same approximation as given in equation (3.28).

4. A MODEL WITH LOSS RATE A FUNCTION OF TOTAL LENGTH OF SERVICE AND PROMOTION AT RANDOM

4.1. General Theory

Promotion is said to be 'at random' whenever the choice is made without regard to seniority. Strictly speaking we should use the description: 'at random with respect to length of service' since selection might well be on the basis of some other observable characteristic. However, provided that any such characteristic is independent of the individual's propensity to leave, our theory is applicable. Since we shall be concerned almost entirely with wastage and promotion densities we shall have no need to specify the promotion rule more precisely. If we were interested in such things as the distribution of 'ability' throughout the organization we should have to postulate how promotion depended on ability. For present purposes the promotion rule states that there is a probability equal to n_j^{-1} that any given member of grade j will be promoted when a vacancy occurs in grade $j + 1$ ($j = 1, 2, \ldots, k - 1$).

The general theory for this promotion rule is more difficult than it was for promotion by seniority. Nevertheless it is possible to develop a general theory which can be made the basis for deriving usable approximations. In order to formulate the theory we require the following definitions.

(a) Let $f_j(t|T)$ ($j = 1, 2, \ldots, k - 1$) be the probability density function of the remaining length of service of a person selected at random from grade j when the system is aged T. We may also define $f_0(t|T) \equiv f(t)$. The distribution function is denoted by $F_j(t|T)$ and its complement by $G_j(t|T)$.

(b) Let $Q_j(t|T)$ ($j = 1, 2, \ldots, k - 1$) be the probability that a member of grade j is not promoted in the interval $(T, T + t)$ given that he has not left in the same interval.

(c) Let $m_j(t|T)$ ($j = 1, 2, \ldots, k - 1$) be the number of promotions from grade j to grade $j + 1$ in the interval $(T, T + t)$. This number is, of course, a random variable.

The first step in the analysis is to express the expected number of losses from grade j in $(T, T + \delta T)$ in terms of the functions defined above. To do this let us classify the losses according to the time at which they entered the grade. The contribution from the initial members who were in grade j at $T = 0$ is clearly

$$n_j f_0(T|0) Q_j(T|0) \delta T.$$

For those who entered between $T - x$ and $T - x + \delta x$ the corresponding expected number is

$$n_{j-1} h_{j-1}(T - x) f_{j-1}(x|T - x) Q_j(x|T - x) \delta x \delta T.$$

Summing these contributions we have that

$$n_j w_j(T) = n_j f_0(T|0) Q_j(T|0) + n_{j-1} \int_0^T h_{j-1}(T-x) f_{j-1}(x|T-x) Q_j(x|T-x) \mathrm{d}x$$

$$(j = 1, 2, \ldots, k). \quad (4.1)$$

As they stand, these equations involve two unknown functions. The next step in the argument is to express these in terms of known quantities.

First let us consider the probability $Q_j(t|T)$. If we calculate the probability conditional upon the event $m_j(t|T) = i$, say, then it follows at once from the promotion rule that

$$Q_j(t|T, m_j(t|T) = i) = \left(1 - \frac{1}{n_j}\right)^i. \tag{4.2}$$

The unconditional probability may thus be expressed in the form

$$Q_j(t|T) = \sum_{i=0}^{\infty} Pr\{m_j(t|T) = i\} \left(1 - \frac{1}{n_j}\right)^i$$

$$= E\left(1 - \frac{1}{n_j}\right)^{m_j(t|T)} \quad (j = 1, 2, \ldots, k - 1). \tag{4.3}$$

In order to complete the determination we require the distribution of $m_j(t|T)$. This is not easy to obtain for any CLS distribution other than the exponential. In that case the promotion process from any grade is a Poisson process and hence $m_j(t|T)$ has a Poisson distribution. This result may be established as follows. The residual length of service distribution at any stage of a member's career always has the same exponential distribution. Hence grade k behaves like a simple renewal process. A standard result of renewal theory (see Cox, 1962, Section 3.1), states that the input to such a system is a Poisson process. Now grade $k - 1$ is subject to two kinds of removal each being independent Poisson processes. Hence the total output of that grade, which is identical to the input, must be a Poisson process. By repeating the argument for each grade in turn the result is established. The mean number of promotions from grade j in $(T, T + t)$ is clearly $n_j h_j t$ so that

$$Q_j(t|T) = \sum_{i=0}^{\infty} \frac{(n_j h_j t)^i}{i!} e^{-n_j h_j t} \left(1 - \frac{1}{n_j}\right)^i$$

$$= e^{-h_j t} \quad (j = 1, 2, \ldots, k - 1). \tag{4.4}$$

When the CLS distribution is not exponential we have only been able to make further progress by assuming that the grade sizes are large. Under these circumstances we can approximate $Q_j(t|T)$ by replacing $m_j(t|T)$ in equation (4.3) by its expectation. From the definition of the promotion density we have that

$$Em_j(t|T) = n_j \int_T^{T+t} h_j(x)dx. \tag{4.5}$$

Hence, substituting in equation (4.3) and taking the limit as $n_j \rightarrow \infty$, we find

$$Q_j(t|T) \sim \exp\left\{-\int_T^{T+t} h_j(x)\mathrm{d}x\right\} \quad (j = 1, 2, \ldots, k - 1). \quad (4.6)$$

The second function which we have to find in order to determine $n_j w_j(T)$ from equation (4.1) is $f_j(t|T)$. If we were told that a member of grade j had been in that grade for time x before his promotion to grade $j + 1$ at time T then it would follow that

$$f_j(t|T, x) = f_{j-1}(t + x|T - x)/G_{j-1}(x|T - x) \quad (j = 1, 2, \ldots, k - 1), \quad (4.7)$$

where $f_j(t|T, x)$ is the conditional distribution for given x. The distribution of x can be obtained as follows: the probability that we require is

Pr\{length of service in grade j is in $(x, x + \delta x)$ when promoted to grade $j + 1$ at time T\}

$= Pr$\{promotion from grade j with length of service in $(x, x + \delta x)$ at time T\}/Pr\{stay in grade j ended by promotion\}.

Of the two probabilities appearing on the right hand side of this equation only the numerator depends on x. It may be expressed as

Pr\{no loss in $(T - x, T)$\}Pr\{no promotion in $(T - x, T)$\}

$\times Pr$\{promotion in $T, T + \delta x$\}

$$= G_{j-1}(x|T - x)Q_j(x|T - x)h_j(T)\delta x. \quad (4.8)$$

Combining this probability with that given by equation (4.7), we find that

$$f_j(t|T) = C\int_0^T f_{j-1}(x + t|T - x)Q_j(x|T - x)\mathrm{d}x \quad (j = 1, 2, \ldots, k - 1). \quad (4.9)$$

The constant C is obviously given by

$$C^{-1} = \int_0^T G_{j-1}(x|T - x)Q_j(x|T - x)\mathrm{d}x. \quad (4.10)$$

The wastage densities, $\{w_j(T)\}$, can be determined in principle by the following method. First, solve equation (4.1), with $j = 1$. The equation then depends only on $f(T)$ and $h(T)$; $f(T)$ is given and $h(T)$ is found by solving the renewal equation. Secondly, knowing $w_1(T)$ and hence $h_1(T)$, determine $f_1(t|T)$ from equation (4.9). When this is known $w_2(T)$ can be found by putting $j = 2$ in equation (4.1). This is used to find $f_2(t|T)$ which, in turn, is needed to obtain $w_3(T)$, and so on. These steps can be carried out by numerical methods for any CLS distribution but the work involved is very heavy especially if k is large. The only CLS distribution for which a simple solution is available is the exponential. If

$$f(T) = \lambda e^{-\lambda T} \quad (T \geq 0)$$

we have already noted that

$$f_j(t|T) = \lambda e^{-\lambda T} \quad (T \geq 0)$$

for all j and T. Also we have shown in this case that

$$Q_j(t|T) = e^{-h_j t} \quad (j = 1, 2, \ldots, k - 1).$$

Making the appropriate substitutions in equation (4.1) it is easy to show that

$$w_j(T) = \lambda$$

and

$$h_j(T) = (N - N_j)\lambda/n_j \quad (j = 1, 2, \ldots, k - 1).$$

These values are identical with those obtained by assuming that promotions were made on the basis of seniority. The reason for this coincidence is that loss is independent of length of service for this distribution. Hence a rule which selects on the basis of length of service will be no different in its effect from one which selects at random. In no other case has it been found possible to obtain the full transient solution but some further progress can be made in the limiting case when $T \to \infty$.

4.2. The Equilibrium Solution

The direct method of investigating the limiting behaviour of the system would be to let T tend to infinity in equation (4.1). An alternative and somewhat simpler method is as follows. Let us treat grades $j + 1$ to k as a single grade. This composite grade will behave like a simple renewal process with a CLS distribution having the density function given by

$$\lim_{T \to \infty} f_j(t|T) = f_j(t) \text{ say.}$$

In the limit the renewal density for this process is known to be

$$(N - N_j)\Big/ \int_0^\infty t f_j(t)\mathrm{d}t \quad (j = 1, 2, \ldots, k - 1).$$

By definition it is also equal to $n_j h_j$. We shall now show that the mean of the residual CLS distribution depends upon h_j and h_{j-1} so that the equations

$$n_j h_j = (N - N_j)\Big/ \int_0^\infty t f_j(t)\mathrm{d}t \quad (j = 1, 2, \ldots, k - 1), \quad (4.11)$$

provide recurrence relations between h_j and h_{j-1}. Since the distribution $f_j(t)$ is of interest in its own right we shall first show how it can be found and then determine its mean. Letting $T \to \infty$ in equation (4.9), and using the approximate form of $Q_j(t|T)$ we find

$$f_j(t) = \int_0^\infty f_{j-1}(x+t)e^{-h_j x} dx / G_{j-1}^*(h_j), \qquad (4.12)$$

where

$$G_{j-1}^*(h_j) = \int_0^\infty G_{j-1}(x)e^{-h_j x} dx \quad (j = 1, 2, \ldots, k-1). \qquad (4.13)$$

It will be clear from the form of equation (4.13) why we have adopted the notation used earlier (Chapter 5, Section 4.1) for the Laplace transform. Once the limiting promotion densities have been found, equation (4.12) provides the means of determining the residual CLS distributions recursively beginning with $f_0(t) \equiv f(t)$.

Equation (4.12) can be expressed in terms of Laplace transforms. On transforming each side we obtain

$$f_j^*(s) = \frac{1}{G_{j-1}^*(h_j)} \left(\frac{f_{j-1}^*(s) - f_{j-1}^*(h_j)}{h_j - s} \right) \quad (j = 1, 2, \ldots, k-1). \quad (4.14)$$

Differentiating each side of this equation and setting $s = 0$ gives

$$\left. \frac{df_j^*(s)}{ds} \right|_{s=0} = \frac{1}{G_{j-1}^*(h_j)} \left(\frac{\left. \frac{df_{j-1}^*(s)}{ds} \right|_{s=0}}{h_j} + \frac{1 - f_{j-1}^*(h_j)}{h_j^2} \right). \qquad (4.15)$$

But

$$\left. \frac{df_j^*(s)}{ds} \right|_{s=0} = - \int_0^\infty t f_j(t) dt$$

$$= (N - N_j)/n_j h_j,$$

from equation (4.11). Making this substitution in equation (4.16) and simplifying we have

$$G_{j-1}^*(h_j) = n_j / n_{j-1} h_{j-1} \quad (j = 1, 2, \ldots, k), \qquad (4.16)$$

where $n_0 h_0$ is read as $N \mu^{-1}$ and

$$G_0^*(h_1) = \int_0^\infty G(x)e^{-h_1 x} dx.$$

Thus using equation (4.16) in conjunction with equation (4.14) the complete set of promotion densities, and hence the wastage densities, can be found. It can easily be verified that this procedure yields the same solution for the exponential distribution as we obtained in the last section.

An example of practical interest for which a complete equilibrium solution can be obtained is provided by the mixed exponential distribution. The recurrence relations for the residual length of service density functions can be simplified by using equation (4.16), to give

$$
\left.
\begin{aligned}
f_j(t) &= \frac{n_{j-1}h_{j-1}}{n_j} \int_0^\infty f_{j-1}(x+t)e^{-h_j x}dx \quad (j = 2, 3, \ldots, k-1) \\
f_1(t) &= \frac{N}{n_1\mu} \int_0^\infty f(x+t)e^{-h_1 x}dx,
\end{aligned}
\right\} \quad (4.17)
$$

where

$$
f(t) = p\lambda_1 e^{-\lambda_1 t} + (1-p)\lambda_2 e^{-\lambda_2 t} \quad (t \geq 0).
$$

Repeated application of equation (4.17) easily yields

$$
f_j(t) = \frac{N}{n_j\mu} \prod_{i=1}^{j} h_{i-1} \left(\frac{p\lambda_1 e^{-\lambda_1 t}}{\prod_{i=1}^{j}(\lambda_1 + h_i)} + \frac{(1-p)\lambda_2 e^{-\lambda_2 t}}{\prod_{i=1}^{j}(\lambda_2 + h_i)} \right)
$$
$$
(j = 1, 2, \ldots, k-1), \quad (4.18)
$$

where $h_0 = 1$. We thus have the very useful result that the successive residual life distributions all have the mixed exponential form. A similar result is arrived at if we take a mixed exponential distribution with more than two components. This fact makes it easy to find $G_j(t)$ and hence $G_j^*(s)$ for all j. On substituting the result in equation (4.16) the recurrence relation becomes

$$
\prod_{i=1}^{j} h_{i-1} \left(\frac{p}{\prod_{i=1}^{j}(\lambda_1 + h_i)} + \frac{1-p}{\prod_{i=1}^{j}(\lambda_2 + h_i)} \right) = \frac{n_j\mu}{N} \quad (j = 1, 2, \ldots, k), (4.19)
$$

where $h_0 = 1$ and $h_k = 0$. When $j = 1$, equation (4.19) gives a quadratic equation for h_1. The solution of this equation may then be substituted in equation (4.19) with $j = 2$ to give a quadratic for h_2. This procedure may be repeated for each grade in turn until the complete solution has been obtained. The wastage densities can then be determined from equation (2.1). As a simple illustration we have given some values of h_1 in Table 7.3 for different values of the ratio λ_1/λ_2 when $p = \frac{1}{2}$ and $\mu = 1$.

TABLE 7.3

Values of h_1 when the CLS distribution is mixed
exponential with $p = \frac{1}{2}$, $\mu = 1$ and $n_1 = \frac{1}{2}N$.

λ_1/λ_2	1	2	5	10	∞
h_1	1.00	0.94	0.76	0.64	0.50

It is clear from the table that the chances of promotion from grade 1 decrease as the dispersion of the CLS distribution increases. The corresponding value of h_1 for promotion by seniority when $\lambda_1/\lambda_2 = 10$ can be calculated from the results plotted in Figure 7.1. We take the curve for $N = \infty$ because our present theory has been derived on the assumption of large grade sizes and find that $h_1 = 2 - w_1 = 0.55$. *The random promotion rule thus offers better promotion prospects from grade 1 than does the seniority rule.*

A second comparison of the effects of the two rules can be made by considering the structure necessary to achieve equal promotion densities. An exact comparison is not possible for $k > 2$ because our results for the seniority rule were for the Type XI distribution and those in the present case are for the mixed exponential. However, the two distributions are similar in shape so we shall choose parameter values for the mixed exponential distribution which enable us to make a qualitative comparison with the figures given in Table 7.2.

If the h_j's are to have a common value h it is clear from equation (4.19) that the n_j's must satisfy the equations

$$\frac{ph^{j-1}}{(\lambda_1 + h)^j} + \frac{(1 - p)h^{j-1}}{(\lambda_2 + h)^j} = \frac{\mu n_j}{N} \quad (j = 1, 2, \ldots, k - 1), \qquad (4.20)$$

since $h_k = 0$. The grade sizes are thus expressible as a mixture of two geometric series. There is a close link here with the result for the simple exponential CLS distribution. In fact the latter can be obtained as a special case by putting $\lambda_1 = \lambda_2$ or $p = 0$ or 1. Some numerical values of the relative grade sizes are given in Table 7.4 for $k = 5$.

TABLE 7.4

Relative grade sizes required to give equal equilibrium promotion densities for a mixed exponential CLS distribution with $p = \frac{1}{2}$, $\mu = 1$ and $h = 2$ when promotion is at random.

	Grade				
	1	2	3	4	5
$\lambda_1/\lambda_2 = 10$	0.263	0.172	0.125	0.096	0.345
$\lambda_1/\lambda_2 = 1$ (exponential)	0.333	0.222	0.148	0.099	0.198

In broad terms the conclusion to be drawn from this table is the same as that from Table 7.2 which related to the rule of promotion by seniority.

The structure is slightly less top-heavy when promotion is at random but it is clearly the form of the CLS distribution rather than the promotion rule which is the main determinant of the grade sizes required. This analysis serves to underline our earlier conclusion that equal promotion opportunities and a tapering structure are incompatible in practice. Modifying the promotion rule can, at best, produce only a marginal improvement.

The determination of the full solution for other CLS distributions is a formidable task but it is relatively easy to obtain h_1 for any distribution. Thus, from equation (4.16), h_1 satisfies

$$\int_0^\infty G(x)e^{-h_1 x}dx = n_1\mu/N, \qquad (4.21)$$

and this equation can always be solved numerically. An upper bound for h_1 is found by observing that the left-hand side of equation (4.21) is maximized for *given* h_1 by taking

$$G(x) = 1 \text{ for } 0 \le x \le \mu$$
$$= 0 \text{ for } x > \mu.$$

($G(x)$ must be a non-increasing function with

$$\int_0^\infty G(x)dx = \mu,$$

and $G(x) \le 1$ for all x.) Hence, if equation (4.21) is satisfied when $G(x)$ has this form, then any change in its form will require a reduction in h_1 if the equation is still to hold. Therefore, the solution of

$$\int_0^\mu e^{-h_1' x}dx = \frac{1 - e^{-h_1' x}}{h_1'} = \frac{n_1\mu}{N},$$

is an upper bound for h_1. Tables of the solution of this equation are given in Barton *et al.* (1960). If $\mu = 1$, $n_1 = \frac{1}{2}N$ we find $h_1' = 1.59$ which may be compared with the values in Table 7.3. The bound is not attainable since the extremal form of $G(x)$ implies that the CLS is constant in which case the renewal density does not exist.

4.3. Adequacy of the Assumption of Large Grade Sizes

The whole of the foregoing theory for random promotion rests on the assumption that the grade sizes are large enough to warrant the replacement of $Q_j(t|T)$ as given in equation (4.3) by the approximation of equation (4.6). We shall make a partial test of this assumption by comparing our results with the exact values in a particularly unfavourable case. This occurs when $n_i = 1$ for all i. In this case all promotion rules are equivalent because there is no scope for choice. We can therefore use the exact theory developed for promotion by seniority to make our comparison. Some calculations for the case $k = 2$ are presented in Table 7.5. We have again assumed a mixed exponential CLS distribution with $p = \frac{1}{2}$ and $\mu = 1$.

TABLE 7.5

Comparison of exact and approximate values of
h_1 for random promotion when $n_1 = n_2 = 1$.

λ_1/λ_2	1	2	5	10	∞
Approximate ($N = \infty$)	1.00	0.94	0.76	0.64	0.50
Exact ($N = 2$)	1.00	0.94	0.78	0.67	0.50

The approximation slightly underestimates the true promotion density and hence slightly overestimates the wastage density but the agreement is remarkably good.

5. A MODEL WITH LOSS RATE DEPENDING ON SENIORITY WITHIN THE GRADE AND PROMOTION BY SENIORITY

5.1. Introduction and General Theory

In this and the following section we shall suppose that the loss intensity for a given individual is a function only of his seniority in his current grade. The course which we shall follow runs parallel to that followed in the earlier part of this chapter. First we shall assume that promotion is by seniority and secondly, in Section 6, that it is at random. The symbol τ will be used in the remainder of this chapter to denote length of service within a given grade. Otherwise, we shall use the same notation as before although the roles which the various quantities play will be somewhat different.

The models of this section imply that it is a man's experience in his current job rather than his experience with the firm which influences his propensity to leave. Thus an ambitious person might become increasingly dissatisfied with waiting for promotion and so become more likely to leave with the passage of time. Alternatively increasing achievement or stronger personal ties might make the member less likely to leave as his seniority increases. In practice it seems probable that length of service both within the grade and within the firm will exert their influence. A general model embodying both features would be intractable so we shall adopt our usual strategy of concentrating on extreme but relatively simple cases.

The wastage and promotion densities will continue to be our main concern but, in addition, we shall meet a new feature of considerable interest. Previously the CLS distribution has been part of the data of the problem when it has sometimes been specified in terms of its associated loss intensity. In the present case it is not given but must be deduced from the loss intensities within the grades and the structure of the system. As a by-product of the analysis we shall therefore have a new class of models for the leaving process to add to those in Section 2 of Chapter 6. It is of interest to see whether they have the same characteristics as those we have seen to be typical in practice.

The methods used in Section 3 for obtaining the transient behaviour of the system do not carry over to the present case. Neither has any alternative approach been found apart from the special cases noted below. For the most part, therefore, we shall have to rely on equilibrium results valid when the grade sizes are large. The principal exception to this remark is provided by the highest grade. Since each member 'begins again' on promotion to grade k this behaves exactly like a simple renewal process. The CLS distribution appropriate to this grade has a known loss intensity which we shall denote by $\lambda_k(\tau)$. This distribution plays the same role as the residual length of service distribution which appeared in the last section, so its density function will be denoted by $f_{k-1}(\tau)$. Corresponding functions for other grades have the same notation with an appropriate change of subscript. The expected number of entrants to grade k in $(T, T + \delta T)$ is $n_{k-1}h_{k-1}(T)$ and this must clearly satisfy the following integral equation

$$n_{k-1}h_{k-1}(T) = n_k f_{k-1}(T) + n_{k-1} \int_0^T h_{k-1}(T - \tau) f_{k-1}(\tau) d\tau. \qquad (5.1)$$

This equation may be solved for $n_{k-1}h_{k-1}(T)/n_k$ by the methods of Chapter 6 and so $h_{k-1}(T)$ and $w_{k-1}(T)$ can both be found. No such equation holds for the lower grades because removals from those grades are partly due to natural loss and partly to promotions to the next higher grade. The general transient solution can be obtained, however, when the loss intensities $\{\lambda_j\}$ are constants and we shall justify this remark in Section 6.

5.2. Equilibrium Theory When the Grade Sizes are Large

Let $\mu_{(j)}$ be the average time spent in grade j ($j = 1, 2, \ldots, k$) regardless of whether the stay there ends in promotion or wastage. When the system has reached equilibrium the total removal density from that grade must be $n_j/\mu_{(j)}$. Since the grade sizes must remain fixed, this density can be equated to the input density of that grade. Thus

$$
\left.\begin{aligned}
n_{j-1}h_{j-1} &= n_j/\mu_{(j)} \quad (j = 2, 3, \ldots, k) \\
R &= n_1/\mu_{(1)}.
\end{aligned}\right\} \tag{5.2}
$$

To make further progress we must assume that the grade sizes are large. In Section 3 we showed that this restriction was of little practical consequence and we anticipate that the same will be true here. Under this assumption the seniority at which promotions occur from grade j will approach a limiting value which we shall denote by τ_j $(j = 1, 2, \ldots, k - 1)$. Of those who enter grade j a proportion

$$
F_{j-1}(\tau_j)
$$

will leave before reaching the seniority in that grade at which they would be promoted. The input to grade j must therefore be sufficient to allow for this wastage and provide just enough candidates to fill the vacancies occurring in grade $j + 1$. This requires that

$$
\left.\begin{aligned}
n_{j-1}h_{j-1}G_{j-1}(\tau_j) &= n_jh_j \quad (j = 2, 3, \ldots, k - 1) \\
RG_0(\tau_1) &= n_1h_1.
\end{aligned}\right\} \tag{5.3}
$$

The final step in the argument is to express $\mu_{(j)}$ in terms of τ_j. We shall then be able to eliminate τ_j between equations (5.2) and (5.3), and so obtain a recurrence relation between h_j and h_{j-1}.

In view of the fact that everyone leaves grade j not later than τ_j after entering it we have

$$
\begin{aligned}
\mu_{(j)} &= \int_0^{\tau_j} \tau f_{j-1}(\tau)\mathrm{d}\tau + \tau_j G_{j-1}(\tau_j) \\
&= \int_0^{\tau_j} G_{j-1}(\tau)\mathrm{d}\tau \quad (j = 1, 2, \ldots, k; \tau_k = \infty). \tag{5.4}
\end{aligned}
$$

Substituting for $\mu_{(j)}$ in equation (5.2) gives

$$
\left.\begin{aligned}
\frac{n_j}{n_{j-1}h_{j-1}} &= \int_0^{\tau_j} G_{j-1}(\tau)\mathrm{d}\tau \quad (j = 2, 3, \ldots, k; \tau_k = \infty) \\
\frac{n_1}{R} &= \int_0^{\tau_1} G_0(\tau)\mathrm{d}\tau.
\end{aligned}\right\} \tag{5.5}
$$

If we solve these equations for $\{\tau_j\}$ and substitute the solution in equation (5.3), we obtain a recurrence relation from which the h_j's can be calculated. Equation (5.5) gives h_{k-1} directly and the remaining h_j's are found in decreasing order of their subscripts.

As a first example suppose that the loss intensity is constant but has a different value in each grade. Thus we may write $\lambda_j(\tau) = \lambda_j$ $(j = 1, 2, \ldots, k)$. We know of no direct empirical evidence in support of this form but we shall show later that it can lead to a CLS distribution similar to those observed in practice. Under this assumption

$$f_{j-1}(\tau) = \lambda_j e^{-\lambda_j \tau}, \quad G_{j-1}(\tau) = e^{-\lambda_j \tau}$$

and

$$\int_0^\tau G_{j-1}(x)dx = (1 - e^{-\lambda_j \tau})/\lambda_j \quad (j = 1, 2, \ldots, k).$$

On substituting these expressions in equations (5.3) and (5.5) and eliminating

$$e^{-\lambda_j \tau_j}$$

between them we find

$$n_{j-1}h_{j-1} = n_j h_j + n_j \lambda_j$$

and hence

$$\left. \begin{aligned} h_j &= \sum_{i=j+1}^{k} n_i \lambda_i / n_j \quad (j = 1, 2, \ldots, k - 1) \\ R &= \sum_{i=1}^{k} n_i \lambda_i. \end{aligned} \right\} \tag{5.6}$$

When $\lambda_j = \lambda$, for all j, these expressions reduce to those given in equations (3.13) and (3.14). In this case the differences between the various models vanish and the same solution is obtained. The effect of increasing (decreasing) the loss intensity in grade i is to increase (decrease) the promotion density h_j $(j < i)$ by an amount proportional to n_i/n_j. Equation (5.6) can also be used to determine the grade structure necessary to achieve any desired set of promotion densities.

For our second example we suppose that the loss intensity decreases monotonically with

$$\lambda_j(\tau) = \left(\frac{v_j}{\kappa_j + \tau} \right) \quad (j = 1, 2, \ldots, k). \tag{5.7}$$

In this case

$$f_{j-1}(\tau) = \frac{v_j}{\kappa_j} \left(1 + \frac{\tau}{\kappa_j} \right)^{-(v_j+1)} \quad G_{j-1}(\tau) = \left(1 + \frac{\tau}{\kappa_j} \right)^{-v_j}$$

and

$$\int_0 G_{j-1}(x)dx = \mu_j \left\{ 1 - \left(1 + \frac{\tau}{\kappa_j} \right)^{-v_j+1} \right\} \quad (j = 1, 2, \ldots, k),$$

where $\mu_j = \kappa_j/(\nu_j - 1)$. Following the same procedure as in the previous example the recurrence relation for the h_j's is found to be

$$\mu_j n_{j-1} h_{j-1} = n_j \bigg/ \left\{ 1 - \left(\frac{n_j h_j}{n_{j-1} h_{j-1}} \right)^{(\nu_j-1)/\nu_j} \right\} \quad (j = 1, 2, \ldots, k), \quad (5.8)$$

where $h_k = 0$.

The grade structure needed to give equal promotion densities is easily obtained in this case. Setting $h_j = h$ for $j = 1, 2, \ldots, k - 1$ in equation (5.8) we see that the n_j's must satisfy the equations

$$\left. \begin{aligned} \frac{n_j}{n_{j-1}} &= \mu_j h \left\{ 1 - \left(\frac{n_j}{n_{j-1}} \right)^{(\nu_j-1)/\nu_j} \right\} \quad (j = 2, 3, \ldots, k - 1) \\ \frac{n_k}{n_{k-1}} &= h\mu_k. \end{aligned} \right\} \quad (5.9)$$

The solution of equation (5.9) gives n_j/n_{j-1} as a function of $\mu_{(j)}$, h and ν_j. If $\nu_j = \nu$ and $\kappa_j = \kappa$ for all j we reach the interesting conclusion that the grade sizes, except for grade k, must form a geometric series. It is a little surprising to find here the same result as in the case of a constant loss intensity. In the example of Section 3.4 the loss intensity had the same form but was a function of total length of service instead of seniority within the grade. In that case the equilibrium structure giving equal h_j's was not geometric (see equation 3.29 and Table 7.2). A numerical comparison of

TABLE 7.6

Relative grade sizes, n_j/N, required to give equal promotion densities for the models of Sections 3 and 5, when promotion is according to seniority.

	$\nu = 2$		$\nu = \infty$
j	Model of Section 3	Model of Section 5	Both Models
1	0.333	0.437	0.333
2	0.167	0.235	0.222
3	0.100	0.126	0.148
4	0.067	0.067	0.099
5	0.333	0.135	0.198

the two cases is given in Table 7.6 for $k = 5$, $h = 2$ and $\mu = 2$. The parameter κ is a scale parameter and does not enter into the comparison. In the last column of the table we have given the limiting case as $\nu \to \infty$; both models then coincide, having a constant loss intensity.

The familiar pattern of a tapering structure with a very large top grade occurs in both cases. The model of Section 3 shows the greater divergence from the limiting case in all grades except the first. In the case of this model, *the effect of a decreasing loss rate is to increase the relative size of the highest grade*.

Our third example is almost identical mathematically with the second but its practical implications are very different. Suppose that the loss intensities are given by

$$\lambda_j(\tau) = \frac{v_j}{\kappa_j - \tau} \quad (0 \leq \tau < \kappa_j; j = 1, 2, \ldots, k). \tag{5.10}$$

In this case the propensity to leave *increases* with seniority until, after a time κ_j, the person leaves automatically. We considered a similar function in Chapter 5 (equation 6.6), but there the loss intensity was a function of total length of service. Our choice of $\lambda_j(\tau)$ for this example would describe the behaviour of someone who became increasingly dissatisfied until a point was reached at which he felt compelled to leave.

The recurrence formula for the promotion densities holds for this example also if we replace μ_j by $\kappa_j/(v_j + 1)$ and $(v_j - 1)/v_j$ by $(v_j + 1)/v_j$.

5.3. The CLS Distribution

As we remarked in Section 5.1, the CLS distribution is no longer given but must be found from the loss intensities and the grade sizes. When promotion is by seniority the distribution is easily obtained as follows. Let $\lambda(T)$ be the loss intensity for a person who has been in the organization for length of time T. Then it is clear that, under the assumption of large grade sizes and in equilibrium,

$$\left. \begin{aligned} \lambda(T) &= \lambda_1(T) & 0 \leq T < \tau_1 \\ &= \lambda_2(T - \tau_1) & \tau_1 \leq T < \tau_2 \\ & \quad \cdots \\ &= \lambda_k(T - \tau_{k-1}) & \tau_{k-1} \leq T < \infty, \end{aligned} \right\} \tag{5.11}$$

where $\tau_1, \tau_2, \ldots, \tau_{k-1}$ are the seniorities at which promotions take place. The CLS distribution is then given by

$$f(T) = \lambda(T)e^{-\int_0^T \lambda(x)dx} \quad (T \geq 0).$$

The discontinuities in $\lambda(T)$ will lead to discontinuities in $f(T)$. A full investigation of the shapes to which this model can give rise has not been undertaken but a simple example will illustrate some of the possibilities.

Let $k = 2$ and $\lambda_j(\tau) = \lambda_j$ $(j = 1, 2)$. Then

$$\left.\begin{aligned}
f(T) &= \lambda_1 e^{-\lambda_1 T} \quad 0 \leq T < \tau_1 \\
&= \lambda_2 e^{-\lambda_1 \tau_1 - \lambda_2(T - \tau_1)} \quad \tau_1 \leq T < \infty.
\end{aligned}\right\} \tag{5.12}$$

The point of discontinuity τ_1 is found from equation (5.5), which becomes in this case

$$e^{-\lambda_1 \tau_1} = n_2 \lambda_2 / N(\lambda_1 + \lambda_2). \tag{5.13}$$

The density function $f(T)$ thus has the form of an exponential density with parameter λ_1 over the first part of its range and the same form with parameter λ_2 over the second part. Its most obvious characteristic is the discontinuity at $T = \tau_1$ and one would be able to recognize this in practice if the model applied. However, whether or not this simple form of the model is realistic, we may note that it possesses one feature which has been observed in CLS distributions. If $\lambda_1 > \lambda_2$ there will be an excess of frequency at the lower and upper ends of the range if we compare the distribution with the exponential curve having the same mean. A similar result holds if we consider an organization with more than 2 grades provided that the loss intensities decrease as we move up the hierarchy. These facts lead us to expect that models in which loss rates are constant within the grades may be capable of describing observed distributions. This point will be taken up again in Section 6.3, where it will be seen that the form of $f(T)$ is mixed exponential when promotion is at random.

6. A MODEL WITH LOSS RATE DEPENDING UPON SENIORITY WITHIN THE GRADE AND PROMOTION AT RANDOM

6.1. Exact Theory in the Transient Case

When promotion is at random it is relatively easy to obtain integral equations for the promotion and wastage densities in the transient case. Unfortunately, the solutions to these equations are not always easy to find. In this section we shall formulate the basic theory and obtain an explicit solution in one case. It will again be necessary to assume that the grade sizes are large. In the next section we shall use the exact theory to obtain the equilibrium solution by letting T tend to infinity.

We begin by recalling that the behaviour of grade k does not depend upon the promotion rule and hence that $h_{k-1}(T)$ can be obtained as in Section 5.1 from equation (5.1). Let us now consider grade j and attempt to treat it as a simple renewal process. This would be possible if the length of time spent in that grade by any individual had a distribution independent of T. However, this is not so because there are two intensities of removal acting on members of this grade. There is the loss intensity $\lambda_j(\tau)$ depending only on seniority within the grade and there is also the promotion intensity which is a function of T only. When promotion is at random the probability that any given member of grade j will be promoted in $(T, T + \delta T)$ is $h_j(T)\delta T$. Hence, since promotion and loss are independent, the total force of removal acting on a member of grade j with seniority τ at time T is

$$\lambda_j(\tau) + h_j(T) \quad (j = 1, 2, \ldots, k - 1). \tag{6.1}$$

The sojourn time distribution for grade j thus depends on the time of joining the grade and on the length of service. Renewal processes of this kind were discussed in Section 3.5 of the last chapter. In order to use the results given there we must first find the distribution of the sojourn time.
Let

$$\lambda_{(j)}(\tau|X) = \lambda_j(\tau) + h_j(X + \tau)$$

denote the intensity of removal for a member of grade j who entered grade j at time X and has a length of service τ in that grade. It is tempting to write down the density function of sojourn time as

$$f_{(j)}(\tau|X) = \lambda_{(j)}(\tau|X)\exp - \int_0^T \lambda_{(j)}(x|X)\mathrm{d}x. \tag{6.2}$$

However, this step requires the assumption that the probability of removal from the grade with seniority in $(\tau, \tau + \delta\tau)$ at time $X + \tau$ is independent of events prior to that time. This is certainly true for the loss probability but it does not hold in general for the promotion process. The probability of promotion in any small increment of time depends in general on the time of the last promotion. The exceptional case occurs when the promotion process is also a Poisson process. This happens if all the loss rates are constant since then the losses from any grade constitute a Poisson process and hence so must the promotions. It also happens asymptotically as the grade sizes increase, as may be deduced from a result of Khintchine (1960, Chapter 5). In order to make use of equation (6.2) in the general case we shall therefore have to assume that the grade sizes are large. Under these conditions it follows from equation (3.15) of Chapter 6 that the promotion densities are given by:

$$n_{j-1}h_{j-1}(T) = n_j f_{(j)}(T|0) + n_{j-1}\int_0^T f_{(j)}(\tau|T - \tau)h_{j-1}(T - \tau)\mathrm{d}\tau$$

$$(j = 1, 2, \ldots, k). \tag{6.3}$$

Substituting for $f_j(\tau|T - \tau)$ from equation (6.2), we arrive at equations connecting $h_{j-1}(T)$ with $h_j(T)$. We therefore begin by finding $h_{k-1}(T)$ in the way described above and then use equation (6.3) to compute the remaining densities recursively.

Although it is easy to construct these equations it is difficult to find analytical solutions. One exception to this rule occurs when the loss intensities are constant within the grade. Thus if $\lambda_j(\tau) = \lambda_j$ $(j = 1, 2, \ldots, k)$, the solution proceeds as follows. Putting $j = k$ in equation (6.2) gives

$$f_{(k)}(\tau|T - \tau) = \lambda_k e^{-\lambda_k \tau} \quad (\tau \geq 0),$$

and hence, by solving equation (6.3) with $j = k$, we have

$$\frac{n_{k-1}h_{k-1}(T)}{n_k} = \lambda_k \text{ and hence } h_{k-1}(T) = \frac{n_k \lambda_k}{n_{k-1}}. \tag{6.4}$$

This result follows from the fact that, in this case, equation (6.3) reduces to the standard integral equation of renewal theory. Next we put $j = k - 1$ in equation (6.2) and so find

$$f_{(k-1)}(\tau|T - \tau) = \left(\lambda_{k-1} + \frac{n_k \lambda_k}{n_{k-1}}\right) \exp\left\{-\lambda_{k-1}\tau - \frac{n_k \lambda_k}{n_{k-1}}\tau\right\} \tag{6.5}$$

which is an exponential distribution with parameter $(n_{k-1}\lambda_{k-1} + n_k \lambda_k)/n_{k-1}$. Substitution of this result in equation (6.3), with $j = k - 1$, yields another integral equation of the same form from which we find that

$$\frac{n_{k-2}h_{k-2}(T)}{n_{k-1}} = \frac{n_{k-1}\lambda_{k-1} + n_k \lambda_k}{n_{k-1}}$$

and hence

$$h_{k-2}(T) = \frac{n_{k-1}\lambda_{k-1} + n_k \lambda_k}{n_{k-2}}. \tag{6.6}$$

This procedure can be repeated for each grade to give

$$h_j(T) = \frac{\sum_{i=j+1}^{k} n_i \lambda_i}{n_j}, \quad R = \sum_{i=1}^{k} n_i \lambda_i \quad (j = 1, 2, \ldots, k - 1), \tag{6.7}$$

which agrees with the equilibrium solution for the case of promotion by seniority given in equation (5.6). Under the assumption of constant loss rates the two promotion rules are identical in the way in which they affect the promotion or wastage densities. The exact theory derived above thus applies equally to both rules and so establishes that the equilibrium result given in equation (5.6) is, in fact, the transient solution also.

It would be possible to solve equation (6.3) by numerical methods for any other kind of loss intensity. A practical question of more immediate concern for the application of the theory is to find whether the assumption of constant loss rates is valid in practice. This could be tested by seeing whether the promotion and wastage rates remain constant over time. Here we have a good example of how the analysis of a theoretical model can guide empirical research.

6.2. Equilibrium Theory

The equilibrium theory can be readily deduced from equations (6.2) and (6.3) by taking limits as $T \to \infty$. Beginning with $h_{k-1}(T)$ we know from standard renewal theory that

$$\frac{n_{k-1}h_{k-1}}{n_k} = \frac{1}{\mu_{(k)}},$$

where $\mu_{(k)}$ is the mean of the sojourn time distribution for the kth grade. A closely related result also states that

$$\lim_{T \to \infty} \int_{T-\tau}^{T} h_j(x)dx = \tau h_j \quad (j = 1, 2, \ldots, k-1)$$

for fixed τ. The limiting form of the sojourn density function for finite τ may thus be written

$$f_{(j)}(\tau) = \{\lambda_j(\tau) + h_j\} \exp\left\{-\int_0^\tau \lambda_j(x)dx - h_j\tau\right\} \quad (j = 1, 2, \ldots, k; h_k = 0\}$$

(6.8)

In the limit, therefore, grade j may be treated as a simple renewal process with a renewal distribution given by equation (6.8). It then follows that

$$\left.\begin{aligned} n_{j-1}h_{j-1} &= n_j/\mu_{(j)} \quad (j = 1, 2, \ldots, k-1) \\ R &= n_1/\mu_{(1)}. \end{aligned}\right\}$$

(6.9)

Now

$$\mu_{(j)} = \int_0^\infty \tau f_{(j)}(\tau)d\tau = \int_0^\infty G_{(j)}(\tau)d\tau,$$

where

$$G_{(j)}(\tau) = \int_\tau^\infty f_{(j)}(x)dx = \exp\left\{-\int_0^\tau \lambda_j(x)dx - h_j\tau\right\}.$$

Therefore

$$\mu_{(j)} = \int_0^\infty G_j(\tau)e^{-h_j\tau}d\tau = G_j^*(h_j) \quad (j = 1, 2, \ldots, k). \quad (6.10)$$

On substituting this result in equation (6.9) we obtain the following recurrence relation for the h_j's:

$$\left.\begin{aligned} n_{j-1}h_{j-1} &= n_j/G_j^*(h_j) \quad (j = 1, 2, \ldots, k-1) \\ R &= n_1/G_1^*(h_1). \end{aligned}\right\}$$

(6.11)

These equations are identical with those obtained in Section 4, for the same promotion rule when the loss intensity depended on total length of service. They may, in fact, be derived by the same argument, the only difference being that the known and unknown quantities are now interchanged. Thus in the former case we had to calculate h_j from h_{j-1}; now we have to find h_{j-1} from h_j. This is very much easier because the unknown no longer appears in the integrand of a Laplace transform.

To illustrate these results we shall use a parametric form for $\lambda_j(\tau)$ which includes both increasing and decreasing functions of τ. This is achieved if $f_j(\tau)$ has the form of a gamma density function. We therefore suppose that

$$f_j(\tau) = \frac{\lambda_j^{\nu_j}}{\Gamma(\nu_j)}\, \tau^{\nu_j - 1} e^{-\lambda_j \tau} \quad (\tau \geq 0,\ \nu_j > 0,\ \lambda_j > 0;\ j = 1, 2, \ldots, k). \quad (6.12)$$

The loss intensity associated with this distribution is always a monotonic function unless $\nu_j = 1$ when $\lambda_j(\tau) = \lambda_j$. If $\nu_j > 1$, $w_j(\tau)$ increases with τ and approaches a horizontal asymptote. If $0 < \nu_j < 1$, $\lambda_j(\tau)$ is a decreasing function of τ and has an infinite ordinate at $\tau = 0$. By varying ν_j we can thus change the form of dependence of the loss rate on τ.

The Laplace transform of $f_j(\tau)$ is

$$f_j^*(s) = \left(\frac{\lambda_j}{\lambda_j + s}\right)^{\nu_j} \quad (j = 1, 2, \ldots, k).$$

Since $G_j^*(s) = \{1 - f_j^*(s)\}/s$ and $\mu_j = \nu_j/\lambda_j$ equation (6.11) becomes

$$n_{j-1}h_{j-1} = n_j h_j \left\{ 1 - \left(1 + \frac{h_j \mu_j}{\nu_j}\right)^{-\nu_j} \right\}^{-1} \quad (j = 1, 2, \ldots, k;\ h_k = 0).$$

$$(6.13)$$

Equation (6.13) can be used to investigate the dependence of the limiting promotion densities on the grade structure. In order to make a comparison with our earlier results we shall use this equation to find the grade structure required to make $h_1 = h_2 = \ldots = h_{k-1} = h$. For this to be so we must have

$$\left.\begin{aligned}
\frac{n_j}{n_{j-1}} &= 1 - \left(1 + \frac{h\mu_j}{\nu_j}\right)^{-\nu_j} \quad (j = 2, 3, \ldots, k - 1) \\[2mm]
\frac{n_k}{n_{k-1}} &= h\mu_k.
\end{aligned}\right\} \quad (6.14)$$

If ν_j and λ_j are independent of j for all grades we note that the grade sizes, except for the highest, will form a geometric series. We have found the same result for two of our previous models. Thus it holds when $\lambda_j(T) = \lambda_j(\tau) = \lambda$ for all grades and both promotion rules and also when

$$\lambda_j(\tau) = \frac{\nu}{\kappa + \tau},$$

for all j if promotion is by seniority. Further, when the loss intensity was supposed to depend on the total length of service, we met an example (see Table 7.2) with a structure very close to the geometric form. This is particularly interesting in view of the fact that many hierarchical organizations conform approximately to this pattern. The reason for this is that each man at any given level is often responsible for the work of x people in the level below him. According to Simon (1957), this number seldom varies very much within a firm; at executive levels x usually lies between 3 and 10. However we would not expect to find equal h_j's in such organizations because the large grade k's which our theory requires rarely, if ever, occur in practice.

The conclusion about geometric structure does not depend on whether $\lambda_j(\tau)$ is an increasing or decreasing function of τ. The value of ν does, of course, help to determine the constant ratio of the grade sizes. Since the right-hand side of equation (6.14) is an increasing function of ν the structure tapers more rapidly if ν is large.

6.3. The Equilibrium CLS Distribution

The CLS distribution for a recruit to the organization will be a function of the time at which he joins. No general theory is available but the equilibrium distribution can be found when the grade sizes are large. The method can be most easily understood by visualizing the situation as shown on Figure 7.2.

On this diagram we have plotted a man's grade as a function of his length of service. The vertical jumps correspond to promotions and the horizontal segments to the lengths of service in the various grades. We shall find the probability that a new entrant remains in the organization for a length of time exceeding T. If $f(T)$ is the equilibrium CLS density function then the probability which we shall determine is $G(T)$. To calculate this probability we shall express it in the form

$$G(T) = \sum_{i=0}^{k-1} Pr\{\text{man promoted } i \text{ times } and \text{ does not leave in } (0, T)\}.$$

$$(6.15)$$

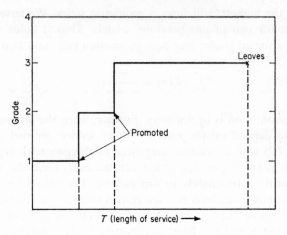

Figure 7.2.

First consider the case $i = 0$. We have already seen in Section 6.1 that, in equilibrium, the promotions from any grade constitute a Poisson process. Therefore

$$Pr\{\text{no promotion in } (0, T)\} = e^{-h_1 T}.$$

Further, since the loss intensity in grade 1 is $\lambda_1(T)$ (T and τ are equivalent in this grade),

$$Pr\{\text{no loss in } (0, T)\} = G_1(T).$$

The promotion and loss processes are independent and so the first term in equation (6.15) is

$$G_1(T)e^{-h_1 T}.$$

When $i = 1$ the probability which we need is obtained as follows. First suppose that promotion takes place from grade 1 to grade 2 in the interval $(T_1, T_1 + \delta T_1)$. The probability of this event is

$$h_1 e^{-h_1 T_1} \delta T_1.$$

Given T_1, the probability of no loss occurring is

$$G_1(T_1)G_2(T - T_1).$$

and the probability of no promotion occurring while the member is in grade 2 is

$$e^{-h_2(T - T_1)}.$$

Therefore the total probability required for the second term on the right-hand side of equation (6.15) is

$$\int_0^T h_1 e^{-h_1 T_1} e^{-h_2(T-T_1)} G_1(T_1) G_2(T-T_1) dT.$$

The above argument extends immediately to the general case. If the promotions take place at times $T_1, T_2, \ldots, T_i$ then

$Pr\{\text{man promoted } i \text{ times and does not leave in } (0, T)\}$

$$= \int\limits_{0 \le T_1 < \ldots} \int\limits_{< T_i \le T} \left\{ \prod_{j=1}^i h_j e^{-h_j(T_j - T_{j-1})} G_j(T_j - T_{j-1}) \right\} e^{-h_{i+1}(T - T_i)}$$

$$G_{i+1}(T - T_i) dT_1 dT_2 \ldots dT_i \quad (i = 1, 2, \ldots, k-1), \quad (6.16)$$

where $T_0 \equiv 0$, $h_k = 0$.

When we sum over i and add in the term for $i = 0$ obtained above, we arrive at the expression for $G(T)$. This apparently cumbersome result is easily handled by means of the Laplace transform. The expression on the right-hand side of equation (6.16) has the form of a convolution integral. Hence, apart from a constant, its Laplace transform is the product of the transforms of the functions

$$G_j(T) e^{-h_j T} \quad (j = 1, 2, \ldots, i+1).$$

Thus we find

$$G^*(s) = \sum_{i=1}^k \prod_{j=1}^i h_{i-1} G_j^*(s + h_j) \quad (h_0 = 1). \quad (6.17)$$

In general, equation (6.17) will not be easy to invert unless there is some simplifying feature such as equal promotion densities or constant loss rates. When we considered promotion by seniority we found that the assumption of constant but unequal loss rates could give a CLS distribution with greater dispersion than the exponential. We shall therefore examine the same case for the random promotion rule by setting $\lambda_j(\tau) = \lambda_j \ (j = 1, 2, \ldots, k)$. This gives

$$G_j(\tau) = e^{-\lambda_j \tau}$$

and

$$G_j^*(s + h_j) = \frac{1}{\lambda_j + s + h_j} \quad (j = 1, 2, \ldots, k; h_k = 0). \quad (6.18)$$

Substituting in equation (6.17) and using the fact that

$$f^*(s) = 1 - s G^*(s)$$

we obtain

$$f^*(s) = \frac{\lambda_1}{\lambda_1 + h_1 + s} + \sum_{i=2}^{k} \left(\frac{\lambda_i}{\lambda_i + h_i + s}\right) \prod_{j=1}^{i-1} \left(\frac{h_j}{\lambda_j + h_j + s}\right) \quad (h_k = 0).$$

(6.19)

As a check it may be verified that this transform reduces to $\lambda/(\lambda + s)$ if $\lambda_j = \lambda$ for all j and to 1 if $s = 0$. The expression on the right-hand side of equation (6.19) can be resolved into partial fractions and inverted term by term to give a density function of the form

$$f(T) = \sum_{i=1}^{k} p_i(\lambda_i + h_i)e^{-(\lambda_i + h_i)T},$$

(6.20)

where $h_k = 0$ and

$$\sum_{i=1}^{k} p_i = 1.$$

This is the familiar mixed exponential distribution although the p_i's need not all be positive as we shall see below.

In the simplest case when $k = 2$

$$p_1 = (\lambda_1 - \lambda_2)/(\lambda_1 - \lambda_2 + h_1)$$
$$= n_1(\lambda_1 - \lambda_2)/\{n_1(\lambda_1 - \lambda_2) + n_2\lambda_2\},$$

which satisfies $0 \le p_1 \le 1$ if $\lambda_1 \ge \lambda_2$. Thus, whenever the loss intensity is higher in the first grade than in the second, we shall have a mixed exponential distribution of the kind we have met before. This is the third probability model we have discussed which gives rise to this particular distribution: the first was Herbst's model described in Chapter 4, the second was in Chapter 6, where it occurred as a special case. When fitting this distribution we found that fairly typical parameter values were $p_1 = \frac{1}{2}$ and $(\lambda_1 + h_1)/\lambda_2 = 10$. To achieve these values with the present model we should need $\lambda_1/\lambda_2 = 5.5$ and $n_2/n_1 = 4.5$. If this model represented the true state of affairs we should not be able to distinguish it from the others if we only observed the total length of service. To do so it would be necessary to identify the two grades, test whether their loss intensities were constant and, if so, to see whether or not their values agreed with those predicted by the fitted distribution.

For $k > 2$ the CLS distribution can take on a variety of shapes. In order to illustrate some of the possibilities we shall list four examples below for the case $k = 3$.

(a) $n_1 = n_2 = n_3$, $\lambda_j = \lambda/j$ $(j = 1, 2, 3)$

$$f(T) = \frac{\lambda}{324} (209e^{-11\lambda T/6} + 75e^{-5\lambda T/6} + 40e^{-\lambda T/3}).$$

(b) $n_1 = n_2 = n_3$, $\lambda_j = \lambda/(4-j)$ $(j = 1, 2, 3)$

$$f(T) = \frac{\lambda}{60}(209e^{-11\lambda T/6} - 405e^{-3\lambda T/2} + 216e^{-\lambda T}).$$

(c) $n_1 = 2n_2 = 3n_3$, $\lambda_j = \lambda/j$ $(j = 1, 2, 3)$

$$f(T) = \frac{\lambda}{18}(14e^{-4\lambda T/3} + 3e^{-2\lambda T/3} + e^{-\lambda T/3}).$$

(d) $n_1 = 2n_2 = 4n_3$, $\lambda_j = \lambda/(4-j)$ $(j = 1, 2, 3)$

$$f(T) = \frac{\lambda}{6}(20e^{-4\lambda T/3} - (18 - 9T)e^{-\lambda T}).$$

The term involving the factor T in (d) arises because, in that example, $\lambda_2 + h_2 = \lambda_3$ so that the inversion leading to equation (6.20) breaks down. The difficulty can be overcome by finding the limit of $f(T)$ as given in equation (6.20) when $\lambda_3 \rightarrow \lambda_2 + h_2$.

In those cases where the loss intensities decrease as we move up the hierarchy we have a mixed exponential distribution with positive p_i's for both structures considered. In the other two cases, when the loss intensities increase with j, the distribution is less skew and rises to a mode. It is the former kind of distribution which occurs in practice and so our present model can only provide a satisfactory explanation if there is a decreasing sequence of loss intensities. This is what one might expect to find in practice but empirical evidence on the question is lacking.

7. LENGTH OF SERVICE STRUCTURE OF THE GRADES

7.1. Theory

The whole emphasis in the preceding part of this chapter has been on the determination of the wastage and promotion densities. These quantities do not provide a complete picture of the system and we shall now remedy one of the most important omissions. The efficient operation of an organization may depend critically on there being enough experienced persons available at each level. It may, therefore, be more important from the firm's point of view to achieve an adequate distribution of experienced staff than to ensure good promotion prospects. The basic mathematical requirement for such studies is the distribution of length of service for serving members. This distribution can be obtained quite easily in the equilibrium state for both promotion rules. The formulae which we shall obtain depend only on the CLS distribution $f(T)$; they therefore apply whether the loss intensity depends upon seniority within the grade or within the organization. In the former case this distribution must be found by the methods of Section 6.3.

Let $a_j(t)$ denote the probability density function of total length of service for serving members of grade j, $(j = 1, 2, \ldots, k)$ when the system has reached equilibrium. We shall continue to use the notation $a(t)$ for the corresponding density function for the system when viewed as a whole. From these definitions it follows that

$$Na(t) = \sum_{j=1}^{k} n_j a_j(t). \tag{7.1}$$

When promotion is according to seniority the solution of our problem is almost immediate. We saw in Section 3.1 that, under this promotion rule, no member of grade j can have longer service than any member of grade $j + 1$. This means that the grades divide the total membership according to their length of service. Let the critical length of service at which promotion takes place from grade j to grade $j + 1$ be t_j $(j = 1, 2, \ldots, k - 1)$. If the model of Section 5, applies, then t_j will be given by

$$t_j = \sum_{i=1}^{j} \tau_i \quad (j = 1, 2, \ldots, k - 1).$$

It thus follows that

$$a_j(t) = a(t) \Big/ \int_{t_{j-1}}^{t_j} a(x)\mathrm{d}x \quad t_{j-1} \leq t < t_j$$

$$= \frac{Na(t)}{n_j} \quad (j = 1, 2, \ldots, k), \tag{7.2}$$

where $a(t) = \mu^{-1}G(t)$, $t_0 = 0$, $t_k = \infty$.

When promotion is at random the derivation starts with the observation that

$$a_j(t) \propto a(t)Pr\{\text{member having length of service } t \text{ is in grade } j\}. \tag{7.3}$$

A person will be in grade j at time t if, and only if, he has experienced exactly $j - 1$ promotions in $(0, t)$. The probability of this event can be determined if it can be assumed that the promotions between adjacent pairs of grades constitute a Poisson process. For this to be so, either the loss intensities must be constant, or the system must have large grade sizes and have reached its equilibrium. Under these conditions

$Pr\{\text{promotion from grade } j \text{ after total service in } (t, t + \delta t)\}$

$$= h_j \delta t \quad (j = 1, 2, \ldots, k - 1).$$

The probability of $j - 1$ promotions in $(0, t)$, given that there is no loss in this interval, follows at once from the theory of the time-homogeneous birth process (see also Chapter 8, equation (2.6), and Bartlett 1955, Section 3.2). In the present notation this probability is

$$P(j - 1|t) = \prod_{i=1}^{j-1} h_i \sum_{i=1}^{j} e^{-h_i T} \prod_{\substack{l=1 \\ l \neq i}}^{j} \frac{1}{(h_l - h_i)} \quad (j = 1, 2, \ldots, k - 1). \quad (7.4)$$

If some of the h_i's are equal, the approximate form of the probabilities can be found by a limiting operation on equation (7.4). In particular, if all of the promotion intensities have a common value h, the distribution of the number of promotions is Poisson for $j < k - 1$ with

$$P(j - 1|t) = \frac{(ht)^{j-1}}{(j - 1)!} e^{-ht} \quad (j = 1, 2, \ldots, k - 2)$$

$$P(k - 1|t) = 1 - \sum_{i=0}^{k-2} P(i|t). \quad (7.5)$$

Returning to equation (7.3) we may therefore write the density function of length of service in the jth grade as

$$\left. \begin{array}{c} a_j(t) = a(t)P(j - 1|t) \Big/ \int_0^\infty a(x)P(j - 1|x)\mathrm{d}x \\ (j = 1, 2, \ldots, k - 1) \\ \text{with} \\ a_k(t) = \frac{1}{n_k} \{Na(t) - \sum_{i=1}^{k-1} n_i a_i(t)\}. \end{array} \right\} \quad (7.6)$$

7.2. Examples

We shall illustrate the foregoing theory by supposing that the CLS distribution is mixed exponential with density function

$$f(T) = p\lambda_1 e^{-\lambda_1 T} + (1 - p)\lambda_2 e^{-\lambda_2 T} \quad (T \geq 0).$$

It has been shown in Section 6 that this form can arise in those models in which the loss rate depends on the grade. However, our discussion will be primarily in terms of the models of Sections 3 and 4. In those cases we saw that the mixed exponential distribution gave a satisfactory description of observed CLS distributions except, perhaps, in the region of the upper tail.

When promotion is by seniority the length of service distribution for the jth grade is, from equation (7.2)

$$a_j(t) = \left(\frac{N}{n_j}\right) \frac{pe^{-\lambda_1 t} + (1-p)e^{-\lambda_2 t}}{p/\lambda_1 + (1-p)/\lambda_2} \quad t_{j-1} \leq t < t_j, \quad (7.7)$$

where the $\{t_j\}$ satisfy

$$\int_0^{t_j} \{pe^{-\lambda_1 t} + (1-p)e^{-\lambda_2 t}\}dt = \frac{N_j}{N}\left(\frac{p}{\lambda_1} + \frac{1-p}{\lambda_2}\right)$$

$$(j = 1, 2, \ldots, k-1). \quad (7.8)$$

If promotion is at random it is clear from equations (7.3) and (7.4) that $a_j(t)$ is a linear combination of exponential terms. For simplicity we consider the case where the grade structure is such that the promotion densities are equal. In this case equation (7.5) applies and we find

$$\left. \begin{aligned} a_j(t) &= \frac{pt^{j-1}e^{-(\lambda_1+h)t} + (1-p)t^{j-1}e^{-(\lambda_2+h)t}}{(j-1)!\left\{p\left(\frac{1}{\lambda_1+h}\right)^j + (1-p)\left(\frac{1}{\lambda_2+h}\right)^j\right\}} \quad (t \geq 0) \\ &\qquad\qquad\qquad\qquad (j = 1, 2, \ldots, k-1) \\ a_k(t) &= \{Na(t) - \sum_{i=1}^{k-1} n_i a_i(t)\}/n_k. \end{aligned} \right\} \quad (7.9)$$

Inspection of the first part of equation (7.9) shows that it is a weighted average of two gamma densities each with index $j-1$. This fact enables us to write down the moments of the distribution and, in particular, the mean which is

$$\left. \begin{aligned} \xi_j &= \frac{j\left\{\frac{p}{(\lambda_1+h)^{j+1}} + \frac{1-p}{(\lambda_2+h)^{j+1}}\right\}}{\left\{\frac{p}{(\lambda_1+h)^j} + \frac{1-p}{(\lambda_2+h)^j}\right\}} \quad (j = 1, 2, \ldots, k-1) \\ \xi_k &= \{N\mu - \sum_{i=1}^{k-1} n_i \xi_i\}/n_k. \end{aligned} \right\} \quad (7.10)$$

These expressions yield simple bounds on ξ_j. Without loss of generality we may assume that $\lambda_1 > \lambda_2$ in which case

$$\frac{j}{\lambda_1+h} < \xi_j < \frac{j}{\lambda_2+h} \quad (j = 1, 2, \ldots, k-1).$$

The bounds cannot be attained unless either $p = 1$, $p = 0$ or $\lambda_1 = \lambda_2$. In the latter case the CLS distribution reduces to the exponential and the bounds coincide.

In order to give a clearer idea of the practical implications of these formulae we shall make numerical calculations for two special cases. For the first example we consider a hierarchy with only two grades; for the second we assume an exponential CLS distribution (the case $\lambda_1 = \lambda_2$). One of our principal objects will be to compare the effect of the two promotion rules. Before embarking on this investigation we may remark that there is one obvious difference. If promotion is by seniority the variation of length of service in grade j, for example, is restricted to the interval (t_{j-1}, t_j); under random promotion the range is unlimited. An organization with random promotion will thus be characterized by a greater spread of experience in each grade.

First suppose that $k = 2$ with N large and $n_1 = 2n_2$. Let us use the same parameter values as in several of our earlier examples and take $p = \frac{1}{2}$, $\lambda_1 = 5.5$, $\lambda_2 = 0.55$ with $\mu = 1$. When promotion is by seniority t_1, the length of service at promotion, satisfies equation (7.8), with $j = 1$,

$$\frac{e^{-5.5t_1}}{5.5} + \frac{e^{-0.55t_1}}{0.55} = \frac{2}{3}.$$

The solution of this equation is $t_1 = 1.8240$. This implies that all members of grade 1, have a length of service less than 1.8240; those in grade 2, have a greater length of service. A useful way of comparing the seniority structure for two promotion rules is to compute the average seniority for each grade. This can easily be found from equation (7.7) for grade 1. The means for grade 2 can be obtained from the last member of equation (7.10), which holds for all promotion rules. Numerical values for the above parameter values are given in Table 7.7.

When promotion is at random $a_1(t)$ is given by equation (7.9), with $j = 1$. For the system we are considering h_1, the renewal density, satisfies

$$\frac{1}{5.5 + h_1} + \frac{1}{0.55 + h_1} = \frac{4}{3}.$$

(see equation 4.21). Thus $h_1 = 0.3111$ and on substituting this value in equation (7.9), we find

$$a_1(t) = 0.7500(e^{-0.8611t} + e^{-5.8111t}) \quad (t \geq 0). \tag{7.11}$$

For grade 2, $a_2(t)$ can be found from equation (7.1), and it too is mixed exponential in form. Numerical values of the average seniority have been calculated from these distributions and the results given in Table 7.7.

It may seem surprising that the average length of service for the whole organization, 1.669, is greater than the average CLS which is 1. This happens because the serving members contain a disproportionate number

TABLE 7.7

Average seniority in grades 1 and 2 for the two promotion rules and a mixed exponential CLS distribution with $p = \frac{1}{2}$, $\lambda_1 = 5.5$, $\lambda_2 = 0.55$.

Grade	Seniority Rule	Random Rule
1	0.683	1.041
2	3.642	2.927
Whole organization	1.669	1.669

who will have 'greater than average' lengths of completed service. As we might have expected, random promotion gives a higher average seniority in grade 1 but a lower average in grade 2, than does promotion by seniority. An apparently paradoxical situation is revealed if we look at the average seniority *within each grade* instead of within the organization as a whole. Consider grade 2, from this point of view. Under promotion by seniority we showed that promotion takes place at seniority 1.824. The average time spent by members of grade 2, in that grade is thus 3.642 − 1.824 = 1.818. If promotion is at random the average length of service of members when they are promoted must be equal to their average seniority in grade 1. In this example the figure is 1.041: the average length of service in grade 2 is therefore 2.927 − 1.014 = 1.886. Thus random promotion gives greater average seniority within *both* grades. This conclusion takes no account, of course, of the greater variability which will occur in the random case.

Secondly, we shall consider the case of general k when the CLS distribution is exponential. Let us assume that the grade sizes satisfy

$$n_{k-1} = n_k, \quad n_j = n_{k-1}2^{k-j-1} \quad (j = 1, 2, \ldots, k-2). \qquad (7.12)$$

In such an organization each grade is half the size of the one below it except for grade k which is equal in size to grade $k - 1$. This structure has the property that the promotion and wastage densities are all equal to λ, the parameter of the CLS distribution (see Section 3.2).

When promotion is by seniority t_j satisfies

$$\int_0^{t_j} e^{-\lambda x} dx = \frac{N_j}{N\lambda} \quad (j = 1, 2, \ldots, k-1),$$

whence

$$t_j = -\frac{1}{\lambda} \log_e (N - N_j)/N.$$

For the structure given by equation (7.12) this equation simplifies to

$$t_j = \frac{j}{\lambda} \log_e 2 = \frac{0.6932j}{\lambda}.$$

The times of successive promotions thus increase in arithmetic progression. The average lengths of service for the members of each grade can easily be calculated. Thus we find

$$\left.\begin{aligned}\xi_j &= \frac{\lambda N}{n_j} \int_{((j-1)\log_e 2)/\lambda}^{(j\log_e 2)/\lambda} te^{-\lambda t}dt = \frac{1}{\lambda}\{1 + (j-2)\log_e 2\} \\ &\qquad\qquad\qquad\qquad (j = 1, 2, \ldots, k-1) \\ \xi_k &= \frac{1}{\lambda}\{1 + (k-1)\log_e 2\}.\end{aligned}\right\} \quad (7.13)$$

The average length of time which a member has spent in a given grade is

$$\begin{aligned}\xi_j - t_{j-1} &= \frac{1 - \log_e 2}{\lambda} = \frac{0.3068}{\lambda} \quad (j = 1, 2, \ldots, k-1; t_0 = 0) \\ \xi_k - t_{k-1} &= \frac{1}{\lambda}.\end{aligned}$$

This system has the rather interesting property that the average experience within a particular grade is the same for all grades except the highest.

When promotion is at random the mean lengths of service in the grades may be obtained from equation (7.10), because h_j is independent of j for the above structure. Setting $\lambda_1 = \lambda_2 = \lambda$ and $h = \lambda$ (from equation 3.14), we find

$$\left.\begin{aligned}\xi_j &= j/2\lambda \quad (j = 1, 2, \ldots, k-1) \\ \xi_k &= (k+1)/2\lambda.\end{aligned}\right\} \quad (7.14)$$

On comparing the results given in equation (7.14) with those of equation (7.13) we see that ξ_2 is the same in both cases. For $j > 2$ the average length of service is greater when promotion is by seniority but when $j = 1$ it is smaller. In the random case the average length of service in each grade is given by

$$\left.\begin{aligned}\xi_j - \xi_{j-1} &= 1/2\lambda \quad (j = 1, 2, \ldots, k-1; \xi_0 = 0) \\ \xi_k - \xi_{k-1} &= 1/\lambda.\end{aligned}\right\} \quad (7.15)$$

As in the previous example we find that random promotion leads to greater average experience within each grade.

These two examples suggest that *there may be practical advantages in adopting promotion policies which are not too rigidly tied to such things as seniority*. However, much more detailed calculation of the kind illustrated here would be needed to establish this as a firm conclusion.

CHAPTER 8

MODELS FOR THE DIFFUSION OF
NEWS AND RUMOURS

1. INTRODUCTION

The diffusion of information in a social group is a phenomenon of considerable interest and importance. A large amount of research has been devoted to the subject and some of this has involved the construction of mathematical or stochastic models. A brief review of the published work on such models is given by Coleman (1964) in Chapter 17 of his *Introduction to Mathematical Sociology*. Our object in this chapter is to describe some stochastic models for diffusion of information and to use them to gain understanding of the phenomenon. As in the earlier part of the book the treatment is theoretical but we have been guided in our choice of assumptions by the limited amount of experimental evidence which is available. A brief review of some of this work is given in the final section of the chapter.

The system which we shall study may be described as follows. There is a population of N units which we shall usually describe as people but which may be groups of people as, for example, families. Information is transmitted to members of the group from a source either at an initial point in time or continuously. For example, the source may be a television commercial, a newspaper, a roadside advertisement hoarding or a group of people introduced into the population from outside. Persons who receive the information may become 'spreaders' themselves by transmitting the information to others whom they meet. The process of diffusion continues until all have heard the news or until transmission ceases.

In many cases a stochastic model will be required to provide an adequate description of the process. The chance element enters at two points. Whether or not a given person hears the information will depend on (a) his coming into contact with the source or a spreader and (b) on the information being transmitted when contact is established. In social systems such as the armed forces where there are well-defined channels of communication the chance factor is negligible. In less rigidly organized systems neither (a) nor (b) is a certain event and so the development of the process is unpredictable. Hence it can only be described stochastically.

In spite of the obvious stochastic nature of the process much of the existing theory is deterministic. The reason for this is found in the mathematical intractability which often attends the development of the stochastic models. We shall sometimes find that we have to fall back on a deterministic analysis in order to make progress. However, the deterministic model will be treated as an approximation to the stochastic version, in terms of which the original problem will be formulated.

Not all aspects of the diffusion process are amenable to stochastic analysis. In Section 2 of this chapter we shall be interested mainly in the number of persons who have received the information at any time. For this purpose we shall study two random variables. The first is the number who have received the information (called 'hearers') at time T. This number is denoted by $n(T)$ or, when there is no risk of confusion, by n. A second way of describing the state of the system is to use the time taken for the number of hearers to reach n. This time is denoted by T_n. These two random variables bear an inverse relation to one another and for many practical purposes either will serve. Our choice between them will be determined chiefly by the mathematical advantages which each offers in a particular instance. Many practical questions about the rate of spread or the number of ultimate hearers can be answered when the distributions of $n(T)$ and T_n are known. In later sections we shall be interested not only in the total number of hearers but, for example, in the number of hearers who are active spreaders.

A second class of random variables which we shall study is defined in relation to the stage at which a person becomes informed. A person who first receives the information from the source is described as a first generation hearer. Those who first hear from members of the first generation belong to the second generation and so on. The number of people in the gth generation will be denoted by n_g, where g takes integer values from 1 to N. The random variables $\{n_g\}$ are of particular interest for the diffusion of a rumour because it is is liable to distortion. We can thus use them to study the extent to which the news is likely to be known with reasonable accuracy.

The diffusion of information in a social group bears obvious similarities to the spread of an epidemic in a population of susceptibles. Two of our models are, in fact, taken over from the theory of epidemics. A comprehensive account of the theory is given in Bailey's *Mathematical Theory of Epidemics* (1957) to which the reader is referred for a full discussion. In spite of this similarity there are important differences between the two kinds of processes which will become apparent as we proceed. The word 'epidemic' provides a convenient short-hand description of either process and we shall use it extensively.

The plausibility of the various assumptions which we shall have to make depends partly on the kind of information which is being transmitted. The term 'information' is being used in a neutral sense to include such diverse things as rumours, news, public warnings and advertisements. Our models should not therefore be regarded as being universally applicable but as pointers to what would happen under various sets of conditions.

2. THE BIRTH PROCESS MODEL

2.1. Description of the Model

Our basic model is a special case of the pure birth process. Let E_S denote the transmission of the information from a source to any given member of the population. This is assumed to be a random event with

$$Pr\{E_S \text{ in } (T, T + \delta T)\} = \alpha\delta T \quad (\alpha > 0), \tag{2.1}$$

where α is described as the *intensity of transmission of the source*. In this model we treat contact with the source and reception of information from the source as a single event. The above assumption may thus be expressed by saying that all members are equally exposed to the source. It would be a plausible assumption if the source were a television commercial and if the population consisted of regular viewers. It would not be realistic if the population also included people who rarely view the programme. Our model can be generalized to include variable exposure. However, we shall show that, in most circumstances, α plays a minor role in the development of the process; a simple assumption will therefore suffice.

Let us denote the transmission of news between any given pair of individuals by E_I. Our second assumption about the process is that

$$Pr\{E_I \text{ in } (T, T + \delta T)\} = \beta\delta T \quad (\beta > 0), \tag{2.2}$$

where β is the *intensity of transmission between individuals*. We assume that this probability is the same for all pairs of individuals. This, in turn, implies that we have a homogeneously mixing population. In such a population any uninformed member is equally likely to receive the news from any of the n persons who are active spreaders. The assumption of homogeneous mixing seems plausible only in very small groups and the experimental evidence referred to in Section 6 supports this view. Nevertheless there are advantages in studying the simple model first and then introducing greater realism by way of appropriate generalizations. Finally we assume that all transmissions, whether from the source or between pairs of individuals, are independent of each other.

We are now in a position to relate the process that we have described to the pure birth process. When exactly n people have received the information we shall say that the system is in state n. A stochastic process is a time-homogeneous birth process if the probability of a transition from state n to state $n + 1$ is given by

$$Pr\{n \rightarrow n + 1 \text{ in } (T, T + \delta T)\} = \lambda_n \delta T \quad (\lambda_n \geq 0) \qquad (2.3)$$

and if no other types of transition (for example, $n \rightarrow n - 1$) are possible. It is obvious that n can only increase and the identification of the two processes will be complete when we have expressed λ_n in terms of the parameters of our model. The number who have heard can be increased in one of two ways. Either the next person to hear will receive the information from the source or from another person. As there are $N - n$ persons who have not heard, the total contribution to λ_n from the source is $(N - n)\alpha\delta T$. The contribution from communication between persons is obtained as follows. Of all the possible pairs which could be formed there are $n(N - n)$ which consist of one 'knower' and one 'ignorant'. These are the only pairs which can give rise to the transition $n \rightarrow n + 1$ and the total probability associated with them is $n(N - n)\beta\delta T$. Combining these results we have

$$\lambda_n = (N - n)(\alpha + \beta n) \quad (n = 0, 1, \ldots, N - 1). \qquad (2.4)$$

The theory associated with our model can thus be developed from that for the birth process with quadratic birth rate, given by equation (2.4).

The model which we have described was proposed by Taga and Isii (1959) but it is almost identical with the simple epidemic model discussed, for example, in Bailey (1957). In epidemic theory the source consists of one or more persons who introduce the infection to the group. Thus if one person starts the epidemic we have to put $\alpha = \beta$ when we find

$$\lambda_n = \beta(n + 1)(N - n) \quad (n = 0, 1, \ldots, N - 1). \qquad (2.5)$$

This particular case has received the greatest attention and we shall return to it later. In the application to diffusion of news it is not necessary that $\alpha = \beta$ or that β should be a multiple of α as in epidemic theory. It is also worth drawing attention to the fact that the assumptions of the model seem more reasonable when it is applied to the diffusion of news. For example, the application to the epidemic requires that we ignore the incubation period of the disease and that each infected individual remains infectious until the epidemic is over. Both assumptions are unrealistic for many infectious diseases but are quite reasonable for the diffusion of some kinds of information. They then require that the information is transmitted instantaneously and that it is not forgotten. Another difference between the two applications is that the epidemiologist and the sociologist are not necessarily interested in the same features of the process. Both are interested in the rate of spread but only the sociologist is likely to want to know how many people hear direct from the source.

2.2. Analysis of the Model

We shall now use the birth process model to make deductions about the development of the diffusion process in time. In view of the fact that our model is a pure birth process it is natural to begin by studying the distribution of $n(T)$. Historically this was the course followed and we shall begin by briefly describing some of the results which have been obtained. However, it is now clear that the approach via the random variables $\{T_n\}$ is capable of yielding more information about the process in a much simpler fashion.

The expression for the distribution of $n(T)$ may be found in Bartlett (1955, Section 3.2). It is given by

$$Pr\{n(T) = 0\} = e^{-\lambda_0 T},$$

$$Pr\{n(T) = n\} = \prod_{i=0}^{n-1} \lambda_i \sum_{i=0}^{n} \frac{e^{-\lambda_i T}}{\prod_{\substack{j=0 \\ j \neq i}}^{n} (\lambda_j - \lambda_i)}. \tag{2.6}$$

Since λ_i can be found from equation (2.5) in terms of α, β and N the problem is solved in principle. Even for small values of N the computation of the distribution is formidable; it is given by Bailey (1957, Table 5.1) for $N = 10$ and $\alpha = \beta$. For large values of N the task is not practicable. The feature of the distribution which is of greatest interest is the mean $\bar{n}(T)$. When plotted as a function of T it gives a visual representation of the expected development of the process. If we are primarily interested in the rate at which the news is spreading at T we would wish to plot the derivative of $\bar{n}(T)$. This latter curve is often called the 'epidemic curve' and provides a clearer picture of the growth and subsequent decline of the epidemic. The expressions for $\bar{n}(T)$ and its derivative were obtained by Haskey (1954) and are given by Bailey (1957). The formulae are rather complicated but computations have been carried out by Haskey (1954), Bailey (1957) and Mansfield and Hensley (1960) for $N \leq 40$. Two epidemic curves, plotted from their calculations, are given in Figure 8.1 for the case $\alpha = \beta$.

The abscissa on Figure 8.1 is plotted in units of β^{-1}. This is the expected time taken for any given pair of people to meet—a fact which follows directly from equation (2.2). Thus, for example, it is clear that the diffusion is completed in the case $N = 40$ in about one third of the average time taken for two given persons to meet. It will be noted that the spread is

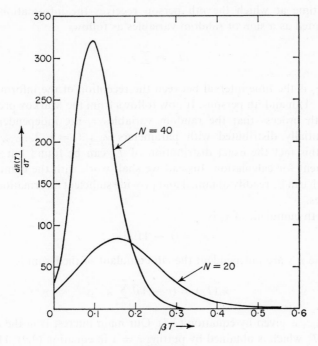

Figure 8.1

more rapid in the larger of the two populations shown on the figure. We shall encounter this phenomenon again below where the reason for it will be made clear.

The investigation of the form of the epidemic curve for larger N is facilitated by the following observation. Let T' denote the time taken for the news to reach a specified member of the population and let $F(T')$ be its distribution function. Then it is clear that

$$\bar{n}(T) = NF(T) \qquad (2.7)$$

and

$$\frac{d\bar{n}(T)}{dT} = Nf(T). \qquad (2.8)$$

Equation (2.8) shows that the epidemic curve is proportional to the probability density function of the time taken to inform a given member of the population. Williams (1965) exploited this relationship to deduce the moments and asymptotic form of the epidemic curve. We shall derive similar results by considering the random variables $\{T_n\}$.

The time at which the nth person receives the information can be represented as a sum of random variables as follows

$$T_n = \sum_{i=1}^{n} \tau_i,$$

where τ_i is the time interval between the reception of the information by the $(i - 1)$th and ith persons. It now follows from the Markov property of the birth process that the random variables τ_i are independently and exponentially distributed with parameters λ_{i-1} $(i = 1, 2, \ldots, N - 1)$. Using this fact the exact distribution of T_n can be found but it is not convenient for calculation. Instead we shall work with the cumulants of T_n which can be readily obtained and provide sufficient information for our purposes.

The rth cumulant of τ_i is

$$\kappa_r = (r - 1)!/\lambda_{i-1}^r.$$

Since the τ_i's are independent the rth cumulant of their sum is

$$\kappa_r(T_n) = (r - 1)! \sum_{i=1}^{n} \lambda_{i-1}^{-r}, \tag{2.9}$$

where λ_{i-1} is given by equation (2.4). Our main interest is in the expectation of T_n which is obtained by putting $r = 1$ in equation (2.9). This gives

$$E(T_n) = \kappa_1(T_n) = \sum_{i=0}^{n-1} \frac{1}{(N - i)(\alpha + \beta i)}$$

$$= \frac{1}{\alpha + \beta N} \sum_{i=0}^{n-1} \frac{1}{N - i} + \frac{\beta}{\alpha + \beta N} \sum_{i=0}^{n-1} \frac{1}{\alpha + \beta i},$$

$$= \frac{1}{\beta(N + \omega)} \{\phi(N) - \phi(N - n) - \phi(\omega - 1) + \phi(n + \omega - 1)\} \tag{2.10}$$

where $\omega = \alpha/\beta$ and

$$\phi(x) = \sum_{i=1}^{\infty} \frac{x}{i(i + x)} = \sum_{i=1}^{\infty} \left(\frac{1}{i} - \frac{1}{i + x}\right)$$

is the digamma function. This function is tabulated in the British Association Mathematical Tables, volume I (1951), for $x = 0.0(0.01)1.0$ and $10.0(0.1)60.0$. For large x

$$\phi(x) \sim \log_e x + \gamma$$

where $\gamma = 0.5772\ldots$, is Euler's constant.

We can now use equation (2.10) to study the expected development of the diffusion process. Nothing essential will be lost if we suppose that N is large. The limiting behaviour of $E(T_n)$ depends on whether or not n is near to zero or N. Initially let us suppose that n/N is fixed and denoted by p. Then if N is large and $p \neq 0$ or 1

$$E(T_{Np}) \sim \frac{1}{\beta(N + \omega)} \left\{ \log_e \frac{pN + \omega - 1}{1 - p} + \gamma - \phi(\omega - 1) \right\}. \quad (2.11)$$

If ω is fixed we have approximately that

$$E(T_{Np}) \sim \frac{\log_e N}{N\beta} + \frac{1}{N\beta} \log_e \frac{p}{1 - p}. \quad (2.12)$$

Two important conclusions follow from these formulae. First it is clear that the parameter β is much more important than ω, and hence α, in determining the rate of diffusion. Secondly, a proportion p will be reached faster in a large than in a small population. Both of these phenomena can be explained by reference to the form of λ_n. Except near the start and finish the coefficient of β in λ_n is an order of magnitude larger than that of α. Also λ_n is an increasing function of N.

The above formulae do not hold if p is zero or one because, in deriving them, we had to assume that N, $N - n$ and n were large. The case $p = 1$, or $n = N$, is of particular interest because T_N is then the *duration* of the epidemic. Proceeding to the limit we find the expression comparable to equation (2.11) to be

$$E(T_N) \sim \frac{2 \log_e N - \phi(\omega - 1) + \gamma}{\beta(N + \omega)}. \quad (2.13)$$

Thus equation (2.12) shows that half of the population will have heard in time $(\log_e N)/N\beta$; equation (2.13) that all will have heard in twice that time.

Equation (2.11) also enables us to find the asymptotic form of the function $\bar{n}(T)$. This follows from the fact that, when n and N are both large with $0 < p < 1$,

$$\frac{n}{N} = p \doteq F(T)|_{T = E(T_n)}. \quad (2.14)$$

Hence the function on the right-hand side of equation (2.11) is $F^{-1}(p)$. It follows that, for large N and $\bar{n}(T)$ not near 0 or N,

$$\bar{n}(T) \sim N \left(\frac{e^X - \omega + 1}{e^X + N} \right) \quad (2.15)$$

where $X = \{\beta(N + \omega)T - \gamma + \phi(\omega - 1)\}$. For small values of ω/N this is an S-shaped function, similar to the normal ogive. Under the conditions discussed below, $\bar{n}(T)/N$ becomes the same as the probability integral of a logistic distribution. The epidemic curve is easily obtained by differentiating equation (2.15). It is a unimodal curve with some degree of positive skewness. An illustrative diagram is given in Williams (1965).

We have already found an expression for the median of the epidemic curve. It is a simple matter to find its mean which is the time that a randomly selected individual can expect to wait before hearing the news. If we write this quantity as $E(T')$ it is obvious that

$$E(T') = \frac{1}{N} \sum_{n=1}^{N} E(T_n).$$

The summation over n on the right-hand side of equation (2.10) involves the manipulation of double sums but readily yields

$$E(T') = \frac{1}{\beta N} \{\phi(N + \omega - 1) - \phi(\omega - 1)\}. \qquad (2.16)$$

This equation is a slight generalization of equation (21) in Williams (1965), whose analysis was restricted to the case when ω is an integer. As we should expect from the result for the median, the mean of the epidemic curve is of order $(\log_e N)/N$.

The consideration of mean values does not tell us how far an actual realization of the process may depart from our expectation. To investigate this we may consider the distribution of the random variables $\{T_n\}$. We already have a general expression for the rth cumulant of T_n in equation (2.9). This result will now be used to show that the time taken for n people to hear is subject to considerable variation. Using the identity

$$\frac{1}{x^r y^r} \equiv \frac{1}{(x + y)^{2r}} \sum_{i=1}^{r} \binom{2r - i - 1}{r - 1} (x + y)^i \left(\frac{1}{x^i} + \frac{1}{y^i}\right)$$

the cumulants given by equations (2.9) in conjunction with (2.4) may be written

$$\kappa_r(T_n) = \frac{(r - 1)!}{\beta^r} \sum_{i=1}^{r} \binom{2r - i - 1}{r - 1} \frac{1}{(N + \omega)^{2r-i}}$$

$$\left\{\sum_{j=1}^{n} \left(\frac{1}{(N + 1 - j)^r} + \frac{1}{(j + \omega - 1)^r}\right)\right\} \qquad (r > 1). \qquad (2.17)$$

Introducing the polygamma functions defined by

$$\phi^{(s)}(x) = (-1)^s (s - 1)! \sum_{i=1}^{\infty} \frac{1}{(i + x)^s} \qquad (s > 1)$$

the cumulants may be written

$$\kappa_r(T_n) = \frac{(r-1)!}{\beta^r} \sum_{i=1}^{r} \binom{2r-i-1}{r-1} \frac{(-1)^{i-1}}{(i-1)!(N+\omega)^{2r-i}}$$

$$\times \{\phi^{(i)}(N-n) - \phi^{(i)}(N) + \phi^{(i)}(\omega-1) - \phi^{(i)}(\omega+n-1)\}. \quad (2.18)$$

In the limit as $N \to \infty$, with $n/N = p$ held fixed with $0 < p < 1$,

$$\kappa_r(T_n) \sim \frac{(-1)^r}{\beta^r(N+\omega)^r} \phi^{(r)}(\omega-1), \quad (r > 1). \quad (2.19)$$

On the other hand, if $(N-n)$ is fixed so that $p \to 1$ as $N \to \infty$ a different limiting form is obtained. For example, in the case $n = N$

$$\kappa_r(T_N) \sim \frac{(-1)^r}{\beta^r(N+\omega)^r} \{\phi^{(r)}(\omega-1) + \phi^{(r)}(0)\} \quad (r > 1). \quad (2.20)$$

A notable feature of equation (2.19) is that it does not depend on n. In particular the asymptotic variance of T_n is independent of n. The polygamma functions are tabulated in the British Association Tables referred to above so that numerical values for the cumulants are readily obtainable. It follows from (2.19) that the variance of T_n is a decreasing function of ω which means that its variability goes down as the 'strength' of the source is increased. The extent of this reduction in variance can be gauged from the fact that $\phi^{(2)}(0) = 1.6449$ and $\phi^{(2)}(1) = 0.6449$. Even when n is large the distribution of T_n may have considerable skewness and kurtosis. Although T_n is representable as a sum it does not have a limiting normal distribution. This is because the $\{\tau_i\}$ do not satisfy the conditions of the Lindeberg-Feller central limit theorem for non-identically distributed random variables. (For these conditions see Fisz (1963), Theorem 6.9.2, p. 206, or Feller (1965), Theorem 3, p. 256). Some illustrative calculations are given in Table 8.1.

TABLE 8.1

Asymptotic values of the skewness, $\sqrt{\beta_1}$, and the kurtosis, β_2, of T_n.

		ω				
		1	2	5	10	∞
$0 < p < 1$	$\sqrt{\beta_1}$	1.14	0.73	0.47	0.32	0.00
	β_2	5.40	4.19	3.44	3.21	3.00
$p = 1$	$\sqrt{\beta_1}$	0.81	0.81	0.97	1.04	1.14
	β_2	4.20	4.33	4.90	5.12	5.40

The covariance of any pair of T_n's can be found at once from the fact that

$$\text{cov}\,(T_n, T_{n+j}) = \text{var}\,(T_n) \quad (j \geq 0). \tag{2.21}$$

2.3. The Deterministic Approximation

With the simple birth process model there was no need to have recourse to deterministic methods. All that we required to know about the expected behaviour of the process was determined from the stochastic model. Nevertheless it is instructive to consider a deterministic version of the model as a preparation for the analysis of the more intractable models which occur later. We treat $n(T)$ as a continuous function. According to equation (2.4) the expected amount by which it will increase in $(T, T + \delta T)$ is $(N - n)(\alpha + \beta n)\delta T$. In the deterministic treatment we suppose that it increases by exactly this amount in each small increment of time. This implies that $n(T)$ satisfies the differential equation.

$$\frac{dn(T)}{dT} = (N - n(T))(\alpha + \beta n(T)). \tag{2.22}$$

Solving this with the boundary condition $n(0) = 0$ we have for $T > 0$,

$$n(T) = N \frac{\{\exp \beta(N + \omega)T - 1\}}{\exp \{\beta(N + \omega)T\} + N/\omega}. \tag{2.23}$$

A comparison of this with equation (2.15) shows that the stochastic solution and the deterministic approximation are not the same. The deterministic curve lags behind the stochastic curve by an amount which varies with both N and ω. The position for small N is illustrated by Bailey (1957, Figures 4.2 and 4.3). For large N the same conclusion follows from a comparison of the means of the two epidemic curves. In the deterministic case

$$E(T') = \frac{1}{N\beta} \log_e \left(\frac{N + \omega}{\omega}\right). \tag{2.24}$$

Williams (1965) showed that this is always less than the stochastic version given by equation (2.16). In order for the deterministic solution to be equivalent to the asymptotic stochastic solution it is necessary for ω to be large. It may easily be verified that equations (2.15) and (2.23) become identical in the limit as $\omega \to \infty$. For fixed ω the difference between the deterministic and stochastic means is of the order of N^{-1}. This may appear to be insignificant until it is recalled that the duration of the whole epidemic is of order $(\log N)/N$. On this time scale a difference of order N^{-1} can be of practical importance for moderate values of N. We must therefore be on the alert for this kind of occurrence when we come to more complex models.

2.4. Models with Imperfect Mixing

The principal assumptions of the birth process model are (a) that all members are equally exposed to the source and (b) that all pairs of members have equal likelihood of communicating. Assumption (a) is not crucial unless α is large compared to β because the main contribution to λ_n, once the process has started, comes from the term $\beta(N - n)n$. The second assumption is certainly invalid in most human populations. It is therefore necessary to investigate the effect of relaxing (b).

We begin by going to an extreme and suppose that there is no communication at all between members of the population. The diffusion is thus entirely attributable to the source. This case is, in fact, covered by our model and is obtained by setting $\beta = 0$. Expressions for the epidemic curve and duration can be obtained from those already given by letting $\omega \to \infty$ with N fixed.† However, they can easily be obtained from first principles along with other results which cannot be found in the general case. When $\beta = 0$ we have what is called the pure death process (see Bailey (1964), Section 8.5). The exact distribution of $n(T)$ turns out to be binomial with

$$Pr\{n(T) = n\} = \binom{N}{n} e^{-\alpha(N-n)T}(1 - e^{-\alpha T})^n \quad (n = 0, 1, \ldots, N). \quad (2.25)$$

Hence

$$\bar{n}(T) = N(1 - e^{-\alpha T}) \quad (2.26)$$

and the epidemic curve is

$$\frac{d\bar{n}(T)}{dT} = N\alpha e^{-\alpha T}. \quad (2.27)$$

There is thus a marked qualitative difference between this case and that illustrated on Figure 8.1. The rate of diffusion declines continuously with time instead of first rising to a maximum. It should therefore be possible, in practice, to form some judgment about the relative importance of interpersonal and source-personal diffusion by an inspection of the empirical epidemic curve. In a study of the diffusion of information about a new drug reported in Coleman (1964, Figure 17.2) it was found that the growth

† Note that this is not the same set of conditions which led to the equivalence of the deterministic and stochastic epidemic curves in Section 2.3. In that case N was allowed to tend to infinity.

of knowledge was roughly exponential. This can be interpreted to mean that advertising rather than personal recommendation led to adoption of the new drug.

The time taken for a proportion p of the population to hear the news is also easy to obtain. Since the T_n's are partial sums of the T's it follows at once that

$$E(T_n) = \frac{1}{\alpha} \sum_{i=1}^{n} \frac{1}{N - i + 1}. \tag{2.28}$$

If N is large and $p \ (=n/N)$ is not near to 1

$$E(T_{Np}) \sim -\frac{1}{\alpha} \log_e (1 - p). \tag{2.29}$$

This result stands in marked contrast to equations (2.11) and (2.12). In the present model the time taken to reach a given proportion does not depend on N. By combining the results obtained from our two extreme assumptions we may conclude, in general, that the time taken to reach a proportion p cannot be an increasing function of population size. This argument does not cover the limiting case $p = 1$. In this case equation (2.29) must be replaced by

$$E(T_N) \sim \frac{1}{\alpha} \log_e N. \tag{2.30}$$

Thus the total duration does increase with size but only slowly.

In order to chart the territory between the two extreme degrees of mixing we shall consider the case of a stratified population. One such model was discussed by Haskey (1954). He supposed that the population was composed of two strata with different rates of contact between and within groups. A similar kind of model for a population with $N/3$ strata was solved semi-deterministically by Coleman (1964, Chapter 17). We shall consider a simpler model of the same kind.

Suppose that the population is made up of k strata of equal size. The members of all strata are equally exposed to the source and the rate of contact between members of the *same* stratum is β, as before. However, there is no contact at all between the members of different strata. Under these conditions the diffusion in each stratum develops according to the theory of the preceding sections. The diffusion in the system as a whole is then found by pooling the results; no new theory is required.

Coleman (1964) developed the theory for the case $N = 2k$. In this case each stratum is of size 2 and there is no difficulty in obtaining the exact distribution of $n(T)$ from equation (2.6). Let $n_i(T)$ denote the number who have heard at time T in the ith stratum ($i = 1, 2, \ldots, N/2$) then

$$\lambda_0 = 2\alpha, \quad \lambda_1 = \alpha + \beta, \quad \lambda_2 = 0.$$

Hence

$$\left.\begin{array}{l}
Pr\{n_i(T) = 0\} = e^{-2\alpha T} \\[2mm]
Pr\{n_i(T) = 1\} = \dfrac{2\alpha(e^{-2\alpha T} - e^{-(\alpha+\beta)T})}{\beta - \alpha} \\[2mm]
Pr\{n_i(T) = 2\} = 1 - Pr\{n_i(T) = 0 \text{ or } n_i(T) = 1\}.
\end{array}\right\} \quad (2.31)$$

The limiting forms appropriate when $\alpha = \beta$ are easily deduced. Since

$$n(T) = \sum_{i=1}^{N/2} n_i(T)$$

it follows that

$$\bar{n}(T) = \frac{N}{2}\,\bar{n}_i(T) \text{ and var } n(T) = \frac{N}{2}\,\text{var } n_i(T),$$

and that $n(T)$ is approximately normal. The moments of $n_i(T)$ are readily found from equation (2.31); in particular

$$\left.\begin{array}{l}
\bar{n}_i(T) = 2 - \dfrac{2(\omega e^{-(\alpha+\beta)T} - e^{-2\alpha T})}{\omega - 1} \quad \omega \neq 1 \\[3mm]
\bar{n}_i(T) = 2\{1 - (1 + \beta T)e^{-2\beta T}\} \quad \omega = 1 \quad (\text{i.e. } \alpha = \beta).
\end{array}\right\} \quad (2.32)$$

The epidemic curve in the case $\alpha = \beta$ has the form

$$\frac{1}{N}\frac{d\bar{n}(T)}{dT} = \beta\{1 + 2\beta T\}e^{-2\beta T}. \quad (2.33)$$

The density on the right-hand side of equation (2.33) is decreasing with mean $3/4\beta$. This may be compared with the approximate value of $(\log_e N)/N\beta$ for a homogeneously mixing population. The mean for a population with no mixing at all and transmission intensity $\alpha = \beta$ from the source is $1/\beta$. With the limited degree of communication permitted by our stratified model the expected time to hear is reduced but is still independent of the population size. If $\beta = \infty$ the second member of each stratum automatically receives the news at the same time as the first member. Our model is then equivalent to a freely mixing population made up of $N/2$ pairs.

The foregoing analysis expresses in quantitative form the obvious conclusion that incomplete mixing reduces the rate of diffusion—at least in a population of small non-communicating strata. This conclusion can be strengthened by considering the duration of the diffusion for general k. Let us denote by $T_{(i)}$ the duration for the ith stratum. Then

$$T_N = \max_i T_{(i)}.$$

The probability distribution of T_N is then that of the largest member of a sample of size k from the distribution of the duration in a stratum. It is possible to make progress with the general theory of the distribution of T_N but an inequality due to Gumbel (1958) provides sufficient information for our purposes. For any random variable x with finite mean μ and variance σ^2 he states that

$$E(x_{\max}) \leq \mu + \sigma \frac{k-1}{\sqrt{2k-1}}$$

where k is the sample size. Applying this result to the case of T_n, μ is the average duration for a stratum and σ^2 is its variance. If N/k is large we may use the asymptotic forms and obtain

$$E(T_N) \leq \frac{2 \log_e (N/k)}{\beta(N/k + \omega)} + \frac{\sqrt{\phi^{(1)}(\omega - 1)}}{\beta(N/k + \omega)} \frac{(k-1)}{\sqrt{2k-1}}$$

$$= k \frac{2 \log_e N}{N\beta} + O(N^{-1}), \tag{2.34}$$

for fixed ω. This result suggests but does not prove, because of the inequality, that division into k strata multiplies the duration by a factor k. These conclusions confirm that the assumption of homogeneous mixing is crucial and they caution against undue reliance on the model in cases where it is known to be suspect. In spite of this severe limitation a careful study of the pure birth model will yield valuable insight into the mechanism of diffusion and provide a good preparation for the more general models which follow in Sections 3–5.

2.5. The Proportion Who Received the Information from the Source

When considering the diffusion of something like a rumour, which is liable to distortion as it passes from mouth to mouth, we may be interested in the degree of distortion which occurs. As this is likely to be a function of g, the generation of the hearer, it is relevant to study the distribution of the random variables $\{n_g\}$. For the birth process model the distribution of n_g is known only for the case $g = 1$†. However, this is the case of greatest interest, because the members of the first generation receive the news free from distortion.

† Results for $g > 1$ have now been obtained by D. J. Daley in unpublished work.

Let $n_1(T)$ denote the number of first generation hearers who have been informed by time T. We shall find the distribution of $n_1(T)$ given $n(T)$. The distribution of the ultimate number of hearers in the first generation is then obtained by putting $n(T) = N$. The analysis is made much simpler by a result due to Taga and Isii (1959) who first considered this problem. This result states that the distribution of $n_1(T)$ given $n(T)$ is independent of T. It is almost obvious when we consider that the probability of the next person hearing the news from the source depends only on the strength of the source and the number of spreaders. We may thus drop the argument from $n_1(T)$ and $n(T)$ and denote the conditional distribution of n_1 by $P(n_1|n)$ ($n_1 = 1, 2, \ldots, n$). The transition of the system to the state represented by (n_1, n) can have taken place in one of two ways. Previously it must have been in one of the states ($n_1, n - 1$) or ($n_1 - 1, n - 1$). The probability that the system was formerly in ($n_1, n - 1$) is, by Bayes's theorem,

$$\frac{(n - 1)(N - n + 1)\beta}{(n - 1)(N - n + 1)\beta + (N - n + 1)\alpha} = \frac{n - 1}{(n - 1) + \omega}.$$

Similarly the probability that the transition was from ($n_1, n - 1$) is

$$\frac{\omega}{n - 1 + \omega}.$$

The probability that the system is in the state (n_1, n) can therefore be related to the probabilities associated with the states ($n_1, n - 1$) and ($n_1 - 1, n - 1$) by the following difference equation.

$$P(n_1|n) = \frac{n - 1}{n - 1 + \omega} P(n_1|n - 1) + \frac{\omega}{n - 1 + \omega} P(n_1 - 1|n - 1)$$

$$(1 \leq n_1 \leq n, n \geq 1), \quad (2.35)$$

with initial conditions

$$P(0|0) = 1, \quad P(0|n) = 0, \quad n \geq 1.$$

Prior to Taga and Isii's derivation of equation (2.35), the special case $\omega = 1$ had been studied in another context. This work is summarized in Barton and Mallows (1965), and we shall draw upon their results later.

Equation (2.35) may be solved by introducing the generating function

$$\Pi_n(s) = \sum_{n_1=1}^{n} P(n_1|n)s^{n_1} \quad (|s| \leq 1, n \geq 1),$$

and $\Pi_0(s) = 1$. Multiplying both sides of equation (2.35) by s^{n_1} and summing over n_1 we find

$$\Pi_n(s) = \Pi_{n-1}(s) \left(\frac{n - 1 + \omega s}{n - 1 + \omega}\right). \quad (2.36)$$

This equation easily yields

$$\Pi_n(s) = \frac{s(1 + \omega s)(2 + \omega s) \ldots (n - 1 + \omega s)}{(1 + \omega)(2 + \omega) \ldots (n - 1 + \omega)}$$

$$= \frac{\Gamma(n + \omega s)\Gamma(\omega)}{\Gamma(n + \omega)\Gamma(\omega s)} \tag{2.37}$$

where $\Gamma(x)$ is the gamma function. Extracting the coefficient of s^{n_1} we have

$$P(n_1 | n) = \frac{\omega^{n_1} \Gamma(\omega) |S_n^{n_1}|}{\Gamma(n + \omega)} \quad (n_1 = 1, 2, \ldots, n), \tag{2.38}$$

where $S_n^{n_1}$ is the Stirling number of the first kind. As is clear from (2.37), $|S_n^{n_1}|$ is the coefficient of x^{n_1} in $x(x + 1) \ldots (x + n - 1)$. Miles (1959) discussed the distribution when $\omega = 1$ and tabulated the Stirling numbers for $n = 1(1)12$. In order to illustrate the shape of the distribution for small n we have tabulated the distribution in Table 8.2 for $n = 10$. It is important to remember that these results can be applied to any population with $N \geq 10$. However, n_1 only has the meaning we gave to it originally when $N = 10$ in which case it can be more accurately written as $n_1(\infty)$.

In small groups it is clear that n_1/n is highly variable except for the extreme values of ω. As the last column shows, the mean number informed by the source increases with ω but not as rapidly as might have been expected. The only way to ensure that most people first hear the news from the source is to have a very high value of ω. This can only be achieved by increasing the strength of the source or decreasing the degree of contact between members of the population. It is a characteristic of rumours that the source is weak, consisting, perhaps, of a single person. Under these circumstances it is not surprising that distortion often occurs because almost everyone receives the rumour at second hand or worse. These conclusions apply also when n is large as we shall now show.

The exact mean and variance of n_1 given n can be found directly from the generating function. They are

$$\left. \begin{aligned} E(n_1 | n) &= \omega \left\{ \frac{1}{\omega} + \frac{1}{\omega + 1} + \ldots + \frac{1}{n + \omega - 1} \right\} \\ &= \omega \{\phi(n + \omega - 1) - \phi(\omega)\} \\ \text{var}\,(n_1 | n) &= E(n_1 | n) - \omega^2 \sum_{i=0}^{n-1} \frac{1}{(i + \omega)^2}. \end{aligned} \right\} \tag{2.39}$$

TABLE 8.2
The distribution $P(n_1|n = 10)$ and $E(n_1|n = 10)$ for various ω.

ω	n_1										$E(n_1|n = 10)$
	1	2	3	4	5	6	7	8	9	10	
0	1.0000	—	—	—	—	—	—	—	—	—	1.00
1	0.1000	0.2829	0.3232	0.1994	0.0742	0.0174	0.0026	0.0002	0.0000	0.0000	2.93
2	0.0182	0.1029	0.2350	0.2901	0.2159	0.1014	0.0303	0.0056	0.0006	0.0000	4.04
5	0.0005	0.0071	0.0404	0.1245	0.2317	0.2722	0.2032	0.0936	0.0242	0.0027	5.84
10	0.0000	0.0003	0.0035	0.0216	0.0803	0.1887	0.2819	0.2595	0.1342	0.0298	7.19
∞	—	—	—	—	—	—	—	—	—	1.0000	10.00

If ω is fixed and n is large

$$E(n_1|n) \sim \omega \log_e n$$

and hence, the proportion who have heard direct from the source is

$$\frac{E(n_1|n)}{n} \sim \omega \frac{\log_e n}{n}. \tag{2.40}$$

The proportion who hear first hand from the source under these conditions thus tends to zero as the population size increases. In order for the source to communicate directly with a high proportion of the population it will obviously be necessary to make ω very large. When ω is large

$$\left. \begin{array}{c} E(n_1|n) \sim \omega \log_e \left(\dfrac{n + \omega - 1}{\omega} \right) \\[2ex] \dfrac{E(n_1|n)}{n} \sim \dfrac{\omega}{n} \log_e \left(\dfrac{1 + \omega/n}{\omega/n} \right). \end{array} \right\} \tag{2.41}$$

and

If $\omega = \frac{1}{2}n$ the expected proportion of hearers is 0.55 and if $\omega = n$ it is 0.69. Thus, for example, if the source consists of N spreaders introduced into a population of size N about 70 per cent would hear the information at first hand.

The formula for the variance given in equation (2.39) suggests that the limiting distribution may be Poisson in form because the limiting value of $E(n_1|n)/\text{var}(n_1|n)$ is 1. This is not so. The asymptotic form of the probability generating function is

$$\Pi_n(s) \sim n^{\omega(s-1)} \Gamma(\omega)/\Gamma(\omega s) \tag{2.42}$$

which is not the generating function of a Poisson distribution. It was shown by Barton and Mallows (1961) that the form of $P(n_1|n)$ for fixed n_1, large n and $\omega = 1$ was that of a Poisson distribution with parameter $\log_e n$. This result can be extended to cover the case of general ω but it relates only to the lower tail of the distribution and yields nothing of real value for our present purposes.

It will be clear that the analysis which we have carried out is far from complete. The distribution of n_g for $g > 1$ and the distribution of the number of times that a given individual hears the information would both be useful additions to present knowledge.†

---

† D. J. Daley has shown in unpublished work that $E(n_g/N) \sim \omega(\log_e N)^g/Ng!$ using a deterministic argument.

3. THE GENERAL EPIDEMIC MODEL

3.1. The Model

This model is so-called because it occurs in the theory of epidemics under that name. It is no more—or less—general than those we shall describe later in Sections 4 and 5. Most of the basic theory is well known and is given in Bailey (1957). Our initial formulation is a little different from Bailey's and we shall give the topic a slant more suited to the application to the diffusion of news.

An assumption common to all variants of the pure birth process model is that all hearers are spreaders and remain so, continuing to spread the information indefinitely. In consequence all members of the population will eventually hear. The emphasis in our analysis for that model was thus upon the rate of diffusion; there was no question of whether or not an epidemic would develop. In this and the following sections we discuss a class of models in which spreaders may cease their activities before the epidemic has terminated. Under these circumstances we shall see that the information may not reach the whole population—in fact it may make very little progress at all. One of the main concerns of our analysis will therefore be to find the distribution of $n(\infty)$, the number of people who ultimately hear the news. Common experience and the experimental work described in Section 6 suggest that news does not always reach everyone even if there is a high degree of mixing. We may thus hope to achieve a greater degree of realism by introducing a mechanism for cessation of spreading.

People may cease to be spreaders for a variety of reasons. They may forget, lose interest, or gain the impression that 'everybody knows'. It is too much to expect that a single model will cover all these possibilities. We shall therefore consider three different models in the remainder of this chapter and show that they may lead to striking qualitative differences in the development of the process.

The general epidemic model considered here is identical with the pure birth model with the additional feature that spreaders are only active for a random period of time. More precisely we assume that this period is an exponentially distributed random variable with mean μ^{-1}. We further assume that once a person has ceased spreading they cannot resume their activity. An essential characteristic of this model is that cessation is independent of the state of knowledge in the population. An individual will thus spread the information with the same zeal whether many or few of his hearers have heard before. The plausibility of this assumption must be judged by the success with which the model accounts for observed diffusion. It would seem most reasonable if the item of news is fairly trivial so that the cessation of spreading is due to forgetfulness. Obviously there would be individual variation in the time taken to forget but the choice of the exponential distribution to describe this variability is more questionable. We shall see later that the form of this distribution is not crucial for some purposes.

At any time, T, the members of the population belong to one of three groups set out below:

$m(T)$ persons who have not heard, described as 'ignorants'.

$n(T)$ persons who have heard and are actively spreading, called 'spreaders' as before.†

$N - m(T) - n(T)$ persons who, having heard the news, have ceased to spread it.

Because the size of the population is fixed, the state of the process at any time T can be defined by the values of any two of these numbers. We shall use the first two and say that the system is in state (m, n) if $m(T) = m$ and $n(T) = n$. One way of studying the development of the process in time is to consider the joint probability distribution of $m(T)$ and $n(T)$. Let us write this as

$$Pr\{m(T) = m, n(T) = n\} = P_{m,n}(T).$$

Another way would be to study the time taken for the system to reach the state (m, n). However, the system need not reach a given state (m, n) and so the simple inverse relation which existed in the analogous situation in the pure birth model is lost and there are no compensating mathematical advantages.

We shall not be able to obtain explicit formulae for the joint distribution of $m(T)$ and $n(T)$. It is nevertheless a worthwhile exercise to set up equations for them for the light which they throw on the process. From the state (m, n) two transitions are possible. They are set out below with the probabilities that they take place in $(T, T + \delta T)$.

$$\text{(a)} \quad (m, n) \rightarrow (m - 1, n + 1) : \quad m(\alpha + \beta n)\delta T$$

for $m = 1, 2, \ldots, N, n = 0, 1, \ldots, N - 1$ such that $0 \leq n + m \leq N$.

$$\text{(b)} \quad (m, n) \rightarrow (m, n - 1) : \quad n\mu\delta T$$

for $n = 1, 2, \ldots, N - 1$.

† $n(T)$ is not now the total number of hearers but a sub-set of them. There is no inconsistency in the new definition because, in the birth model, all hearers were also spreaders.

The transition (a) takes place when a spreader meets an ignorant; transition (b) occurs when a spreader forgets and ceases to spread.

Using these transition probabilities we can relate the joint probability at time $T + \delta T$ to that at T in the usual way and obtain the following bivariate differential-difference equation for $P_{m,n}(T)$.

$$
\left.
\begin{aligned}
P'_{m,n}(T) &= -\{m(\alpha + \beta n) + n\mu\}P_{m,n}(T) + (m + 1) \\
&\qquad (\alpha + \beta(n - 1))P_{m+1,n-1}(T) + (n + 1)\mu P_{m,n+1}(T) \\
P'_{N,0}(T) &= -N\alpha P_{N,0}(T) \\
P_{N,0}(0) &= 1 \\
&\quad 0 \le m \le N, \;\; 0 \le n < N, \;\; 0 \le m + n \le N
\end{aligned}
\right\}
\tag{3.1}
$$

where it is to be understood that probabilities with subscripts not satisfying $0 \le m + n \le N$, $n, m \ge 0$ are zero. It may be deduced that $P_{m,n}(T)$ can be expressed as a series of descending exponentials but the quadratic coefficients in equation (3.1) make further progress difficult.

We can draw certain general conclusions about the process by noting that the pure birth model is a special case. If $\mu = 0$ there is no forgetting and it is intuitively obvious that the rate of spread must therefore be greater than when $\mu > 0$. Thus, for example, $\bar{n}(T)$ for the pure birth model provides an upper bound for the same function in our present model. Secondly, if $\beta = 0$ or $\mu = \infty$ forgetting is irrelevant since then no one is ever actively spreading the news and hence $n(T)$ is always zero. By putting $\mu = \infty$ our model thus becomes identical with the pure birth model with $\beta = 0$. The rate of diffusion will be greater if $\beta > 0$ than if $\beta = 0$ so, this time, we can obtain a lower bound for $\bar{n}(T)$. The two bounds provided by considering the extreme values of μ will usually be rather wide but no further progress has been made with the stochastic model in this form.

The foregoing model does not allow for the possibility, which we envisaged at the beginning of the section, of the epidemic dying out. This is because the source continues to transmit indefinitely and thus, ultimately, all people will be informed. An interesting variant is obtained by supposing that the source transmits for a limited period only. One way in which this could happen is if the source consists of a group of a individuals with the same law of forgetting as the other members of the population. Under these circumstances the infinitesimal transition probabilities become

$$
\text{(a) } \beta mn \quad \text{and} \quad \text{(b) } \mu n,
$$

where n now refers to the total number of spreaders whether they originate from inside or outside the population. The differential-difference equations for the probabilities $P_{m,n}(T)$ are now

$$
\begin{aligned}
P'_{m,n}(T) &= -\beta mn P_{m,n}(T) + \beta(m+1)(n-1)P_{m+1,n-1}(T) \\
&\qquad\qquad\qquad\qquad\qquad + \mu(n+1)P_{m,n+1}(T) \\
P'_{N,a}(T) &= -\{\beta aN + \mu a\}P_{N,a}(T) \\
P_{N,a}(0) &= 1 \\
&\quad 0 \le m \le N, \quad 0 \le n < N+a, \quad 0 \le m+n \le N+a.
\end{aligned}
\right\} \tag{3.2}
$$

We again define probabilities to be zero if their subscripts are outside the stated ranges. The equations (3.2) are those that arise in epidemic theory and a considerable body of information has accumulated about their solution. Gani (1965) and Siskind (1965) have obtained methods for finding explicit solutions using a generating function technique. Their methods are extremely unwieldly unless N is very small and so are of little immediate practical value. Two other approaches remain open. One is to concentrate on finding partial solutions, in particular, for the limiting distribution of the number of ignorants. The second is to use a deterministic approximation for the system of equations (3.2). We shall follow both of these courses but, before doing so, we point out a second way in which the present model can arise.

Suppose that the source transmits the information to exactly a people before the diffusion starts and then ceases to operate. From that point onwards the system behaves like one of size $N' = N - a$ into which a spreaders are introduced. It only requires trivial modifications of notation to make the theory cover a situation of this kind.

3.2. The Terminal State of the System

Although the equations (3.2) are difficult to solve it is relatively easy to find the limiting values of the probabilities $P_{m,n}(T)$ as $T \to \infty$. After a sufficiently long period the diffusion will cease either because everyone has heard or because the spreaders have ceased to be active. In either event $n(\infty)$, the final number of spreaders, is zero with probability 1. Consequently

$$
P_{m,n}(\infty) = 0 \text{ if } n > 0. \tag{3.3}
$$

When $n = 0$, $P_{m,0}(\infty)$ will be the probability distribution of the terminal number of ignorants. We shall determine this distribution by exploiting the existence of an embedded random walk.

Let $P_{m,n}$ denote the probability that, *at some time* during the diffusion, there are m ignorants and n spreaders. Then clearly

$$
P_{m,0} = P_{m,0}(\infty). \tag{3.4}
$$

If we consider the process only at those points in time when a change of state takes place we may represent it as following a random walk over the lattice points (m, n). The situation is illustrated in Figure 8.2. We imagine a

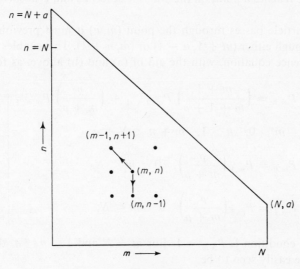

Figure 8.2

particle starting at the point (N, a) and moving, at each step, either diagonally upwards or vertically downwards as shown. When the system is in state (m, n) the two transitions which it can make and their associated probabilities are

(a) $(m, n) \rightarrow (m - 1, n + 1) : \dfrac{m}{m + \rho}$

(b) $(m, n) \rightarrow (m, n - 1) : \dfrac{\rho}{m + \rho}$

except that every state $(m, 0)$ is an absorbing state. These probabilities are the relative values of the infinitesimal transition probabilities given in (a) and (b) of Section 3.1. The random walk is Markovian because the transition probabilities depend only on the present state of the system. Here, $\rho = \mu/\beta$ and is often called the *relative removal rate*. In words, it may be expressed as

$$\rho = \frac{\text{Average time taken for a randomly chosen pair to communicate}}{\text{Average length of time for which a spreader is active}}.$$

A large value of ρ indicates that forgetting takes place relatively rapidly and a small value the converse. The m-axis is an absorbing barrier corresponding to the complete elimination of spreaders from the population. If the particle reaches a point on the n-axis it descends and is absorbed at the origin.

If the particle passes through the point (m, n) it must previously have passed through either $(m + 1, n - 1)$ or $(m, n + 1)$. This enables us to set up a difference equation, with the aid of (a) and (b) above, as follows:

$$P_{m,n} = \left(\frac{m + 1}{m + 1 + \rho}\right) P_{m+1,n-1} + \left(\frac{\rho}{m + \rho}\right) P_{m,n+1}$$

$$m \geq 0, \quad n > 1, \quad m + n < N + a$$

$$P_{m,0} = P_{m,1}\left(\frac{\rho}{m + \rho}\right), \quad 0 < m \leq N \tag{3.5}$$

$$P_{m,1} = P_{m,2}\left(\frac{\rho}{m + \rho}\right) \quad 0 < m \leq N.$$

The initial condition is $P_{N,a} = 1$. For $m = N$ and $1 \leq n \leq a$, the probabilities are easily seen to be

$$P_{N,a-i} = \left(\frac{\rho}{N + \rho}\right)^i, \quad (i = 0, 1, \ldots, a) \tag{3.6}$$

while those on the diagonal $m + n = N + a$ are given by the recurrence formula

$$P_{N-i,a+i} = P_{N-i+1,a+i-1}\left(\frac{N - i + 1}{N - i + 1 + \rho}\right) \quad (i = 1, 2, \ldots, N). \tag{3.7}$$

These results can be used to compute the complete probability distribution from equation (3.5). Bailey (1957) has given an explicit formula for $P_{m,0}$ (equation 5.53) and Siskind (1965) gave an alternative expression. The probability distribution was computed by Bailey for $a = 1$ and $N = 10$, 20 and 40. Some further calculations have been made for $N = 100, 200$ and 400 and various values of a. These form the basis of Figure 8.3 and Tables 8.3, 8.4 and 8.5. We follow Bailey and express the results in terms of the number $n_H = N - m$.

The distribution of $n_H = N - m$ has a variety of shapes depending on the values of N and ρ. Figure 8.3 illustrates the three principal forms for $a = 1$. If $N \leq \rho$ the distribution is J-shaped indicating that the information seldom reaches more than a handful of people. If N is a little greater than ρ a mode appears in the upper tail. As N/ρ increases the mode becomes larger and moves to the end of the range until the distribution is U-shaped.

Further increase in N/ρ results in a reduction in the probability concentrated near the origin. Finally, in the limit, the process degenerates into a pure birth model with all of the probability at $n_H = N$. The development of the diffusion thus depends critically on the relative sizes of N and ρ. There may be no epidemic at all, there may be an epidemic of uncertain

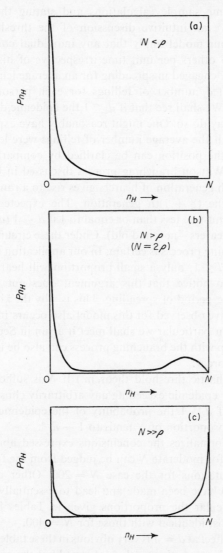

Figure 8.3. Forms of the distribution of n_H, the ultimate number who hear.

size or there may be an epidemic in which everyone is almost certain to receive the information. These conclusions hold good in broad outline for any fixed a but the position will be investigated quantitatively in more detail below.

The discussion given above is based on extensive calculations of the exact distribution and on Whittle's (1955) stochastic threshold theorem. Before giving some sample calculations and stating the theorem it is instructive to give an intuitive discussion of the threshold effect. The assumptions of our model imply that any individual communicates, on average, with $N\beta$ others per unit time irrespective of his own state. He himself is actively engaged in spreading for an average length of time μ^{-1}. Hence the expected number of tellings for each person will be $N\beta/\mu = N/\rho = d$, say. We shall see that if $d \leq 1$ the epidemic does not develop and if $d > 1$ it may do so. One might reasonably have expected the diffusion to peter out if the average number of tellings were less than one per head. However, the position can be clarified by comparing our process with the Galton-Watson branching process discussed in Chapter 2. Any member of the gth generation of hearers gives rise to a random number of *new* hearers in the $(g + 1)$th generation. The expected value of this random number must be less than or equal to 1 if $d \leq 1$ (d is the expected total number of hearers—new and old). Under these circumstances extinction of the branching process is certain. In our application this means that, if N is large and $d \leq 1$, only a small proportion will hear the news. It is very important to notice that this argument does not depend on the distribution of the period of spreading. This is why the kind of threshold effect which we have observed for this model also occurs in a much larger class of models. In particular we shall meet it again in Section 3.4.

The relationship with the branching process can also be used to establish the following theorem:

Theorem. (Stochastic threshold theorem.) If N is sufficiently large the probability of the epidemic exceeding any arbitrarily chosen size tends to zero for $d \leq 1$. If $d > 1$ the probability of the epidemic exceeding any arbitrarily small proportion of N tends to $1 - d^{-a}$.

This theorem formalizes the conclusions expressed above. The extent to which it holds for moderate N can be judged from the following tables. They give computations for the case $N = 200$. Other calculations for $N = 100$ and 400 have been made and lead to essentially the same conclusions. In particular the proportions given in Tables 8.3 and 8.4 for $N = 200$ are almost identical with those for $N = 400$.

The threshold effect at $d = 1$ is very obvious in these tables. By increasing a it is possible to increase the number informed but the overall characteristics of the process remain the same. From Table 8.5 it can be seen that

TABLE 8.3

Probabilities that the ultimate number of hearers will be small
or large for various values of d and $N = 200$, $a = 1$.

n_H	0	$\frac{1}{2}$	$\frac{2}{3}$	1	2	4	20	∞
0–1	1.000	0.815	0.745	0.626	0.408	0.232	0.050	0.000
0–9	1.000	0.985	0.950	0.830	0.496	0.251	0.050	0.000
0–19	1.000	0.998	0.986	0.889	0.506	0.251	0.050	0.000
181–200	0.000	0.000	0.000	0.000	0.006	0.749	0.950	1.000
191–200	0.000	0.000	0.000	0.000	0.000	0.704	0.950	1.000
199–200	0.000	0.000	0.000	0.000	0.000	0.026	0.950	1.000

TABLE 8.4

Probabilities that the ultimate number of hearers will be
small or large for various values of d and $N = 200$, $a = 5$.

n_H	0	$\frac{1}{2}$	$\frac{2}{3}$	1	2	4	20	∞
0–1	1.000	0.279	0.172	0.071	0.009	0.001	0.000	0.000
0–9	1.000	0.860	0.670	0.322	0.028	0.001	0.000	0.000
0–19	1.000	0.981	0.885	0.495	0.034	0.001	0.000	0.000
181–200	0.000	0.000	0.000	0.000	0.017	0.999	1.000	1.000
191–200	0.000	0.000	0.000	0.000	0.000	0.954	1.000	1.000
199–200	0.000	0.000	0.000	0.000	0.000	0.044	1.000	1.000

TABLE 8.5

Means and variances of n_H for $N = 200$. Upper figure
is the mean and lower figure the variance.

a	0	$\frac{1}{2}$	$\frac{2}{3}$	1	2	4	20	∞
1	0.0	1.0	1.8	7.0	78.2	146.8	190.0	200.0
	0.0	5.3	19.7	265.0	6258.0	7191.5	1900.0	0.0
2	0.0	1.4	3.6	13.3	118.7	183.6	199.5	200.0
	0.0	10.4	37.7	449.0	4849.8	2260.0	99.8	0.0
5	0.0	4.8	8.7	28.8	154.4	196.0	200.0	200.0
	0.0	24.6	83.2	711.2	1011.9	44.2	0.1	0.0
10	0.0	9.3	16.6	47.4	162.9	196.6	200.0	200.0
	0.0	45.1	137.2	747.5	183.6	5.1	0.0	0.0

the expected number of hearers changes smoothly on each side of the threshold value $d = 1$. The variances show very large differences because of the changing shape of the distribution. For $d \leq 1$ it always has a high degree of positive skewness; for $d > 1$ there is a concentration near the origin and a unimodal portion centred in the upper part of the range. As d increases this hump moves to the right until the distribution appears U-shaped. When a is increased the concentration near the origin diminishes rapidly.

Daniels (1966) has shown that if $d > 1$ then $N - n_H$ is asymptotically distributed in the Poisson form. Inspection of Table 8.5 suggests that this will only be a satisfactory approximation in practice for $N = 200$ if a and d are reasonably large. Cane (1966) arrived at a similar result by an approximate method.

3.3. The Deterministic Approximation

The distribution theory for the terminal state of the system tells us nothing about the duration or rate of growth of the epidemic. Except in degenerate cases, the mathematical problems of obtaining this information from the stochastic formulation are formidable. We shall therefore treat the process deterministically. The adequacy of this approach can be judged by comparing its terminal predictions with those already obtained for the stochastic case.

Instead of supposing that the number of transitions from (m, n) to $(m - 1, n + 1)$ in $(T, T + \delta T)$ is a random variable taking the values 0 or 1 with expectation $\beta m(T) n(T) \delta T$, we now assume that N is large enough for the expectation to be treated as the actual increase in $n(T)$ during the interval. Similarly, the decrease in $n(T)$ due to cessation of spreading will be assumed to be exactly $\mu n(T) \delta T$. Thus $n(T)$, $m(T)$ and $l(T)$ are treated as continuous variables no longer being restricted to integer values. As $T \to 0$ the change in $n(T)$ may then be represented by the differential equation

$$\frac{dn(T)}{dT} = n(T)\{\beta m(T) - \mu\}. \tag{3.8}$$

Likewise, the derivatives of $m(T)$ and $l(T) = N + a - m(T) - n(T)$ are given by

$$\frac{dm(T)}{dT} = -\beta m(T) n(T) \tag{3.9}$$

and

$$\frac{dl(T)}{dT} = \mu n(T). \tag{3.10}$$

The initial conditions are $n(0) = a$, $m(0) = N$, $l(0) = 0$ and, throughout the diffusion we must have $n(T) + m(T) + l(T) = N + a$.

An important result concerning the behaviour of the system can be found without actually solving the equations. First we note that $dn(T)/dT$ is negative or zero if $m(T) \leq \rho$ for all T. Since the number of ignorants cannot increase, this condition will certainly be satisfied if $m(0) = N \leq \rho$. Thus no epidemic occurs when $N \leq \rho$, while if $N > \rho$, $dn(T)/dT > 0$ at $T = 0$, the number of spreaders rises initially and an epidemic occurs. This is essentially the same threshold result which we obtained for the stochastic version of the model. The deterministic approximation has therefore been successful in reproducing this important characteristic of the epidemic.

If $N > \rho$, we can find the ultimate size of the epidemic and compare it with the stochastic values given in Table 8.5. To do this we first establish a simple relationship between $m(T)$ and $l(T)$. Dividing each side of equation (3.9) by the corresponding side of equation (3.10) we have

$$\frac{dm(T)}{dl(T)} = -\frac{\beta}{\mu} m(T) = -\frac{m(T)}{\rho}. \tag{3.11}$$

Integrating this equation and substituting the initial conditions we find that

$$\frac{m(T)}{N} = \exp\{-l(T)/\rho\}. \tag{3.12}$$

When the diffusion has ceased $n(T)$ will be zero and hence $m(T) = N + a - l(T)$. We have earlier denoted the ultimate number of hearers by n_H which is the value taken by $l(T)$ when $n(T) = 0$. Hence from equation (3.12) we have

$$1 + \frac{a}{N} - p = e^{-dp}$$

where $p = n_H/N$ and $d = N/\rho$. If a is fixed and N large, p satisfies

$$1 - p = e^{-dp} \tag{3.13}$$

approximately. This equation can easily be solved by using the tables of Barton et al. (1960). A short table is given below.

The last row of the table is included to facilitate the comparison of the deterministic predictions with the values of the stochastic mean given in Table 8.5. In the stochastic case the expected size depends on the value of a. The agreement between the deterministic and stochastic solutions is reasonably good when $a = 5$ or 10 but is very poor for $a = 1$ or 2. It might thus appear that the deterministic approximation is of little value. However, further investigation shows that the agreement is only poor when the distribution of n_H is bi-modal or U-shaped. This happens when there is an

TABLE 8.6

Deterministic approximation to the ultimate number of hearers in the general
epidemic model.

		d		
	1	2	4	20
p	0	0.797	0.980	1.000
$200p$	0	159.4	196.0	200.0

appreciable probability that no epidemic will develop. According to the deterministic model an epidemic *always* occurs if $N > \rho$. We are therefore prompted to ask whether the agreement can be improved by omitting those cases where only a few people hear. There is, of course, some degree of arbitrariness† about where we draw the line but in Table 8.7 we have given the mean of n_H *given that* $n_H > 20$.

TABLE 8.7

Values of $E(n_H | n_H > 20)$ for
$N = 200$.

		d	
a	2	4	20
1	157.3	195.9	200.0
2	157.7	195.9	200.0
5	159.7	196.2	200.0
10	163.1	196.6	200.0

It is clear that the overall agreement between the stochastic and deterministic predictions as given by Table 8.6 and 8.7 is greatly improved. The minor exception to this rule at $a = 10, d = 2$, may be accounted for by the omission of the term a/N from equation (3.13). It thus appears that the deterministic approach provides a satisfactory terminal description of the process *when an epidemic occurs*. The probability of an occurrence is, of course, given by the stochastic threshold theorem.

The number who have heard at time T is $N - m(T)$; the 'epidemic curve', which is defined as the rate of increase of the number of hearers,

---

† D. J. Daley has pointed out that the 'natural' point of cut-off for $d > 1$ is at $n_H = N - \rho$ because, starting with N' between ρ and N still gives an epidemic with the possibility of a major outbreak.

is thus obtained by plotting $(-dm(T)/dT)$ against T. (In the theory of epidemics the epidemic curve is defined by $dl(T)/dT$. This is because only the $l(T)$ members have recognizable symptoms although a further $n(T)$, who are incubating the disease, are actively spreading it.) Combining equations (3.9) and (3.12) we find

$$\frac{-dm(T)}{dT} = \beta m(T)\{N + a - m(T)\} + \mu m(T) \log_e (m(T)/N). \quad (3.14)$$

We may compare this with the corresponding equation for the pure birth model of Section 2.3 which is obtained by putting $\mu = 0$. Since the last term on the right-hand side of equation (3.14) is always negative the epidemic curve for $\mu > 0$ lies everywhere below that for $\mu = 0$. Solving the equation with the appropriate initial conditions we have

$$T = \frac{1}{\beta} \int_{m(T)}^{N} \frac{dx}{x\{N + a - x + \rho \log_e x/N\}}, \quad 0 \leq m(T) < m(\infty). \quad (3.15)$$

Using numerical integration this equation may be used to plot $m(T)$, and hence $-dm(T)/dT$, against T. Some calculations are given in Kendall (1956). It will be recalled that in the birth model the stochastic and deterministic epidemic curves approached one another as a increased. We may expect that the same will be true in the present case but there are no results available for the stochastic model to test this conjecture.

Our analysis of the general epidemic model leaves many gaps to be filled. In particular no results have been obtained for the distribution of the quantities $\{n_g\}$. This omission will be partly rectified in the following section where we consider a very similar model due to Rapoport.

4. RAPOPORT'S MODELS

4.1. The Basic Model

During the period 1948–1954 a number of models for the diffusion of information were proposed by Rapoport and his co-workers (see, for example, Rapoport (1948, 1951, 1953a and b, 1954), Rapoport and Rebhun (1952), Solomanoff and Rapoport (1951)). Their theory was originally developed for the study of the random net which arises in neuro-physiological problems but the relevance to diffusion of information and disease was soon apparent. This work pre-dates much of that described by Bailey (1957) in his book. The close relationship between the two bodies of theory seems to have passed largely unnoticed. Rapoport's model is, in fact, a simple variant of the general epidemic model and both can be regarded as special cases of a more general model discussed on page 246.

Rapoport's assumptions were the same as those of the general epidemic model except for the one governing the cessation of spreading. He supposed that each spreader told the news to exactly d other people and then ceased activity. The choice of person to be told was supposed to be random and hence independent of whether or not they had received the information. It is difficult to imagine a real-life situation in which this assumption would be true. The chain-letter in which each recipient is asked to write to d other persons is perhaps the nearest approximation. The value of studying the model is best seen by considering it as a special case of a more general model in which the number told is a random variable. If this random variable is denoted by $\tilde{d}$, Rapoport stated that his results would hold by taking $d = E(\tilde{d})$. Later in this section we shall discuss the conditions under which this statement can be justified.

The present model thus arises as an extreme case when we take the distribution of $\tilde{d}$ as concentrated at the point d. The general epidemic model is another special case since then $\tilde{d}$ has a geometric distribution. This may be seen as follows. If a spreader is active for length of time x the number of people he communicates with, excluding the initial spreaders, will have a Poisson distribution with mean $\beta N x$. But x has an exponential distribution with parameter μ. Therefore,

$$Pr\{\tilde{d} = j\} = \int_0^\infty e^{-\mu x} \frac{(\beta N x)^j}{j!} e^{-\beta N x} dt$$

$$= \frac{\mu}{\mu + N\beta} \left(1 - \frac{\mu}{\mu + N\beta}\right)^j$$

$$= \frac{1}{1 + d} \left(\frac{d}{1 + d}\right)^j \quad (j = 1, 2, \ldots). \tag{4.1}$$

As another example, take the case where the individual spreads the news for a fixed length of time; $\tilde{d}$ would then have a Poisson distribution. By comparing the results obtained under a variety of fairly extreme assumptions we may hope to establish our results on a broader basis.

Except for the case $d = 1$ we shall not be able to obtain any results about the rate of diffusion. Instead we shall study the random variables $\{n_g\}$—the numbers in the different generations of hearers. Some additional notation is required as follows. Let

$$N_g = \sum_{i=1}^{g} n_i.$$

For some $g \leq N$, N_g will attain its maximum value at which it remains constant. This limiting value is the ultimate size of the epidemic. In

Section 3 we denoted this quantity by n_H but here it is more natural to use N_∞ because it is obtained by allowing g rather than T to tend to infinity. The equivalence between n_H and N_∞ is established by noting that

$$N_\infty = \lim_{g \to \infty} \sum_{i=1}^{g} n_i = \lim_{T \to \infty} \{N - m(T)\} = n_H. \tag{4.2}$$

Finally let

$$p_g = E(n_g)/N.$$

This may be interpreted as the probability that a randomly chosen member of the population belongs to the gth generation.

4.2. Some Exact Distribution Theory

The exact distribution theory for the random variables $\{n_g\}$ and hence of $\{N_g\}$ for fixed d can be obtained by combinatorial methods. This fact is a consequence of the formal equivalence between our diffusion process and the classical occupancy problem in which balls are distributed randomly into boxes. The precise way in which this correspondence is established depends on what assumptions are made about the operation of the source. Two points which must be considered are the following.

(a) The a persons who introduce the news may or may not be able to communicate with one another. Which of the alternatives is adopted will depend on whether or not the initial spreaders are able to recognize one another.

(b) The members of the population may or may not be able to communicate with the initial spreaders. In practice communication may be impossible because the initial spreaders withdraw, or unnecessary because they can be recognized. The four variants of the basic model to which these categories give rise are set out below.

		Initial Spreaders	
		May communicate with one another	May not communicate with one another
Members of Population	May communicate with initial spreaders	Ia	IIa
	May not communicate with initial spreaders	Ib	IIb

If N is large and a is small the difference between the four models is negligible. When $a = 1$ the classifications I and II coincide. For convenience

we shall develop the theory for model IIb. Each of the others can be treated
by essentially similar arguments which we shall indicate at various points.

Consider first the distribution of n_1 under model IIb. We think of the
N members of the population as empty boxes. The $a \times d$ contacts made
by the source can then be thought of as balls distributed randomly among
the boxes. The distribution of first generation hearers is thus the same as
the distribution of the number of non-empty boxes. This is given, for
example, by Barton and David (1962, p. 242) and is

$$Pr\{n_1 = i\} = \binom{N}{i} \sum_{j=0}^{i-1} (-1)^j \binom{i}{j} \left(\frac{i-j}{N}\right)^{ad} \quad (i = 1, 2, \ldots, ad). \quad (4.3)$$

The conditional distribution of n_{g+1} given $n_g, n_{g-1}, \ldots, n_1$ may be found
by an extension of the same argument. Of the $n_g d$ contacts made by the
spreaders of the gth generation suppose that r are with ignorants, then
from equation (4.3),

$$Pr\{n_{g+1} = i \mid n_g, n_{g-1}, \ldots, n_1; r\}$$

$$= \binom{N - N_g}{i} \sum_{j=0}^{i-1} (-1)^j \binom{i}{j} \left(\frac{i-j}{N - N_g}\right)^r$$

$$(i = 1, 2, \ldots, r; r > 0) \quad (4.4)$$

$$= 0 \ (r = 0, i > 0)$$

$$= 1 \ (r = 0, i = 0).$$

To find the required distribution we need the distribution of r. This is
clearly binomial because each contact is made independently with probability $(N - N_g)/(N - 1)$. The denominator here is $N - 1$ rather than N
because a spreader cannot communicate with himself. Combining this
result with equation (4.4), the conditional distribution of n_{g+1} is then

$$Pr\{n_{g+1} = i \mid n_g, n_{g-1}, \ldots, n_1\}$$

$$= \binom{N - N_g}{i} \sum_{j=0}^{i} (-1)^j \binom{i}{j} \left(\frac{i-j+N_g - 1}{N - 1}\right)^{n_g d}$$

$$(i = 0, 1, \ldots, \min(n_g d, N - N_g)). \quad (4.5)$$

In principle our problem is now solved, but the joint distribution of the
n_g's obtained from equation (4.5) is extremely cumbersome. However,
the exact result provides a starting point for, and check on, the approximations of the next section.

Modifying the foregoing theory for the other models is straightforward. In the case of model IIa the only difference is that the binomial probability $(N - N_g)/(N - 1)$ above must be replaced by $(N - N_g)/(N + a - 1)$. Equation (4.5) gives the conditional probability distribution for model Ia for a population of size $(N - a)$ if, instead of equation (4.3), we have

$$Pr\{n_1 = i\} = 1 \text{ if } i = a$$

$$= 0 \text{ otherwise.}$$

The treatment of model Ib is slightly more complicated and is left as an exercise for the interested reader.

The distributions of n_g and N_g, and hence of N_∞, can be found using the theory of Markov chains. This fact was noticed and used by Solomanoff (1952). For moderate or large N the arithmetic is very heavy but can easily be programmed for a computer. For any g we can describe the state of the system by a pair of numbers (x, X), where $x = n_g$ and $X = N_g$. The process defined on these states is a Markov chain because the probabilities of transition between states from one generation to the next depend only on x and X. The numbers x and X must obviously satisfy

$$1 \leq X \leq N, \quad 0 \leq x \leq X$$

so there are $\frac{1}{2}N(N + 3)$ states in all. When $N = 3$ the 9 possibilities are listed in Table 8.8. below. For the present purpose the process begins when the members of the source have communicated with n_1 members of the population. The system is then in the state $(x = i, X = i)$ and the probability of being in this state is $Pr\{n_1 = i\}$ given by equation (4.3). The only transitions with non-zero probabilities are those of the form $(x, X) \to (i, X + i)$ for $i = 0, 1, \ldots, \min (xd, N - x)$. In these cases the transition probability is obtained from equation (4.5) with $x = n_g$, $X = N_g$. Let us agree to list the states in some particular order and denote the $1 \times \frac{1}{2}N(N + 3)$ vector of initial probabilities by $\mathbf{p}_0$. If $\mathbf{P}$ denotes the transpose of the matrix of transition probabilities then the state distribution after i generations will be given by

$$\mathbf{p}_i = \mathbf{P}^i \mathbf{p}_0. \tag{4.6}$$

The states of the form $(0, X)$ are absorbing states. Since the number of generations cannot exceed N we shall find that $\mathbf{p}_i$ contains non-zero entries for the absorbing states when i is at most N. These probabilities give the distribution of N_∞, the number who ultimately receive the information. The intermediate vectors $\mathbf{p}_i$ can be used to find the distribution of n_g and N_g for all g. An illustrative example is given in Table 8.8 for $N = 3$, $d = 2$ and $a = 1$.

TABLE 8.8

Calculations required to find the distributions of n_g, N_g and N_∞ for Rapoport's model when $N = 3$, $d = 2$, $a = 1$.

States	Transition Probabilities									State Probabilities			
	01	11	02	12	22	03	13	23	33	p_3	p_2	p_1	p_0
01	1	0	0	0	0	0	0	0	0	0	0	0	0
11	0	0	0	$\frac{1}{2}$	0	0	$\frac{1}{2}$	0	0	0	0	0	$\frac{1}{3}$
02	0	0	1	0	0	0	0	0	0	$\frac{2}{24}$	$\frac{2}{24}$	$\frac{1}{24}$	0
12	0	0	$\frac{1}{4}$	0	0	0	$\frac{3}{4}$	0	0	0	0	$\frac{1}{6}$	0
22	0	0	$\frac{1}{16}$	0	0	0	$\frac{15}{16}$	0	0	0	0	0	$\frac{2}{3}$
03	0	0	0	0	0	1	0	0	0	$\frac{22}{24}$	$\frac{19}{24}$	0	0
13	0	0	0	0	0	1	0	0	0	0	$\frac{3}{24}$	$\frac{15}{24}$	0
23	0	0	0	0	0	1	0	0	0	0	0	$\frac{1}{6}$	0
33	0	0	0	0	0	1	0	0	0	0	0	0	0

It follows at once from the column headed $\mathbf{p_3}$ that

$$Pr\{N_\infty = 2\} = 1/12, \quad Pr\{N_\infty = 3\} = 11/12$$

and hence that $E(N_\infty) = 35/12$. Solomanoff (1952) made similar calculations for models Ia and IIa for the same values of N, d and a. His version of the model includes the somewhat unrealistic assumption that a person can communicate with himself and thus his calculations are not directly comparable with ours. As a further illustration of the use of Table 8.8 let us find the distribution of n_2. From the $\mathbf{p_1}$ column

$$Pr\{n_2 = 0\} = Pr\{n_2 = 0, N_2 = 1 \text{ or } 2 \text{ or } 3\} = 1/24$$
$$Pr\{n_2 = 1\} = Pr\{n_2 = 1, N_2 = 1 \text{ or } 2 \text{ or } 3\} = 1/6 + 15/24 = 19/24$$
$$Pr\{n_2 = 2\} = Pr\{n_2 = 2, N_2 = 2 \text{ or } 3\} = 1/6.$$

For larger and more realistic values of N the calculations follow the same pattern but the size of the matrix is proportional to N^2.

Methods for finding the distribution of N_∞ and its expectation were given by Landau (1952). These methods take advantage of the Markov property to construct difference equations which can then be solved to give the required probabilities or expectations. In particular Landau showed that, under model Ia when a member can communicate with himself and $a = 1$,

$$E(N_\infty) = \sum_{i=1}^{N-1} b_i \binom{N-1}{i} \left(1 - \frac{i}{N}\right)^{(N-i)d} \tag{4.7}$$

where the b_i satisfy

$$w = \sum_{i=1}^{w} b_i \binom{w}{i} \left(1 - \frac{i}{n}\right)^{(w-i)d}, \quad w = 1, 2, \ldots, N-1. \tag{4.8}$$

4.3. Exact Theory when $a = d = 1$

In this case it is possible to derive a simple explicit expression for the distribution of N_∞. This may be obtained as a special case of the general theory of Section 4.2 but we shall proceed from first principles. Since each spreader tells only one individual who is either an ignorant or former spreader, it follows that $n_g = 0$ or 1 for all g. The process will continue until a spreader tells a former spreader. Suppose that this happens at the ith generation then

$$n_g = 1, \quad i \leq g$$
$$= 0, \quad i > g.$$

The process can be represented as a random walk on the integers $1, 2, \ldots$, N as follows:

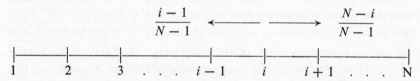

A particle starts at the left-hand end. It moves to the right whenever a spreader tells an ignorant and to the left if a spreader tells a former spreader. The probabilities of each kind of transition are $(N - i)/(N - 1)$ and $(i - 1)/(N - 1)$ respectively and the process terminates as soon as the first move to the left is about to occur. The point of termination is equal to N_∞. A direct argument thus gives that

$$Pr\{N_\infty = i\} = \left(\frac{i - 1}{N - 1}\right) \prod_{j=1}^{i-1} \left(\frac{N - j}{N - 1}\right)$$

$$= \frac{(N - 2)!(i - 1)}{(N - i)!(N - 1)^{i-1}} \quad (i = 2, 3, \ldots, N). \quad (4.9)$$

For small N the distribution is easily tabulated; the result for $N = 11$ is given below.

TABLE 8.9

Distribution of N_∞ for $N = 11$, $d = 1$, $a = 1$.

i	$Pr\{N_\infty = i\}$	i	$Pr\{N_\infty = i\}$
2	0.1000	7	0.0907
3	0.1800	8	0.0423
4	0.2160	9	0.0145
5	0.2016	10	0.0033
6	0.1512	11	0.0004

The distribution is positively skewed with mean value 4.660. If communication with the source is allowed the above table would apply to the case $N = 10$ with i reduced by one.

For large N an approximation to $Pr\{N_\infty = i\}$ can be found as follows. Let K be a constant such that $i = K\sqrt{N}$ and let N be large then

$$\prod_{j=1}^{i-1} \left(1 - \frac{j-1}{N-1}\right) = \exp\left\{\sum_{j=1}^{i-1} \log_e \left(1 - \frac{j-1}{N-1}\right)\right\}$$

$$\sim e^{-K^2/2}.$$

Therefore

$$Pr\{N_\infty = K\sqrt{N}\} \sim \frac{K}{\sqrt{N}} e^{-K^2/2}. \qquad (4.10)$$

Omitting the factor $1/\sqrt{N}$, equation (4.10) gives the probability density function of the continuous approximation to the distribution of N_∞ at $K\sqrt{N}$. As a check, we may note that the density integrates to one. It may be shown that the median of the distribution of N_∞ is at $\sqrt{2\log_e 2N}$ $= 1.177\sqrt{N}$. The asymptotic moments may be deduced by observing that $K = N_\infty/\sqrt{N}$ is distributed like χ^2 with 4 degrees of freedom. Hence

$$\left.\begin{array}{l} E(N_\infty) \sim \sqrt{\dfrac{\pi N}{2}} = 1.253\sqrt{N} \\[4mm] \text{var}\,(N_\infty) \sim \dfrac{4-\pi}{2} N = 0.4292N. \end{array}\right\} \qquad (4.11)$$

and

It thus follows that the expected proportion of the population who eventually hear tends to zero as N increases. When $N = 11$ the asymptotic formula for the mean gives $E(N_\infty) = 4.1557$ as compared with the exact value of 4.6604.

In the case $a = d = 1$ it is also possible to find the distribution of the duration of the diffusion. On the assumption of random mixing the length of time taken for a spreader to communicate with another person has an exponential distribution with mean value $1/\beta(N-1)$. Given that $N_\infty = i$ the distribution of the duration will then be like that of $\chi^2_{2(i-1)}/2\beta(N-1)$. We have already found the distribution of N_∞ so that an expression for the unconditional distribution of the duration can be written down at once. It is simpler to work with the moments for which we find

$$E(T_{N_\infty}) = \sum_{i=2}^{N} Pr\{N_\infty = i\}(i-1)/\beta(N-1)$$

$$= \frac{E(N_\infty) - 1}{\beta(N-1)} \sim \sqrt{\frac{\pi}{\beta^2 N}} = \frac{1.253}{\beta\sqrt{N}}. \qquad (4.12)$$

Similarly,

$$\text{var}\,(T_{N_\infty}) = \sum_{i=2}^{N} Pr\{N_\infty = i\}E(T_i^2|i) - \{E(T_{N_\infty})\}^2$$

$$\sim \left(\frac{2}{\beta^2} - \frac{\pi}{2\beta^2}\right)\bigg/N = \frac{0.4292}{\beta^2 N}. \qquad (4.13)$$

The duration of the epidemic thus decreases as the population size increases as we found with the pure birth model.

4.4. An Approximation to $E(N_\infty)$

The conditional distribution of n_{g+1} given by equation (4.5) can be made the basis of an approximation to $E(N_\infty)$. By elementary methods it can be shown that

$$E(n_{g+1}|n_g, N_g) = (N - N_g)\left\{1 - \left(1 - \frac{1}{N-1}\right)^{n_g d}\right\} \quad (g \ge 1). \qquad (4.14)$$

The same result may be derived by the following direct argument. The probability that a randomly chosen individual does not receive *any* of the $n_g d$ transmissions made by members of the gth generation is

$$\left(1 - \frac{1}{N-1}\right)^{n_g d}.$$

The probability that he receives at least one such transmission is thus

$$1 - \left(1 - \frac{1}{N-1}\right)^{n_g d}.$$

A randomly chosen hearer is an ignorant with probability

$$\left(1 - \frac{N_g - 1}{N-1}\right).$$

Therefore the expected number of new hearers in the gth generation is

$$E(n_{g+1}|n_g, N_g) = (N - 1)\left(1 - \frac{N_g - 1}{N-1}\right)\left\{1 - \left(1 - \frac{1}{N-1}\right)^{n_g d}\right\}$$

which is identical with equation (4.14). A simple re-arrangement gives that

$$E\left\{\frac{N - N_{g+1}}{N - N_g}\bigg|n_g, N_g\right\} = \left(1 - \frac{1}{N-1}\right)^{n_g d} \quad (g \ge 1). \qquad (4.15)$$

Suppose now that we attempt to take the expectations of both sides of equation (4.15) with respect to all the random variables appearing. There is no simple expression for the result but an approximation to the answer can be obtained by replacing all the random variables by their expectations. For this operation we need

$$E(n_g) = Np_g \quad \text{and} \quad E(N_g) = N \sum_{i=1}^{g} p_i.$$

Substitution in equation (4.15) now yields

$$\frac{N - \sum_{i=1}^{g+1} p_i}{N - \sum_{i=1}^{g} p_i} = \left(1 - \frac{1}{N-1}\right)^{Np_g d}. \tag{4.16}$$

Let g^* be the smallest value of g for which $N_{g+1} = N_g$. We now take the product of both sides of equation (4.16) for $g = 1$ to $g = g^*$. On the left-hand side we have

$$N - \sum_{i=1}^{g^*} p_j = N - E(N_\infty)$$

and on the right-hand side

$$\left(1 - \frac{1}{N-1}\right)^{dE(N_\infty)}.$$

Setting $p = E(N_\infty)/N$ the equation thus becomes

$$p = 1 - \left(1 - \frac{1}{N-1}\right)^{Npd} \sim 1 - e^{-dp}. \tag{4.17}$$

This result was first obtained by Solomanoff and Rapoport (1951) but it is identical with that found for the general epidemic in equation (3.13). This should occasion no surprise. The two models differ only in the stochastic aspects of the cessation of spreading and both equations (3.13) and (4.17) were found by deterministic methods involving only averages. Table 8.6 can thus be used for Rapoport's model also.

In this case it is possible to judge the accuracy of the approximation given by equation (4.17) since we also have some exact theory. When $d = 2$ Table 8.6 gives $p = 0.797$ and thus $E(N_\infty) = 0.797N$. For the example discussed in Table 8.8 we found $E(N_\infty) = 3 \times 0.972$ which is considerably larger than the approximation but $N = 3$ is much too small a number for a satisfactory test. A more realistic check can be obtained when $a = d = 1$. In the limit as $N \to \infty$ we have $p = 0$ but we can investigate the situation when N is finite. To do this we re-write equation (4.16) in the form

$$p_{g+1} = \left\{1 - \left(1 - \frac{1}{N-1}\right)^{Npd_g}\right\}\left\{1 - \sum_{i=1}^{g} p_i\right\} \quad (g \geq 1) \quad (4.18)$$

and add

$$p_1 = 1 - \left(1 - \frac{1}{N-1}\right)^{ad}. \quad (4.19)$$

These equations may be solved recursively to give the p_g's and hence p. A comparison of exact and approximate values is given in Table 8.10.

TABLE 8.10

Comparison of Rapoport's recursive approximation to n_H/N with the exact value for $a = d = 1$.

			N			
	10	20	50	100	200	300
Exact	0.366	0.265	0.171	0.122	0.087	0.071
Approximate	0.292	0.237	0.168	0.125	0.092	0.076

The agreement is reasonably good and suggests that the approximation may be used with confidence when N is moderate or large. Further evidence confirming this conclusion for $a = 1$ and $d = 2$ and 4 has been obtained from the simulation studies summarized in Table 8.11.

TABLE 8.11

Average values and standard deviations of n_H/N in 100 simulations of Rapoport's model.

			N			Rapoport's Asymptotic Approximation
		20	100	300	3000	
$d = 2$	Average	0.784	0.799	0.794	0.796	0.797
	S.D.	0.138	0.049	0.031	0.010	—
$d = 4$	Average	0.978	0.981	0.981	0.980	0.980
	S.D.	0.035	0.015	0.010	0.0077	—

By means of equation (4.18) we can also compute the expected number in each generation. Some calculations for the case $N = 300$, $d = 4$, $a = 1$ are given in Table 8.13 where a comparison is made with results for a

9

stratified population. Some further results are summarized in Table 8.12, which gives the most common value of g and a deterministic approximation to the duration of the epidemic. The latter is obtained as the largest value of g for which $Np_g \geq 1$.

TABLE 8.12

The most common value of g and estimated
duration of the epidemic for $N = 300$ and 3000

		d		
		2	4	10
$N = 300$	Mode	7	4	3
	Duration	13	7	4
$N = 3000$	Mode	11	6	4
	Duration	19	9	5

Perhaps the most surprising feature of this table is the small number of generations taken for the news to spread. Nevertheless, even with d as large as 10, most people receive the news at third or fourth hand.

It is convenient at this point to consider the more realistic general model in which each person tells a random number $\tilde{d}$ of persons, where $E(\tilde{d}) = d$. We have already seen that equation (4.17) still holds in one such case when $\tilde{d}$ has a geometric distribution (see equation 4.1). That it holds in general may be demonstrated as follows. Let n_{gi} be the number of people informed by the ith member of the gth generation. Assume that the $\{n_{gi}\}$ are independent. By definition

$$n_{g+1} = \sum_{i=1}^{n_g} n_{gi} \quad (g = 1, 2, \ldots)$$

$$n_1 = \sum_{i=1}^{a} n_{1i}.$$

As before we can find the conditional distribution of n_{g+1} given $\{n_{gi}\}$; it has the same form as equation (4.5). The distribution of n_{g+1} thus depends on the previous n_{gi}'s only through the two sums n_g and N_g. The conditional expectation of n_{g+1} is likewise still given by equation (4.14) and hence equation (4.16) may be arrived at as before because $E(n_g)$ and $E(N_g)$ are unchanged if we interpret d as an expectation. The general result then follows.

4.5. Imperfect Mixing

One of the most crucial assumptions of Rapoport's model is that communication between all possible pairs of persons is equally likely. As it seems highly improbable that this will be the case in most social groups Rapoport extended his theory to systems in which there is 'distance bias'. This means that the likelihood of communication between two people will depend on their distance (social, geographical, etc.) apart. In the present section we shall discuss a simple special case of the general model. This will serve to indicate the broad qualitative effects of distance bias.

Rapoport supposed that the population was divided into large homogeneous strata with different probabilities of communication between and within strata. We shall take the case where there are only two strata of sizes N' and N'' with $N = N' + N''$. The notation is the same as before except that we add one or two primes according to whether we are referring to the first or second stratum. Thus, for example $p'_g = E(n'_g)/N'$ is the expected proportion of gth generation hearers in stratum 1.

In the case of a single homogeneous population the probability of contact between a given spreader and any other member of the population is $1/(N - 1)$. For the purposes of obtaining asymptotic results we can replace this by $1/N$. Since we shall only be concerned with asymptotic theory it will be notationally convenient to make this kind of alteration in what follows without further comment. Consider now the case of a system with two strata. If there were no communication barrier the probability that a spreader in stratum 1 makes his next communication with a member of stratum 2 would be N''/N. When there is imperfect mixing this probability will be reduced. Let us therefore suppose that

$Pr\{$next communication of a spreader in stratum 1 is to stratum 2$\}$

$$= \frac{N''}{(cN' + N'')} \quad (1 \le c < \infty).$$

Similarly let

$Pr\{$next communication of a spreader in stratum 2 is to stratum 1$\}$

$$= \frac{N'}{cN'' + N'} \quad (1 \le c < \infty).$$

$$(4.20)$$

When $c = 1$ we have the case of homogeneous mixing; as $c \to \infty$ the probability of communication between strata approaches zero. We continue to assume that contacts are made at random within any stratum.

We are now in a position to find the conditional expectation of n'_{g+1} by a generalization of the argument which led to equation (4.14). The probability that a randomly chosen member of stratum 1 receives the communication being made by a given spreader in the same stratum is, by equation (4.20),

$$\frac{cN'}{cN' + N''} \times \frac{1}{N'} = \frac{c}{cN' + N''}.$$

The probability that he does not receive any of the $n_g'd$ transmissions emanating from stratum 1 is thus

$$\left(1 - \frac{c}{cN' + N''}\right)^{n_g'd}.$$

By a similar argument the probability of his not receiving any of the $n_g''d$ transmissions originating from stratum 2 is

$$\left(1 - \frac{c}{cN'' + N'}\right)^{n_g''d}.$$

The probability that he receives at least one communication, regardless of its source is therefore

$$1 - \left\{\left(1 - \frac{c}{cN' + N''}\right)^{n_g'd}\left(1 - \frac{c}{cN'' + N'}\right)^{n_g''d}\right\}. \tag{4.21}$$

Finally since he is an ignorant with probability $(1 - (N_g'/N'))$ we have

$$E(n_{g+1}'|n_i', n_i''; 1 \le i \le g)$$

$$= (N' - N_g')\left[1 - \left\{\left(1 - \frac{c}{cN' + N''}\right)^{n_g'd}\left(1 - \frac{c}{cN'' + N'}\right)^{n_g''d}\right\}\right]. \tag{4.22}$$

Dividing both sides of equation (4.22) by N', replacing the random variables by their expectations and allowing N' to tend to infinity we find

$$p_{g+1}' = \{1 - \sum_{i=1}^{g} p_i'\}\left\{1 - \exp\left(-\frac{p_g'dcN'}{cN' + N''} - \frac{p_g''dN'}{cN'' + N'}\right)\right\}. \tag{4.23}$$

A similar expression for p_{g+1}'' follows by interchanging the single and double primes in equation (4.23). The initial conditions will depend on the way in which information is first introduced into the system. If it is introduced by a persons into stratum 1 we shall have

$$p_1' = 1 - \left(1 - \frac{1}{N'}\right)^{ad} \quad \text{and} \quad p_1'' = 0.$$

Using these, or any other appropriate initial conditions, the approximations to the expected proportions can be computed recursively from equation (4.23) and its counterpart in p''_{g+1}.

The foregoing theory can be used to derive approximations to the expected proportion who eventually receive the news. The method is exactly similar to that leading up to equation (4.17). In this case it gives the following equations for $p' = N'_\infty/N'$ and $p'' = N''_\infty/N''$.

$$
\left.
\begin{aligned}
1 - p' &= \exp\left\{-p'd\left(\frac{cN'}{cN' + N''}\right) - p''d\left(\frac{N'}{cN'' + N'}\right)\right\} \\
1 - p'' &= \exp\left\{-p''d\left(\frac{cN''}{cN'' + N'}\right) - p'd\left(\frac{N''}{cN' + N''}\right)\right\}
\end{aligned}
\right\}
\tag{4.24}
$$

The expected proportion who receive the information in the whole population is then

$$
p = \frac{p'N' + p''N''}{N}.
\tag{4.25}
$$

In the case $N' = N''$ the solution of equation (4.24) is easily obtained. The equations are simultaneously satisfied by $p' = p'' = p_0$, where p_0 is the non-zero root of the equation

$$
1 - p = e^{-dp}
$$

which is identical with equation (4.17). This means that the proportion who ultimately hear the information is unaffected by the stratification. The same result holds if $N'/N'' \to 0$ or ∞ with N' and N'' both large. It would be surprising if p depended strongly upon N'/N''. Calculations which we have made show that p is almost independent of c which only affects it in the third decimal. We can easily extend the argument used for two strata to the case of many strata and the conclusions reached are essentially the same. It seems likely that the rate of diffusion will be affected by stratification. Some light is thrown on this question by the results in Table 8.13. The analogue of Rapoport's model for incomplete mixing in the case of the general epidemic model of Section 3 was treated deterministically by Rushton and Mautner (1955). Similar conclusions about the ultimate size of the epidemic hold in that case also.

We have computed the expected proportions of hearers in each generation for a stratified population with $N' = 200$, $N'' = 100$ and $d = 4$.

The case $c = 1$ corresponds to homogeneous mixing and shows that most people hear at second, third or fourth hand. When $c = 20$ there is very little communication between strata. The effect on the values of p_g is not great but the tendency is for people to receive the news at a greater remove from the source.

TABLE 8.13

Expected proportion of hearers, p_g, for $N' = 200$,
$N'' = 100$, $d = 4$.

				g			
c	1	2	3	4	5	6	7
1	0.051	0.172	0.380	0.300	0.058	0.005	0.000
20	0.050	0.160	0.310	0.268	0.142	0.033	0.004

The main pre-supposition of our analysis in this chapter is that the information is spread by means of chance contacts between individuals. A quite different situation arises if there are recognized channels of communication. In most human organizations such channels exist in order to ensure that information reaches every member of the system as quickly as possible. Perhaps the most important general conclusion we have reached from this study is that, even when such channels do not exist, *casual contact is often sufficient to ensure that most people are informed*. The most striking practical illustration of this fact is the way in which rumours spread in human societies. The models which we shall describe in the next section were specifically constructed for studying the diffusion of rumours.

5. DALEY AND KENDALL'S MODEL

5.1. The Basic Model and Some Exact Theory

One important feature of the diffusion of information in human populations has been disregarded when constructing the models given earlier in the chapter. On telling the news the spreader is likely to discover whether his hearer has already heard it. This knowledge may very well influence his enthusiasm for continuing to spread the news. In other words, the cessation of spreading may depend on the state of knowledge in the population. This interaction between spreader and hearer is peculiar to this application and has no counterpart in the theory of epidemics. It is thus necessary to develop new models to assess the importance of this characteristic. A class of models having the property that cessation of spreading depends on the state of knowledge in the population was proposed by Daley and Kendall (1965). Their work forms the basis of the present section.

We retain all the assumptions of the general epidemic model except the one which governs the cessation of spreading. In the simplest version of the model the diffusion proceeds as follows. If a spreader meets an ignorant the news is transmitted and the ignorant becomes a spreader. If a spreader meets someone who has previously been informed he ceases to spread the news. Those who have heard but are no longer spreading are called 'stiflers' because, on contact with a spreader, they cause him to cease spreading. As before, $m(T)$ and $n(T)$ denote the number of ignorants and spreaders, respectively, at time T. The theory for this model has only been worked out for the case when the a persons who initiate the diffusion process are indistinguishable from the other members of the population. Thus they may communicate with one another and they remain present as stiflers throughout the process. The number of stiflers at time T, denoted by $l(T)$, is thus $N + a - m(T) - n(T)$.

When the system is in state (m, n) three transitions are possible as follows:

(a) $(m, n) \rightarrow (m - 1, n + 1)$. This transition occurs whenever a spreader meets an ignorant. The probability that such a meeting occurs in $(T, T + \delta T)$ is $\beta mn\delta T$.

(b) $(m, n) \rightarrow (m, n - 1)$. The number of spreaders is reduced by one whenever a spreader meets a stifler. This happens with probability $\beta nl\delta T$.

(c) $(m, n) \rightarrow (m, n - 2)$. This transition results from contact between two spreaders when both become stiflers. There are $\frac{1}{2}n(n - 1)$ pairs of spreaders so the total probability of contact is $\beta\frac{1}{2}n(n - 1)\delta T$.

It is possible to set up differential-difference equations for the probabilities $P_{m,n}(T)$ in exactly the same way as for the general epidemic model. As in that case they are difficult to solve, except in degenerate cases. Some information can be obtained by comparison with the pure birth process model because the expected number of hearers will always be greater in the absence of stifling. Thus the curve of $N - \bar{m}(T)$ for the birth process will provide an upper bound for the corresponding function of the stifling model. However, we shall see later that the deterministic approximation provides sufficient information.

The distribution of the ultimate number of ignorants, or knowers, can be obtained by the method of the embedded random walk. The situation closely parallels the development in Section 3.2 so we shall give a more condensed treatment here. We construct difference equations for the probabilities $\{P_{m,n}\}$, using the transition probabilities which are as follows:

$$(m, n) \rightarrow (m - 1, n + 1) : \frac{m}{N + a - \frac{1}{2}(n + 1)}$$

$$(m, n) \rightarrow (m, n - 1) : \frac{N + a - n - m}{N + a - \frac{1}{2}(n + 1)}$$

$$(m, n) \rightarrow (m, n - 2) : \frac{\frac{1}{2}(n - 1)}{N + a - \frac{1}{2}(n + 1)}.$$

The equations are:

$$P_{m,n} = \frac{m+1}{N+a-\frac{1}{2}n} P_{m+1,n-1} + \frac{N+a-n-m-1}{N+a-\frac{1}{2}(n+2)} P_{m,n+1}$$

$$+ \frac{\frac{1}{2}(n+1)}{N+a-\frac{1}{2}(n+3)} P_{m,n+2}$$

$$(m \geq 0, n > 1)$$

$$P_{m,1} = \frac{N+a-m-2}{N+a-3/2} P_{m,2} + \frac{1}{N+a-2} P_{m,3} \quad (m \geq 0)$$

$$P_{m,0} = \frac{N+a-m-1}{N+a-1} P_{m,1} + \frac{\frac{1}{2}}{N+a-3/2} P_{m,2} \quad (m \geq 0).$$

(5.1)

If we define $P_{m,n} = 0$ whenever $m + n > N + a$ these equations hold for all m and n satisfying $0 \leq m \leq N$ and $0 \leq m + n \leq N + a$. The initial condition is $P_{N,a} = 1$. The m-axis is an absorbing barrier so $\{P_{m,0}\}$ is the probability distribution of ignorants remaining when diffusion ceases. It has not proved possible to obtain an explicit solution of equations (5.1) for this distribution but numerical values can easily be obtained by using a computer.

The shape of the distribution of n_H is illustrated in Figure 8.4 for $N = 50$, $a = 1$. This shows that the number reached will usually be in the neighbourhood of 40 but on a few occasions the diffusion will fail to

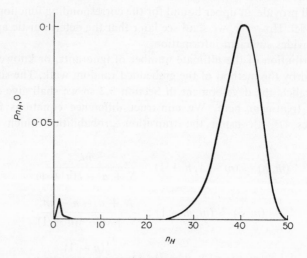

Figure 8.4.

develop. If N is increased the hump near the origin diminishes in size while the major hump becomes more nearly symmetrical with decreasing variance. Provided that N is large the value of a has hardly any effect on the main part of the distribution of n_H for reasons which we shall explain below. Some values of the means and variances of n_H/N are given in Table 8.14.

TABLE 8.14

Means and variances of n_H/N for Daley and Kendall's model.

| a | | N | | | |
		50	100	200	400
1	Mean	0.782	0.790	0.794	0.795
	Variance	0.0139	0.00653	0.00320	0.00158
5	Mean	0.774	0.786	0.792	0.794
	Variance	0.00752	0.00338	0.00165	0.00080

The figures in the table suggest that the mean proportion who hear is approaching an asymptotic value in the neighbourhood of 0.80 independently of a. The variances are nearly proportional to $1/N$ but those for $a = 1$ are almost twice those when $a = 5$. This difference arises because, as Daley and Kendall showed, the hump near the origin accounts for about half of the variance. When $a = 5$ the minor hump makes a negligible contribution to the variance. A more meaningful result can be obtained by omitting the minor hump from the calculations. Daley and Kendall computed the mean and variance of the major part of the distribution only. They investigated the behaviour of these moments for large N by fitting quadratics in N^{-1} to their values when $N = 191$, 383 and 767. The results are expressed in the following formulae:

$$
\left.
\begin{aligned}
E\left(\frac{n_H}{N}\middle| n_H \geq 20\right) &= 0.7968 - \frac{0.2738}{N} - \frac{1.7268}{N^2} \\
\operatorname{var}\left(\frac{n_H}{N}\middle| n_H \geq 20\right) &= \frac{0.3107}{N} + \frac{1.2327}{N^2} + \frac{19.5734}{N^3}.
\end{aligned}
\right\}
\tag{5.2}
$$

At first sight the negligible effect of a on the expectation seems paradoxical. One might expect to achieve a greater coverage of the population by introducing more initial spreaders whereas, in fact, a slightly smaller proportion hear when $a = 5$ than when $a = 1$. The explanation of this phenomenon is quite simple. A system with a initial spreaders is in state

(N, a) at time zero. Its future development is in no way different from a process which began in state $(N + a - 1, 1)$ and is now in state (N, a). Since all processes starting in $(N + a - 1, 1)$ must pass through (N, a), unless the unlikely event of premature extinction takes place, we would expect the two processes to terminate with the same number of ignorants. If a is fixed and N is large the eventual expected proportion of people informed will thus be virtually independent of a. The same argument holds for any other characteristic of the distribution of n_H provided that we ignore the minor hump.

The results obtained for the distribution of the ultimate size of the epidemic are in marked contrast to those for the general epidemic model. There is no threshold effect, by which we mean that the development of the process does not depend radically on the population size. Daley and Kendall's model is like Rapoport's in that a fixed proportion, which is strictly less than one, ultimately receive the information.

5.2. A More General Model

In the simple model described above the spreaders are very easily rebuffed. After meeting only one person who has already heard the news they assume that 'everyone knows' and cease to be spreaders. Various generalizations of this model are possible. We shall describe one of the two proposed by Daley and Kendall. Suppose that when a spreader communicates with another spreader or a stifler he becomes a stifler himself with probability ζ. As a further generalization let η be the probability that communication of the news actually takes place when a spreader meets another person. In our previous model both ζ and η were unity. (We could have introduced the second generalization in any of the models of Sections 2, 3 or 4, but it would have been superfluous. Its only effect would have been to reduce the effective rate of contact to $\eta\beta$. In the stifling model things are a little more complicated.)

The infinitesimal transition probabilities are as follows:

(a) $(m, n) \to (m - 1, n + 1)$: $\eta\beta mn\delta T$

(b) $(m, n) \to (m, n - 1)$: $\beta[\eta\zeta nl + \zeta(1 - \zeta)\{1 - (1 - \eta)^2\}n(n - 1)]\delta T$

(c) $(m, n) \to (m, n - 2)$: $\beta\{1 - (1 - \eta)^2\}\zeta^2\frac{1}{2}n(n - 1)\delta T$.

The transition probabilities for the associated random walk are obtained by expressing (a), (b) and (c) above as proportions of their total. These may then be used to construct difference equations for the probabilities $\{P_{m,n}\}$ after the manner of equation (5.1). Extensive calculations have been made of the terminal probabilities $\{P_{m,0}\}$ in order to assess the effect of these generalizations on the ultimate state of the system. As we should expect the value of a has almost no effect on the expected proportion who finally hear the news. The influence of ζ and η can thus be adequately demonstrated by considering only the case $a = 1$. Table 8.15 gives the expected proportion of hearers for values of ζ and η intermediate between 0 and 1.

TABLE 8.15

The expected proportion of hearers for the general model of Daley and Kendall with $a = 1$.

	$N = 50$			$N = 200$		
			η			
ζ	0.25	0.50	0.75	0.25	0.50	0.75
0.25	0.979	0.983	0.987	0.981	0.985	0.989
0.50	0.892	0.905	0.920	0.899	0.911	0.925
0.75	0.793	0.813	0.834	0.807	0.825	0.844

The general effect of relaxing the assumption that $\zeta = \eta = 1$ is to increase the proportion who ultimately hear. It is clear from the table that η plays a relatively minor role compared with ζ. Inspection of the actual distribution of n_H/N shows that the basic form is preserved under this generalization. That is, it remains true that the diffusion reaches a fixed proportion of the population on average but the actual values of that proportion will depend on the extent to which stifling occurs.

An alternative way of generalizing the simple model is to suppose that a spreader becomes a stifler after k unsuccessful attempts at telling the news. The quantity k could be fixed or it could be a random variable. Using deterministic methods Daley and Kendall obtained the following asymptotic values for the $E(n_H/N)$ when k is fixed.

k	1	2	3
$E(n_H/N)$	0.797	0.940	0.980

It is thus true to say that 'most people' will hear the news in a homogeneously mixing population unless there is a high degree of stifling. By supplementing our analysis by deterministic methods we shall be able to show that $E(n_H/N)$ cannot be less than 0.63 under any of the models we have considered. The deterministic approach also enables us to obtain information about the rate of diffusion.

5.3. Deterministic Approximation

If we treat m and n as continuous variables with rates of change determined by the transition probabilities of Section 5.2, we obtain:

$$\left.\begin{array}{l} \dfrac{dm(T)}{dT} = -\eta\beta m(T)n(T) \\[2em] \dfrac{dn(T)}{dT} = \eta\beta n(T)\{(1 + \zeta)m(T) - \zeta(1 - \eta)n(T) + \zeta(2 - \eta - N - a). \end{array}\right\} \quad (5.3)$$

The initial conditions are $m = N, n = a$. A direct consequence of equation (5.3) is that

$$\frac{dn}{dm} = -(1 + \zeta) + \zeta(1 - \eta)\frac{n}{m} - \frac{\zeta(2 - \eta - N - a)}{m}, \qquad (5.4)$$

where we are now treating n as a function of m. This differential equation may be solved by standard methods to give

$$n = -\frac{(N + a + \eta - 2)}{(1 - \eta)} - \frac{(1 + \zeta)n}{1 - \zeta(1 - \eta)} + \left(\frac{m}{n}\right)^{\zeta(1-\eta)}\left(\frac{2 - \eta}{1 - \eta}\right)$$

$$\times \left[\frac{N}{\{1 - \zeta(1 - \eta)\}} + (a - 1)\right] \quad (\eta \neq 1). \quad (5.5)$$

When $\eta = 1$ the appropriate relationship between $m(T)$ and $n(T)$ can be obtained either directly from equation (5.4) or by a limiting operation on equation (5.5). Equation (5.5) enables us to find $n(T)$ in terms of $m(T)$ at any stage of the process. Hence we may eliminate $n(T)$ from equation (5.3) to obtain a differential equation for $m(T)$. Before doing this we shall check to see whether the deterministic and stochastic methods agree in their predictions of the final number of hearers.

The ultimate number of ignorants is found from equation (5.5) by setting $n = 0$ and solving for m. To effect the comparison with the stochastic solution let us first consider the case of fixed a and large N. Writing $p = n_H/N = (N - m)/N$ and allowing N to tend to infinity the equation for p is

$$(2 - \eta)(1 - p)^{\zeta(1-\eta)} = \{1 - \zeta(1 - \eta) + (1 + \zeta)(1 - \eta)(1 - p)\}$$

$$(\eta \neq 1) \quad (5.6)$$

and

$$\zeta \log_e (1 - p) + (1 + \zeta)p = 0, \quad (\eta = 1). \qquad (5.7)$$

Equation (5.7) is essentially the same as equation (3.13), whose solution is given in Barton and others (1960) and in David and others (1966). When $\zeta = 1$, equation (5.7) is satisfied by $p = 0.7968$ which is exactly equal to the asymptotic mean in the stochastic case as estimated by equation (5.2). Further calculations for $\zeta \neq 1$ and $\eta \neq 1$ confirm the agreement between the two approaches. We may therefore proceed with confidence to use deterministic methods to extend the analysis of the diffusion process.

We have already noted and explained the fact that the terminal behaviour does not depend on a provided that a is fixed and N is large. This conclusion no longer holds if a is of the same order as N. Suppose, for example, that $a = CN$ $(C > 0)$ and, for simplicity, let $\zeta = \eta = 1$. Equation (5.5), with $n = 0$, is then asymptotically equivalent to

$$2p + (1 + C) \log_e (1 - p) + C = 0. \tag{5.8}$$

When $C = 0$ we have shown above that $p = 0.7968$. When $C = 1$, $p = 0.6983$ and as $C \to \infty$, $p \to 1 - e^{-1} = 0.6321$. Here we have a clearer demonstration of a conclusion revealed in Table 8.14, namely, that the proportion who hear is a decreasing function of the number of initial spreaders. Since decreasing either ζ or η increases p, the value $p = 0.6321$ represents the minimum expected proportion of hearers under the general model of Daley and Kendall.

The rate at which the news spreads can be investigated by solving the first member of equation (5.3) for $m(T)$. A solution can be obtained numerically after using equation (5.5) to express $-\eta\beta m(T)n(T)$ as a function of $m(T)$. The method is exactly the same as the one used for the general epidemic model discussed in Section 3.3. We shall merely point out an interesting connexion between the two models in this respect. Let $a = 1$, $\zeta = \eta = 1$ then $m(T)$ satisfies

$$\frac{dm(T)}{dT} = -\beta m(T) \left\{ 2N + 1 - 2m(T) + N \log_e \frac{m(T)}{N} \right\} \tag{5.9}$$

with initial condition $m(0) = N$. If we refer to equation (3.14) the corresponding equation for the general epidemic model, we see that the two equations are very similar. In fact the rate of spread, $dm(T)/dT$, in the present model is the same as it is in the general epidemic model with a population size of $2N$ and $d = 2$. This fact was also noted by Cane (1966).

6. EMPIRICAL DATA ON THE DIFFUSION OF INFORMATION

There have been many experimental investigations of message diffusion. However, the resulting data are rather limited in extent and uncertain in their interpretation. We shall not therefore undertake a detailed test of our models although we hope that new experiments will be undertaken for this purpose. Instead we shall summarize the main conclusions which have emerged and illustrate them in a particular case.

The most extensive collections of data on the diffusion of news have been made by the Washington Public Opinion Laboratory, Seattle. Much of this material was obtained as part of 'Project Revere' which was carried out in the early part of the 1950's. Some of the experiments were made using small populations of school children or college students; others covered the populations of small towns. The work was sponsored by the United States Air Force and was particularly concerned with the diffusion of information contained in leaflets dropped from the air. Another well-documented investigation was carried out among physicians by Coleman *et al.* (1957). This work, which is also described in Coleman (1964), was concerned with the diffusion of knowledge about a new drug. References to some other empirical studies will be found in the chapter entitled 'Diffusion in Incomplete Structures' of Coleman's book.

The data which we shall use to illustrate some of the main conclusions of this research comes from the 'coffee slogan' experiment which formed part of Project Revere. In a United States village of 210 housewives, 42 were told a slogan about a particular brand of coffee. Each housewife thus informed was asked to pass on the information to other housewives. As an incentive it was explained that there would be a reward—a free pound of coffee—for all people who knew the slogan when an interviewer called later. Data were obtained 48 hours afterwards by interviewers calling at each household. It was possible to trace the route by which the slogan had been passed to each hearer so that they could be classified by generations. The results are given in Table 8.16.

TABLE 8.16

Numbers of hearers n_g in successive generations g of the 'coffee slogan' experiment with the expected values $E(n_g)$ on Rapoport's model with $d = 2$, $a = 42$, $N = 168$. (From equations (4.18) and (4.19).)

	Generation g					
	1	2	3	4	5	Total
n_g	69	53	14	2	4	142
$E(n_g)$	66.6	55.8	22.3	5.5	1.1	151.3

When the experiment ended, 142 out of the original 168 housewives (84.5 per cent), had been informed. It seems unlikely that very much, if any, diffusion would have taken place after 48 hours. It thus appears that diffusion ceased before all persons had been informed. This at once rules out models such as the pure birth process. In other experiments the terminal percentage of hearers varied between 60 per cent and 100 per cent. Some of these figures must be accepted with caution because evidence of hearing was sometimes provided by handing in a card containing a completed message. In spite of incentives offered to participants there is no guarantee that all members of the population did take part. Nevertheless it seems reasonable to infer that some kind of forgetting or stifling process did occur. The figure of 84.5 per cent in the 'coffee slogan' experiment is very close to the figure predicted by Daley and Kendall's simple model. Alternatively, Rapoport's or the general epidemic model would lead to this result with d in the neighbourhood of 2.

Another convenient way of comparing the models is by means of the number who heard directly from the 42 source members. On Rapoport's model with $d = 2$ the expected number of first generation hearers is

$$E(n_1) = 168 \left\{ 1 - \left(1 - \frac{1}{168} \right)^{84} \right\} = 66.6$$

as given in the table. The agreement with observation is remarkably good. However, equally good agreement can be obtained using the pure birth model. We have already ruled this out as a complete explanation because it predicts 100 per cent coverage in the long run. However, both the general epidemic and Daley and Kendall's model will be very similar to the birth model near to the beginning of the process. If we use the theory of Section 2.5 and, in particular equation (2.41), we have $\omega = 42$, $N = 168$ and

$$E(n_1) \sim N \log_e \frac{N + \omega - 1}{\omega} = 42 \log_e \frac{209}{42} = 67.4.$$

There is thus no empirical basis for choice between the various models in this comparison. Both methods give excellent predictions of what actually happened.

A more detailed comparison is less favourable to our models. This is evident from Table 8.16, where the observed and expected n_g's are less close for $g > 1$. Similar results were obtained with other data. Dodd and his co-workers collected data giving empirical estimates of the growth of the number of knowers with time. In many cases the whole population was informed before the epidemic died out so that a pure birth model might have been considered appropriate. In fact there were significant departures from the logistic form predicted by this model. It is encouraging to find some agreement between our predictions and the course of actual epidemics but it is also clear that further refinement is necessary.

Our various models are capable of generalization in many ways, some of which have been mentioned in this chapter. One kind of generalization which we have not considered so far was proposed by both Rapoport and Dodd. Rapoport observed that the agreement between the predictions of his model could be made perfect if d was allowed to be a function of g. This would mean that the number of persons told by a spreader would vary with the generation of the spreader. In a similar way, Dodd obtained much better fits of the birth process model to his data when he allowed β to be a function of T. In practice this assumption implies either that meetings become less frequent as time passes or that telling takes place less often as the news becomes stale. Although generalizations of this kind undoubtedly provide a satisfactory basis for prediction it is doubtful whether they have any explanatory value. This statement rests on the fact that both Rapoport's and Dodd's generalization retain the most questionable assumption of the simple models, namely that of homogeneous mixing. Dodd showed, in fact, that in a small community of 184 seventh-grade pupils at a school in Washington state, pairing off in the diffusion process was far from random. Members of the same sex, the same group of friends or the same living group were more likely to communicate among themselves than with members outside their groups. If the assumption is invalid in such apparently homogeneous groups it is most unreasonable to expect it to hold in larger populations. The next step in the development of the theory of diffusion should thus be towards the analysis of systems with a specified communication structure. Some progress on the theoretical side has already been made by Coleman (1964). Dodd and McCurtain (1965) have used Monte Carlo methods to study the effect of clique size on the rate of diffusion. Much more remains to be done.

REFERENCES

Those references marked with an asterisk are not referred to in the text. Some of them provide general background material on the application of mathematical methods in the social sciences. The remainder relate to topics discussed in the text and provide a convenient starting point for further reading. The reader should be able to decide into which of these two categories a reference falls by its title. The list is not exhaustive but contains most of the references which are central to the main theme of the book.

ADELMAN, I. G. (1958), A stochastic analysis of the size distribution of firms, *J. Amer. Statist. Ass.*, **53**, 893–904.

AITCHISON, J. (1955), Contribution to the discussion on Lane and Andrew (1955).

*ALLING, D. W. (1958), The after history of pulmonary tuberculosis: a stochastic model, *Biometrics*, **14**, 527–547.

ARMITAGE, P. (1959), The comparison of survival curves, *J. R. Statist. Soc.*, **A122**, 279–300.

*ARROW, K. J., S. KARLIN, and P. SUPPES (Eds.), (1960), *Mathematical Methods in the Social Sciences*. Stanford University Press.

BAILEY, N. T. J. (1957), *The Mathematical Theory of Epidemics*. London: Griffin.

BAILEY, N. T. J. (1964), *The Elements of Stochastic Processes with Applications to the Natural Sciences*. New York: John Wiley.

BARTHOLOMEW, D. J. (1959), Note on the measurement and prediction of labour turnover, *J. R. Statist. Soc.*, **A122**, 232–239.

BARTHOLOMEW, D. J. (1963a), A multistage renewal process, *J. R. Statist. Soc.*, **B25**, 150–168.

BARTHOLOMEW, D. J. (1963b). An approximate solution of the integral equation of renewal theory, *J. R. Statist. Soc.*, **B25**, 432–441.

BARTLETT, M. S. (1955), *An Introduction to Stochastic Processes*. Cambridge University Press.

BARTON, D. E., and F. N. DAVID (1962), *Combinatorial Chance*. London: Griffin.

BARTON, D. E., and C. L. MALLOWS (1961), The randomization bases of the problem of the amalgamation of weighted means, *J. R. Statist. Soc.*, **B23**, 423–433.

BARTON, D. E., and C. L. MALLOWS (1965), Some aspects of the random sequence, *Ann. Math. Statist.*, **36**, 236–260.

BARTON, D. E., F. N. DAVID, and M. MERRINGTON (1960), Tables for the solution of the exponential equation, $\exp(-a) + ka = 1$, *Biometrika*, **47**, 439–445.

BHARUCHA-REID, A. T. (1960), *Elements of the Theory of Markov Processes and Their Applications*. New York: McGraw-Hill.

BLUMEN, I., M. KOGAN, and P. J. McCARTHY (1955), *The Industrial Mobility of Labour as a Probability Process*. Ithaca, New York: Cornell University Press.

BOAG, J. (1949), Maximum likelihood estimates of the proportion of patients cured by cancer therapy, *J. R. Statist. Soc.*, **B11**, 15–53.

British Association Mathematical Tables: Vol. I, Circular and Hyperbolic Functions, (1951), Cambridge University Press.

*BRYANT, D. T. (1965), A survey of the development of manpower planning policies, *Brit. J. Indust. Rel.*, **3**, 279–290.

BUSH, R. R., and C. F. MOSTELLER (1955), *Stochastic Models for Learning*. New York: John Wiley.

*CARLSSON, G. (1958), *Social Mobility and Class Structure*. Lund, Sweden: CWK Gleerup.

CANE, V. R. (1966), A note on the size of epidemics and the number of people hearing a rumour, *J. R. Statist. Soc.*, **B28**, 487–490.

*COLEMAN, J. S. (1964), *Models of Change and Response Uncertainty*. Englewood Cliffs: Prentice-Hall.

COLEMAN, J. S. (1964), *Introduction to Mathematical Sociology*. The Free Press of Glencoe. London: Collier-Macmillan.

COLEMAN, J. S., E. KATZ, and H. MENZEL (1957), The diffusion of an innovation among physicians, *Sociometry*, **20**, 253–270.

*COLLISON, P. (1962), Career contingencies of English university teachers, *Brit. J. Sociology*, **13**, 286–293.

COX, D. R. (1962), *Renewal Theory*. London: Methuen.

COX, D. R., and H. D. MILLER (1965), *The Theory of Stochastic Processes*. London: Methuen.

*CUTOLO, I. (1963), A stochastic analysis of the patrimonial structure of a firm, *Riv. Pol. Econ.*, **8** and **9**, 1197–1218.

DALEY, D. J., and D. G. KENDALL (1965), Stochastic rumours, *J. Inst. Math. Applns.*, **1**, 42–55.

DANIELS, H. E. (1966), The distribution of the total size of an epidemic, *Fifth Berkeley Symposium on Mathematical Statistics and Probability* (in press).

DAVID, F. N., M. G. KENDALL, and D. E. BARTON (1966), *Symmetric Functions and Allied Tables*. Cambridge University Press.

*DODD, S. C. (1955), Diffusion is predictable: testing probability models for laws of interaction, *Amer. Sociol. Rev.*, **20**, 392–401.

*DODD, S. C., and M. MCCURTAIN (1965), The logistic diffusion of information through randomly overlapped cliques, *Operat. Res. Quart.*, **16**, 51–63.

FELLER, W. (1950), *An Introduction to Probability Theory and Its Applications*, Vol. I (1st ed.). New York: John Wiley.

FELLER, W. (1965), *An Introduction to Probability Theory and Its Applications*, Vol. II. New York: John Wiley.

FISZ, M. (1963), *Probability Theory and Mathematical Statistics* (3rd ed.). New York: John Wiley.

FIX, E., and J. NEYMAN (1951), A simple stochastic model of recovery, relapse, death and loss of patients, *Human Biology*, **23**, 205–241.

FRAZER, R. A., W. J. DUNCAN, and A. R. COLLAR (1946), *Elementary Matrices*. Cambridge University Press.

GANI, J. (1963), Formulae for projecting enrolments and degrees awarded in universities, *J. R. Statist. Soc.*, **A126**, 400–409.

GANI, J. (1965), On a partial differential equation of epidemic theory, I, *Biometrika*, **52**, 617–622.

GLASS, D. V. (Ed.) (1954), *Social Mobility in Britain*. London: Routledge and Keegan Paul.

*GOFFMAN, W. (1965), An epidemic process in an open population, *Nature*, **205**, 831–832.

*GOFFMAN, W., and V. A. NEWILL (1964), Generalization of epidemic theory—an application to the transmission of ideas, *Nature*, **204**, 225–228.

*GOFFMAN, W., and V. A. NEWILL (1967), Communication and epidemic processes, *Proc. Roy. Soc. Series A*, **298**, 316–334.

GOODMAN, L. A. (1961), Statistical methods for the 'mover-stayer' model, *J. Amer. Statist. Ass.*, **56**, 841–868.

GUMBEL, E. J. (1958), *The Statistics of Extremes*. New York: Columbia University Press.

HART, P. E., and S. J. PRAIS (1956), The analysis of business concentration, *J. R. Statist. Soc.*, **A119**, 150–191.

HASKEY, H. W. (1954), Stochastic cross-infection between two otherwise isolated groups, *Biometrika*, **44**, 193–204.

HEDBERG, M. (1961), The turnover of labour in industry, an actuarial study, *Acta Sociologica*, **5**, 129–143.

*HERBST, P. G. (1954), Analysis of social flow systems, *Human Relations*, **7**, 327–336.

HERBST, P. G. (1963), Organizational commitment: a decision process model, *Acta Sociologica*, **7**, 34–45.

*HILL, J. M. M. (1951), A consideration of labour turnover as the resultant of a quasi-stationary process, *Human Relations*, **4**, 255–264.

*HORVATH, W. J. (1966), Stochastic models of behaviour, *Management Science*, **12**, B513–B518.

*HYRENIUS, A. H. (1954), Utredning rörande pråstkärens rekrytering (Statistical studies in the structure and recruitment of the clergy of the Church of Sweden). Stockholm: *Publications of the Statistical Institute*, University of Gothenburg.

*JONES, E. (1946), An actuarial problem concerning the Royal Marines, *J. Inst. Actu. Students Soc.*, **6**, 38–42.

*JONES, E. (1948), An application of the service-table technique to staffing problems, *J. Inst. Actu. Students Soc.*, **8**, 49–55.

KEMENY, J. G., and L. SNELL (1960), *Finite Markov Chains*. New York: Van Nostrand.

KEMENY, J. G., and L. SNELL (1962), *Mathematical Models in the Social Sciences*. Boston: Ginn and Co.

KENDALL, D. G. (1956), Deterministic and stochastic epidemics in closed populations, *Third Berkeley Symposium on Mathematical Statistics and Probability*, Vol. **4**, 149–165.

*KENDALL, M. G. (1961), Natural law in the social sciences, *J. R. Statist. Soc.*, **A124**, 1–19.

KHINTCHINE, A. J. (1960), *Mathematical Methods in the Theory of Queueing*. London: Griffin.

LANDAU, H. G. (1952), On some problems of random nets, *Bull. Math. Biophysics.*, **14**, 203–212.

*LANDAU, H. G., and A. RAPOPORT (1953), Contribution to the mathematical theory of contagion and spread of information I: through a thoroughly mixed population, *Bull. Math. Biophysics*, **15**, 173–183.

LANE, K. F., and J. E. ANDREW (1955), A method of labour turnover analysis, *J. R. Statist. Soc.*, **A118**, 296–323.

LAWRENCE, J. R. (Ed.), (1966), *Operational Research and the Social Sciences*. London: Tavistock Publications.

*LAZARSFELD, P. F. (Ed.), (1954), *Mathematical Thinking in the Social Sciences*. New York: The Free Press of Glencoe.

LITTELL, A. S. (1952), Estimation of the T-year survival rate from follow-up studies over a limited period of time, *Human Biology*, **24**, 87–116.

Manpower Planning. Proceedings of NATO conference Brussels 1965. London: English Universities Press.

MANSFIELD, E., and C. HENSLEY (1960), The logistic process: tables of the stochastic epidemic curve and applications, *J. R. Statist. Soc.*, **B22**, 332–337.

MATRAS, J. (1960a), Comparison of intergenerational occupational mobility patterns: An application of the formal theory of social mobility, *Population Studies*, **14**, 163–169.

MATRAS, J. (1960b), Differential fertility, intergenerational occupational mobility and change in the occupational distribution: Some elementary interrelationships, *Population Studies*, **15**, 187–197.

MATRAS, J. (1966), Social mobility and social structure: Some insights from the linear model, *Paper presented at the Sixth World Congress of Sociology*, Evian, France.

*McPHEE, W. N. (1963), *Formal Theories of Mass Behaviour*. New York: The Free Press.

MILES, R. E. (1959), The complete amalgamation into blocks, by weighted means, of a finite set of real numbers, *Biometrika*, **46**, 317–327.

PARZEN, E. (1962), *Stochastic Processes*. San Francisco: Holden-Day.

POLLARD, J. H. (1966), On the use of the direct matrix product in analysing certain stochastic population models, *Biometrika*, **53**, 397–415.

POLLARD, J. H. (1967), A note on certain discrete time stochastic population models with Poisson immigration, *J. App. Prob.*, **4**, 209–213.

PRAIS, S. J. (1955), Measuring social mobility, *J. R. Statist. Soc.*, **A118**, 56–66.

PRESTON, L. E., and E. J. BELL (1961), The statistical analysis of industry structure: an application to food industries, *J. Amer. Statist. Ass.*, **56**, 925–932.

PYKE, R. (1961a), Markov renewal processes: Definitions and preliminary properties, *Ann. Math. Statist.*, **32**, 1231–1242.

PYKE, R. (1961b), Markov renewal processes with finitely many states, *Ann. Math. Statist.*, **32**, 1243–1259.

RAPOPORT, A. (1948), Cycle distributions in random nets, *Bull. Math. Biophysics*, **10**, 145–157.

*RAPOPORT, A. (1949a), Outline of a probabilistic approach to animal sociology, I, *Bull. Math. Biophysics*, **11**, 183–196.

*RAPOPORT, A. (1949b), Outline of a probabilistic approach to animal sociology, II, *Bull. Math. Biophysics*, **11**, 273–281.

RAPOPORT, A. (1951), Nets with distance bias, *Bull. Math. Biophysics*, **13**, 85–91.

RAPOPORT, A. (1953a), Spread of information through a population with socio-structural bias: I Assumption of transitivity, *Bull. Math. Biophysics*, **15**, 523–533.

RAPOPORT, A. (1953b), Spread of information through a population with socio-structural bias: II Various models with partial transitivity, *Bull. Math. Biophysics*, **15**, 535–546.

RAPOPORT, A. (1954), Spread of information through a population with socio-structural bias: III Suggested experimental procedures, *Bull. Math. Biophysics*, **16**, 75–81.

RAPOPORT, A., and L. I. REBHUN (1952), On the mathematical theory of rumour spread, *Bull. Math. Biophysics*, **14**, 375–383.

*RASHEVSKY, N. (1951), *Mathematical Biology of Social Behaviour*. Chicago: University of Chicago Press.

*RICE, A. K., and E. L. TRIST (1952), Institutional and sub-institutional determinants of social change in labour turnover, *Human Relations*, **5**, 347–371.

RICE, A. K., J. M. M. HILL, and E. L. TRIST (1950), The representation of labour turnover as a social process, *Human Relations*, **3**, 349–381.

ROGOFF, N. (1953), *Recent Trends in Occupational Mobility*. Glencoe, Ill.: The Free Press.

RUSHTON, S., and A. J. MAUTNER (1955), The deterministic model of a simple epidemic for more than one community, *Biometrika*, **42**, 126–132.

SEAL, H. L. (1945), The mathematics of a population composed of k stationary strata each recruited from the stratum below and supported at the lowest level by a uniform annual number of entrants, *Biometrika*, **33**, 226–230.

SILCOCK, H. (1954), The phenomenon of labour turnover, *J. R. Statist. Soc.*, **A117**. 429–440.

SIMON, H. A. (1957), The compensation of executives, *Sociometry*, **20**, 32–35.

SISKIND, V. (1965), A solution of the general stochastic epidemic, *Biometrika*, **52**, 613–616.

*SMITH, A. R. (1967), Manpower planning in management of the Royal Navy, *J. Management Studies*, **4**, 127–139.

SOLOMANOFF, R. (1952), An exact method for the computation of the connectivity of random nets, *Bull. Math. Biophysics*, **14**, 153–157.

SOLOMANOFF, R., and A. RAPOPORT (1951), Connectivity of random nets, *Bull. Math. Biophysics*, **13**, 107–117.

STEINDHL, J. (1965), *Random Processes and the Growth of Firms*. London: Griffin.

*STONE, R. (1965), A model of the educational system, *Minerva*, **3**, 172–186.

SVERDRUP, E. (1965), Estimates and test procedures in connexion with stochastic models of deaths, recoveries and transfers between different states of health, *Skand. Aktuar.*, **46**, 184–211.

*SVALAGOSTA, K. (1959), *Prestige, Class and Mobility*. London: Heinemann.

TAGA, Y. (1963), On the limiting distributions in Markov renewal processes with finitely many states, *Ann. Inst. Statist. Math.*, **15**, 1–10.

TAGA, Y., and K. ISII (1959), On a stochastic model concerning the pattern of communication—Diffusion of news in a social group, *Ann. Inst. Statist. Math.*, **11**, 25–43.

*TAGA, Y., and T. SUZUKI (1957), On the estimation of average length of chains in the communication pattern, *Ann. Inst. Statist. Math.*, **9**, 149–156.

VAJDA, S. (1947), The stratified semi-stationary population, *Biometrika*, **34**, 243–254.

*VAJDA, S. (1948), Introduction to a mathematical theory of a graded stationary population, *Bull. de l'Ass. Actuair, Suisses*, **48**, 251–273.

WHITE, H. (1963), Cause and effect in social mobility tables, *Behavioral Science*, **8**, 14–27.

WHITTLE, P. (1955), The outcome of a stochastic epidemic—a note on Bailey's paper, *Biometrika*, **42**, 116–122.

WIDDER, D. V. (1946), *The Laplace Transform*. Princeton University Press.

WILLIAMS, T. (1965), The simple stochastic epidemic curve for large populations of susceptibles, *Biometrika*, **52**, 571–579.

*WOOD, S. (1965), A simple arithmetic approach to career planning and recruitment, *Brit. J. Indust. Relations*, **3**, 291–300.

*YOUNG, A. (1965), Models for planning recruitment and promotion of staff, *Brit. J. Indust. Relations*, **3**, 301–310.

YOUNG, A., and G. ALMOND (1961), Predicting distributions of staff, *Comp. J.*, **3**, 246–250.

ZAHL, S. (1955), A Markov process model for follow-up studies, *Human Biology*, **27**, 90–120.

AUTHOR INDEX

The following authors appear in the List of References but are not referred to in the text

SUBJECT INDEX

Ability, distribution of, 174
Absorbing state, 227, 239
  barrier, 228, 252
Actuarial, estimate, 86
  method, 86
  risk, 86
  studies, 72
Actuaries, 1
Advertisement hoarding, 204
Advertisements, 206
Advertising, 216
Age structure, 27
Aircraft, 2
ALGOL, 10
American University system, 39
Arithmetic progression, 203
Attitude change, model for, 76
Average, weighted, 27, 141, 200

Barrier, absorbing, 228, 252
Bayes's theorem, 219
Behaviour, animal, 5
  human, 5
  molecular, 5
Beta distribution, 166
Beta function, incomplete, 162, 164, 166, 167
Bi-modal distribution, 233
Binomial distribution, 65, 160, 215, 238
Binomial series, 162
Biologists, 1
Birth and Death process, 77, 102
Birth Process, 206–208, 210
  model, 214, 215, 218, 223–225, 229, 235, 243, 251, 259, 260
  theory of, 199
Birth Rate, 26, 27
  differential, 25, 26
  quadratic, 207
Branching process, 12, 26, 230
British Association Mathematical Tables, 210, 213

Cancer, 4, 71–75, 80, 82, 85–87

Census analysis, 96–97
Census, job, 29
Censuses, 24, 32
Central limit theorem, 129, 139, 213
Chain letter, 236
Characteristic roots, see under Eigen values
Chebychev's inequality, 35
Chi-square distribution, 242
Civil Service, 156
Class, occupational, 8
  social, 8, 12, 16, 20, 27, 38, 76
Class structure, see under Structure, class,
Clique size, 260
Closed models (defined), 8
Coefficient of variation, 138, 148
Coffee slogan experiment, 258, 259
Cohort analysis, 96, 97
Combinatorial methods, 237
Communication, channels of, 204, 250
  structure, 260
Completed length of service distribution (CLS Distribution) (defined), 123
Completed length of service distribution, empirical, 125, 126, 133, 199
Computer, 7, 54, 239, 252
  programmes, 10, 23, 43, 67
Contracting organizations, 39, 124, 146, 150, 151
Convolution, 35, 195
Covariance, of grade sizes, 11, 22, 23, 41, 51–54, 65, 66
  of multinomial distribution, 23
  of predictions, 21
  of time for news to reach n persons, 214
Cumulants, 210, 212, 213

Daley and Kendall's model, 250, 253, 254, 257, 259
Death Process, 215
  rate, 74, 102
Decision process model, 75

269